D1109712

ARITHMETIC OPERATIONS
IN DIGITAL COMPUTERS

R. K. RICHARDS, Ph.D.

Development Engineer
International Business Machines Corporation

FOURTH PRINTING

D. VAN NOSTRAND COMPANY, INC.

PRINCETON, NEW JERSEY

TORONTO   LONDON

NEW YORK

D. VAN NOSTRAND COMPANY, INC.

120 Alexander St., Princeton, New Jersey
257 Fourth Avenue, New York 10, New York
25 Hollinger Rd., Toronto 16, Canada
Macmillan & Co., Ltd., St. Martin's St., London, W.C. 2, England

*All correspondence should be addressed to the
principal office of the company at Princeton, N. J.*

———

Library of Congress Catalog Card No. 55–6234

———

First Printing February 1955
Second (Prepublication) Printing February 1955
Third Printing August 1955
Fourth Printing February 1956

PRINTED IN THE UNITED STATES OF AMERICA

PREFACE

Among the first things that are learned in a study of mathematics are rules and procedures for performing basic arithmetic operations, notably addition, subtraction, multiplication, and division. The rules and procedures taught in school are, for the most part, aimed at making the operations as simple and speedy as possible when a pencil and a piece of paper are the only tools. In the design of more elaborate arithmetical tools, it is usually found necessary or at least highly desirable to devise new methods for executing the various arithmetic operations.

This text has been written to point out the shortcomings of pencil-and-paper rules and procedures when applied to computing machinery and to explain the more important of the schemes which have been worked out for executing arithmetic operations in that class of machinery generally known as "digital computers." Of course, to appreciate the features of the different schemes, many other points must be considered, and these range all the way from the systems of symbols which are to be used to the ideas involved in causing a computer to proceed through a long sequence of arithmetic operations in an automatic fashion. In other words, it might be said that the text has been prepared as an answer to the question: "How does a digital computer work?"

In the design of computers, not only the methods of performing arithmetic operations, but also the fundamental concepts with regard to symbolic representation of quantities have been subjected to critical review. For this reason, the explanation of computer functioning has been started with a discussion of systems of symbols which have been invented for representing the numbers entering into the computations. Relatively little attention is given to actual components, circuits, and other engineering details which must be considered when designing a computer. However, these details have been a great influence in the selection of the arithmetic methods to be presented, and the advantages and disadvantages of the various schemes from an engineering standpoint are pointed out throughout the text. Most of the means for performing arithmetic operations are explained through the use of "functional block diagrams," where it is understood that any set of physical components which provide the indicated functions may be used. A Boolean algebra notation is introduced at any early point and is widely used as a convenient means of representing the block diagrams and, in many cases, as a device for finding improved functional arrangements.

In the descriptions of the arithmetic operations themselves, separate chapters are devoted to the methods employed in the binary and the decimal systems. This separation has been made because, from a machine standpoint, the operations are quite different in spite of the fact that the systems are alike, from a mathematical standpoint, except for a change in the value of the radix. On the other hand, most of the important ideas relating to the organization of a computer and to the programming of it to execute a long series of arithmetic operations are not related to its binary or decimal nature. Since principles of operation have been considered to be of first importance, no attempt has been made to give a complete, detailed description of any one machine, although in some cases the explanations have been patterned after certain machines which seemed to be typical of a category. To explain programming principles, a simplified "specimen" machine was used as a model. By this means it is possible to illustrate the important concepts of programming without the need for describing numerous details which, although highly desirable in an actual machine, tend to cause confusion in explanations and which may be totally different from one machine to the next.

This book was originally prepared as a set of notes to be used with a course of instruction for engineers at IBM's laboratories. I wish to thank all of those at IBM, particularly the students in the classes, who have given assistance either through discussions or through suggesting improvements in the text. Also, I wish to acknowledge with thanks the support and encouragement given me in this project by Mr. Ralph L. Palmer, Director of Engineering at IBM.

R. K. R.

CONTENTS

Chapter 1

SYMBOLIC REPRESENTATION OF QUANTITIES

To those familiar with ordinary arithmetic processes, the symbols which should be used to represent various quantities may appear to offer no problems or even no room for choice. The Arabic numerals together with decimal points, plus and minus signs, exponents, and so on, serve very well for grade-school arithmetic and higher mathematics as well, and there is no self-evident reason why these same symbols cannot be adopted for use in computing machinery. To some extent these symbols can be used; and, since they are so well established, it is desirable that they be used as much as possible. However, it could hardly be expected that a system of symbols which was developed along with pencil-and-paper arithmetic would be the most desirable system when transported to the field of machine computations. There are many problems connected with the use of the decimal system in a computer, especially when attempts are made to employ it in the arithmetic unit, or that portion of the machine which performs the actual computations. It is because of these problems that it is usually desirable to modify the decimal system, sometimes considerably, in order to adapt the computations to machine operations. In some cases it has been found expedient to abandon the decimal entirely in the computer in favor of another system, known as the binary system, which will be described in detail later.

The increase in speed of computations (other factors assumed equal) and the saving in tubes, relays, and other components that can be achieved by the proper choice of symbols are well known to machine designers. Of equal importance is the fact that mathematical progress can be aided or hindered in no small way simply by the properties of the systems of symbols in use by the mathematicians. The Roman numeral system, for example, did much to stall the Romans in their mathematical endeavors. As another example, Leibnitz and his associates on the Continent for a time far outdistanced Newton and his asso-

1

ciates in England in the development of the calculus largely because the English employed a clumsy system of symbols, while the Germans had a more useful means for expressing the operations and ideas involved.

The best system of symbols which may be used for computing machinery applications is difficult, if not impossible, to determine conclusively. Further, it is probably true that the system which is most appropriate for a computer designed for one purpose can be quite unsatisfactory when applied to a computer designed for another purpose. However, it is possible to point out the features and characteristics of the various systems, and this will be done through relating the symbols to the quantities which they represent. Although a reasonably broad coverage of the symbols available for use in computors is presented, it would be well to keep in mind that further modifications or even completely new systems may be invented which will greatly enlarge the usefulness of computing machinery.

Zero. One of the simplest and most elementary quantities which requires a symbol is the quantity of nothing at all, or zero. A common symbol for zero is 0, which may be thought of as representing a hole or empty container. Everyone who is familiar with the Arabic numerals is familiar with the symbol 0 and it may appear ridiculously trivial to mention it here. When discussing computers, however, it is not a trivial point, because, as a matter of fact, 0 is for some applications an inconvenient symbol to use, and other symbols are frequently adopted. One such other symbol is 999999, and another is 0011. The reasons behind the adoption of such symbols are varied, and they depend to a large extent upon the nature and purpose of the particular computer under consideration. Factors such as reliability of operation, ability to detect errors once they occur, savings in components, to name a few, create problems in the design of computers which are quite different from those occurring when the familiar pencil-and-paper method of computation is employed. One unexpected reason for the adoption of an unusual symbol for zero is that, when this symbol is employed in the internal mechanism of the computer, it is actually easier to cause the computer to print the familiar symbol than when the familiar symbol is used throughout. The details of this and other reasons can be made understandable only after certain other topics have been discussed.

One. A single item or unity is called one and may be represented by the symbol 1, which could easily have been derived from a finger or a stick or some similar object used for counting. As in the case of zero, the symbol for one may be, and is frequently, modified to suit the requirements of the machine. These modifications, incidentally, are not merely the substitution of a character of one shape for the character of another shape. The shape of the symbol as written on a piece of paper is of no consequence to a machine because the machines do not handle printed information, except in that portion which prints the final result, and in this printing mechanism the type face may have any desired design without the slightest effect on the computations. If data were entered into the machine in printed form, symbols of some shapes could probably be distinguished and identified more readily than those of other shapes; but in all existing machines the input is of some other nature such as punched cards or magnetic tape. The modifications which are of consequence involve the number of characters, the meaning of each character in the group, and its position in the group.

Two. In choosing a symbol for one plus one, or two, there are three quite different lines of procedure that may be followed.

Probably to a person inventing his own system of symbols the most obvious choice for two is two 1's placed side by side. In examining the systems of ancient peoples it is found that this choice is actually rather common. The Roman numeral system, which is well-known even today, employs this notation for two. As has already been mentioned, Roman numerals are clumsy and awkward, and computations performed with them are much more difficult than those performed with Arabic numerals. It is for this reason that Arabic numerals have replaced Roman numerals in all but simple counting applications, such as the designation of the volumes in a series of books or the recording of the date on the cornerstone of a building. It is debatable, though, that the clumsiness in the Roman numeral system is caused by their choice of a symbol for two. The real difficulties are created by their choice for larger numbers, and the possibility of devising a system useful for computers and based on the use of two 1's for two should not be overlooked, although as yet no such useful system is known.

Another choice for a symbol for two is simply a character of a shape different from 0 or 1. The Arabic numeral 2 is an example of such a choice.

A third idea for the development of a symbol for two is to use the same symbols that were employed for zero and one but to place them in such a manner that their meaning is two. A scheme which has received considerable use and which is based on this idea is to use the symbol 1 for two as well as for one but to place the 1 in a different position when it is indicating two. Then, to indicate that the one is in this different position, it is customary to place a zero in the original position. The binary system of numbers is a continuation of this method of notation.

Three and Larger Integers. No outstanding new ideas that could not have been employed for zero, one, and two are obvious for the designation of three and larger integers. Three may be symbolized by three 1's, a new symbol such as 3, or by a 1 in the different position combined with a 1 in the original position with the meaning of two plus one. If a 1 in the different position were to be interpreted as indicating three, a 0 would be placed in the original position; the ternary system of numbers involves this step in its system of symbols.

For integers larger than three, all of the processes just described may be extended, but the writing of a large number of 1's or the establishment of a great many different symbols to represent large numbers is clearly impractical. Although each of these two systems is by itself impractical for large numbers, a combination of the two systems is not at all out of the question. For example, symbols may be established for one, ten, one hundred, one thousand, and so on, and any reasonable integer could be represented by a reasonable number of these symbols written in any sequence or relative position. No particularly successful system is known which is based on this combination, however. The Roman numeral system is similar but with additional complications.

The greatest advances in arithmetic have been made through the employment of a very few different symbols with their position being used to indicate their value. The ten familiar Arabic numerals 0 through 9 employed in the well-known manner comprise the most outstanding system of this type.

Radix. The number of digit symbols employed in a system such as the Arabic numeral system is called the radix of the system. Consideration of various number systems, particularly when the consideration has been for possible use in digital computing machinery, has been largely limited to systems of the Arabic numeral type but with a variation in the choice of radix. The selection of radix ten was made long before the conception of computing machinery and was probably chosen to facilitate counting on fingers. When chosen for such a reason, radix ten is a good choice. But when finger counting is not practiced, some other radix might appear more attractive. The advantages of radix twelve have been extolled from time to time, and this radix has actually been adopted in a limited way for use with time clocks and in the counting of eggs, tacks, and other objects by the dozen and gross. The advantages of twelve are derived mainly from the fact that twelve is divisible by more numbers than any other small integer. In the design of computing machinery, twelve has no outstanding advantages over ten. However, certain other radices do offer substantial advantages over ten for use in computing machinery when the machinery is designed along certain lines. The phrase, "when the computing machinery is designed along certain lines," is important, because there are ways of going about designing a computer for which radices eight, ten, or eleven, for example, would be approximately equally desirable. For those designs where the radix does make an important difference, radices two, eight, and sixteen offer the best possibilities for an efficient computer. Actually, radix two is the only one which has been found to offer any improvements functionally. Radices eight and sixteen are mentioned because they can be employed with substantially the same designs as used for two. In such cases they amount to little more than an imaginary grouping of the radix two or binary digits except for printed representations of the data and the results. Printed numbers in the binary system are undesirable because it is difficult to handle a large number of nothing but 0's and 1's without making excessive errors.

So far as is known, radices two, three, eight, ten, twelve, and sixteen are the only ones which have ever received serious consideration for use in computing machinery. The list of those which have actually been used is much more restricted. In fact, no computer is known in which a radix other than two or ten is employed. One minor exception to this last statement exists in that at least two companies have built small electromechanical desk computers in which radix eight is used. The purpose of these radix eight computers is to provide a more satisfactory means for manually checking the computations performed on the radix two computers; therefore, it would not be quite correct to consider them in the same category.

The terms binary, ternary, and decimal have already been mentioned as referring to systems of radix two, three, and ten, respectively. Octonary, duodecimal, and sexadecimal are the accepted terms applying to radix eight, twelve, and sixteen, respectively. It is interesting to note that the Standards Committee of the Institute of Radio Engineers has gone to the trouble of listing the adjectives to be used in describing systems of many other radices, including, for example, septendecimal for seventeen and nonagenary for ninety.

The Digits and Numbers. By way of definition, a digit is a single symbol or character representing an integral quantity. A number is a quantity represented by a group of digits. The usual relationship between the digits, d_i, and the number, N, may be expressed mathematically as

$$N = d_0 + d_1R + d_2R^2 + d_3R^3 + \cdots$$

where R is the radix (also an integer) of the number system in use. A further condition which is usually, but not necessarily, applied is that the number of digits be equal to the radix and that $0 \leqq d_i < R$.

When applied to computing machinery, another term frequently used to indicate a group of digits is "word," but the digits in a word may have any of a wide variety of meanings, and there is not necessarily any connection between a word and a quantity.

It is standard practice to write the digits of a number in the opposite order from that shown above; that is,

$$N = \cdots d_3 d_2 d_1 d_0$$

This way, the digits appear from left to right in order of decreasing significance where the significance of a digit refers to the change in N that would be caused by a change in the digit. The term "order" is also used in connection with digit significance, and it means the digit position in the group with high and low orders referring to large and small significance, respectively. The placing of the higher-order digits on the left seems reasonable in view of the practice of reading from left to right, because it is thereby possible to ascertain the relative magnitude of a number at a glance more easily than if the low-order digits were encountered first. Although the arrangement of the digits on a piece of paper is of little consequence, the practice of reading and writing the highest-order digit first in time is sometimes a source of considerable difficulty in the design of computers. The difficulty is especially acute for small computers where the data are sent directly to the arithmetic unit as an operator keys it one digit at a time; and the difficulty arises because it is, in general, awkward to perform computations on numbers where the digits appear in descending order of significance.

A somewhat different requirement often arises in the printing of digits. It is customary to write a number such as 0076, for example, as 76, without any zeros in orders higher than the highest-order nonzero digit. In a computing machine the zeros are not usually nonexistent as may be the marks on a piece of paper, and therefore it is necessary to provide means for suppressing the printing of the unwanted zeros. If the printing is done one digit at a time with the digits in ascending order of significance, the zero suppression function is difficult to incorporate into a machine, but if the digits are printed in descending order of significance, zero suppression is relatively easily accomplished.

The term "significant" has another, slightly different meaning in connection with digits. A digit is significant if it is any of the digits of a number except one of zeros in orders higher than the highest order nonzero digit and if it is known or believed to be of consequence for the accurate representation of the magnitude of the quantity being represented by the number. If, because of round-off errors, inaccuracies in measurement, or otherwise, a digit is believed to be of no consequence for the accurate representation of the magnitude of a quantity, this digit is called "not significant." It usually follows that, if any given digit is not significant because of an inaccuracy, all lower-order digits in the number are also not significant.

It is now almost self-evident that a "digital" computer is a computing device which employs numbers composed of digits to represent the various quantities undergoing the computations. For some computations of purely mathematical interest the numbers or the digits are the end and not just the means, but the functioning of the computer is the same in either case. In a digital computer the individual digits are represented by variations in discrete steps of a different set of physical quantities which may include distance, angle, time, electrical potential, magnetization, and others. The physical quantities undergoing computations are related to the physical quantities in the computer through the medium of digits and numbers, which are symbols used to facilitate the computations in the computer.

There is another class of computing machinery known as "analog" computers, which differ from digital computers in two fundamental respects. The physical quantities in an analog computer are varied continuously instead of in discrete steps, and they are direct representations of the physical quantities undergoing computations rather than representations of intermediate symbols. Since digital computers are the subject of this study, analog computers will not be discussed in more detail.

Economy of Storage "Space" Through Choice of Radix. A factor frequently mentioned in connection with the choice of radix is the amount of equipment necessary to store a given amount of numerical information. This factor is of interest in the design of computers, because it is usually necessary to store, at least temporarily, in the computer itself the numbers making up the input data, results of intermediate computations, and the final results to be printed. In addition, in some computers the "program" for a given problem is stored in the same storage unit with the same system of symbols as other numerical information.

In order to discuss the amount of equipment required to store a number, it is necessary to consider the nature of the equipment. One assumption that may be made is that the amount of equipment required to store one digit is proportional to the radix of the digit. That is, two units of equipment may be required for a binary digit, three for a ternary digit, ten for a decimal digit, etc. In some cases such an assumption is approximately correct. If the storage device is a mechanical wheel, the number of gear teeth or detent positions would be proportional to the radix. Also, it is possible to design electronic storage equipment wherein the required number of vacuum tubes is proportional to the number of stable states of the circuit. It is easy to design a circuit employing two triodes which has two stable states and therefore is capable of storing a binary digit, with the existence of the circuit in one state indicating 0 and its existence in the other state indicating 1. It is not difficult to design a circuit employing three triodes which has three stable states for the storage of a ternary digit. The extension of the design to a circuit with ten stable states and employing ten triodes is possible, but such circuits are generally unreliable and not satisfactory. A different approach to the problem may be made by using a number of circuits, each employing two triodes and each with two stable states. For radix ten, then, ten such twin-triode circuits would be employed, and provision would be made to cause one and only one of the circuits to be in a given state of equilibrium at any one time, with all the other circuits in the opposite state of equilibrium. Although twice as many triodes are required ($2R$, where R is the radix), it is possible to design reliable operating circuits of this type, and the assumption that the amount of equipment required for one digit be proportional to the radix is satisfied.

If n is the number of digits, $R^n = N$ is a measure of the maximum amount of information the digits can represent and is equal to the number of different stable states of the digit-representing devices considered collectively. With the above assumption, the amount of equipment required to store N is proportional to nR. Both n and R are usually integers so that when a change in radix is made there is also of necessity at least a small change in N. Therefore, an exact comparison of the storage efficiency of the various radices is difficult, but for illustrative purposes it will be assumed that N can be held constant as R is varied. Then, $n (\log R) = \log N = K$, where K is a constant. Therefore, the amount of equipment is proportional to $KR/\log R$. To determine the most efficient radix for storage, the expression $R/\log R$ should be examined for minima. By taking the derivative of $R/\log R$ with respect to R, it is found that there is a minimum at $R = e \simeq 2.718$, but the significance of a nonintegral radix is difficult to imagine. A tabulation of the expression for several selected radices is more useful.

Radix	$R/\log R$
2	6.64
3	6.29
4	6.64
5	7.15
8	8.86
10	10.00
12	11.12
16	13.29

The tabulation indicates that radix three is the most efficient, that radices two and four are only slightly less efficient than three, and that radices ten and higher are substantially less efficient.

It should be remembered that these results were obtained after making the rather restrictive assumption that the amount of equipment required to store a digit is proportional to the radix of the digit. Some serious objections may be made to this assumption, because it seldom applies to any practical example. Even in the case of the gear teeth on a storage wheel, it does not apply well. Much more equipment than gear teeth is required to make a complete and useful mechanical storage device. In fact, in this particular case, the additional equipment adds so many complications that a meaningful comparison of radices is almost impossible.

In the case of twin-triode circuits where each circuit has two stable states, a different objection to the assumption may be raised. The objection is that it is not necessary to use, for example, ten such circuits to store a decimal digit, and this is so because each circuit may function independently. Four independent circuits, each with two stable states, are sufficient for the storage of a decimal digit, since the four taken together can exist in any one of $2^4 = 16$ stable states. Six of the stable states may be disregarded, and the other ten may be used to represent the digit. With a scheme such as this, the inferiority of radix three when compared with radix two is clearly evident. To store a ternary digit through the use of bistable twin-triode circuits, two such circuits are required, and of the four stable states available, three are used and one is wasted. To store a binary digit, only one twin-triode circuit is required, and there is no waste in the stable states. Because there is no waste in the stable states, no radix can be more economical with regard to storage space than radix two when bistable storage elements are used, although any radix that is a power of two may be equally economical provided each individual digit is coded properly. If, for example, three twin-triode circuits are used in the storage of an octonary digit, all possible combinations of stable states must be used in designating all possible values of the octonary digit. In this respect the octonary system is practically no different from the binary system; the octonary digits may be considered a grouping by threes of the binary digits.

Most of the various types of storage units used in computers are composed of devices which are essentially binary in character, such as the twin-triode circuits just mentioned. Other examples are a hole punched or not punched in a card or tape, a relay which may be open or held closed by the action of a holding coil, a pulse which may be circulating in a delay-line storage unit or which may be nonexistent, a "dot" or a "dash" in a Williams type electrostatic storage tube, and magnetization in one direction or the opposite direction in a small area of magnetic tape. One of the few exceptions to the rule is the mechanical counter wheel. Some of the devices mentioned as being binary in character could conceivably be used in decimal fashion such as by using the intensity or direction of magnetization to indicate the magnitude of a decimal digit, but little success has been achieved in making devices of this character reliable.

If one of the essentially binary storage devices is employed, the question arises as to how much saving in storage space may be secured by changing from, say, the decimal system to the binary system. The problem may be solved in the following manner. The number of storage elements, D, necessary to store a decimal number of d digits is $D = 4d$. The maximum number of different conditions, M, that can be represented by this number is $M = 10^d$. Similarly, the number of storage elements, B, necessary to store a binary number of b binary digits is $B = b$, and the maximum number of different conditions that can be represented by this binary number is $M = 2^b$. For a given amount of information to be stored,

$$10^d = 2^b \quad \text{and} \quad 10^{0.25D} = 2^B$$

From a solution of this equation it is found that $B \simeq 0.83D$. In other words, a saving of approximately 17% may be obtained by changing from a decimal system employing four storage elements per digit to a binary system.

To illustrate the above result, consider the storage of a ten-digit decimal number through the use of 40 storage elements. A binary number which is nearly as large, $2^{33} = 8,589,934,592$, may be stored through the use of 33 storage elements. The saving is in approximate agreement with the computed result.

It is of interest to solve the problem under the assumption that the amount of storage space is a constant and to compare the amounts of information that may be stored through the use of different radices. For instance, with four storage elements, one out of 10 different conditions may be recorded by employing the decimal system, but one out of 16 different conditions may be recorded by employing the binary system. The increase is 60%. With 32 storage elements, the respective numbers are 10^8 and $2^{32} = 4,294,967,296$, which indicates an increase of over 4000%. Such a comparison is valid if information is defined as being proportional to the number of possible different stable states, but this definition is not very satisfactory. It is better to define information as being proportional to the logarithm of the number of different stable states. The reason for the use of the logarithm may be explained through the use of a simple example. Assume that L letters may be written on one page. Since there are 26 letters in the alphabet, the number of different arrangements of the letters (neglecting spaces, periods, etc.) that may appear on one page is 26^L. The number of different arrangements that may appear on two pages considered together is 26^{2L}. The ratio of the logarithms of these two quantities is two, which indicates the generally accepted fact that twice as much information may be written on two pages as may be written on one page. With the latter definition, the ratios of the quantities of information are

$$\frac{\log 10}{\log 16} = \frac{\log 10^8}{\log (4.29) \, 10^9} \simeq 0.83$$

which is in agreement with the result obtained previously.

The 17% saving in storage space which may be achieved through the use of the binary system when compared with the decimal system is probably worth considering, but it is doubtful that a decision on a choice between the two systems has ever turned on this factor. The differences in the nature of the computer components and circuits which may be or must be used with the respective systems are much more striking.

Other Possible Systems of Symbols. Although the Arabic numeral system and similar systems, but with different radix, are the only ones with which much success has been achieved and which have found general use, it might be well to mention certain other systems. Although zero is a logical starting point for a system of numbers, it is not the only possible starting point. In fact, historically, zero was not recognized and understood until long after the positive integers were in common use. Symbols for the positive integers can then be employed in such a fashion that they signify zero. For example, $1 - 1$, with the meaning of one minus one, is a possibility. Another idea which may be employed in the development of a system of symbols is to have certain symbols in a group be multiplied by certain other symbols in the group. An example would be the assigning to 23 the value of two times three, or six. It is easy to let the imagination run wild on a wide assortment of schemes of this nature; but since they have not been found to have any practical value, they will not be discussed in more detail.

A system that deserves slightly more attention is called the "reflected binary" system, its name being derived from a simple method by which it may be generated. The outstanding feature of the reflected binary system is that the representations of successive integers differ, one from the next, by only one digit. The system starts with the customary 0 for zero and 1 for one. For two and three, the 0 and 1 are written in inverted sequence and then distinguished from zero and one by a 1 in the second position. Therefore, for zero, one, two, and three, the representations are 00, 01, 11, and 10, respectively. For four through seven, these symbols are repeated, again in inverted sequence, with a 1 in the third position to distinguish them from zero through three. The symbols for eight through fifteen and so on are generated in an analogous manner. A list of the symbols for zero through fifteen is shown below to illustrate the process more clearly.

Zero	0000	Eight	1100
One	0001	Nine	1101
Two	0011	Ten	1111
Three	0010	Eleven	1110
Four	0110	Twelve	1010
Five	0111	Thirteen	1011
Six	0101	Fourteen	1001
Seven	0100	Fifteen	1000

Many variations in the above scheme are possible. For one thing, any column of digits may be interchanged with any other column. Actually, it is not difficult to derive such a system by simply changing one digit at a time in an almost random fashion. An example is shown below.

Zero	0000	Eight	0110
One	0001	Nine	1110
Two	0011	Ten	1111
Three	0111	Eleven	1011
Four	0101	Twelve	1001
Five	1101	Thirteen	1000
Six	1100	Fourteen	1010
Seven	0100	Fifteen	0010

A useful application of the reflected binary system or one of its variations is found in some types of analog-to-digital and digital-to-analog conversion equipment. Its advantage is derived from the fact that successive integers differ, one from the next, by only one digit. This property is in contrast with the familiar decimal system and similar systems, because in these systems successive integers may differ by several digits. For example, 3999 and 4000 are successive integers, yet the digits in each of the four orders are different.

Unfortunately, the usefulness of the reflected binary system does not extend to arithmetic operations. Even simple addition is relatively difficult with the system, and therefore it is not expected that it will find much use in digital computers.

Negative Numbers. Negative numbers are in such common use today that it is somewhat surprising to learn that it was in relatively recent centuries that they were first recognized and understood. Probably, negative numbers were slow in coming into use because there is no such thing as negative material or negative space, at least according to the concepts of classical physics. When a quantity is spoken of as being negative, it invariably can, with a simple alteration of viewpoint, be considered as positive. A temperature of minus 10°C is a positive temperature on the Fahrenheit or Kelvin scales; a negative sum of money usually implies a debt and would appear as a positive sum in the creditor's account books; a dimension tolerance may be listed as plus or minus two-thousands of an inch, but in this case positive or negative indicates direction from a given point and it should not be taken to indicate the existence of negative distance. The scoring system used for certain card games comes closer to the use of true negative quantities, if a score may be considered a quantity. For certain eventualities in the game, a player receives points to be added to his score; but for certain other eventualities, points must be taken away from his score. It may well happen that the player loses more points than he gains, in which case his score becomes negative or "in the hole." Even though examples of true negative quantities are difficult to find, the value of negative numbers for representing the application of a quantity should be apparent. The value of negative numbers becomes considerably more outstanding when computations are performed with numbers representing the quantities.

From a purely mathematical standpoint, there is no reason at all why the series of integers has to have an abrupt ending at zero. Mathematical symbols may be devised to indicate solutions to problems such as $2 - 5 = ?$, and the relationship, or lack of it, of the symbols to physical quantities may be ignored. The customary way to indicate the solutions to such problems is to extend the series of integers in the opposite direction from zero and to call the new integers minus or negative. Note that the minus sign in the problem means that 5 is to be taken away, that is, subtracted, from 2. The 5 is not by itself a negative number; if it were negative, the problem would have been written some other way, such as $2 + (-5) = ?$ The minus sign therefore has two different, although related, meanings. One meaning is the designation of the operation of subtraction, and the other is the designation of those integers which continue the series of integers beyond zero in the direction of smaller numbers. The terms "small" and "large" and also the frequently used terms of "less than" and "greater than" are derived from the application of numbers to physical quantities, and although phrases such as "less than nothing" or "smaller than zero" have little meaning when applied to physical quantities, they may assume a useful meaning when applied to negative numbers.

The most familiar system of symbols for negative numbers is the same system which is used for positive numbers, where the group of digits indicates the "distance" from zero, and a sign, plus or minus, indicates the "direction" from zero. It follows that, for a negative number, all coefficients in the expression $d_0 + d_1R + d_2R^2 \cdots$ are negative. For positive numbers, the plus sign is frequently omitted, with the understanding that the absence of a minus sign signifies that the number under consideration is positive.

From a mathematical point of view, the sign of zero is usually of no consequence and may be either plus or minus, or, in other words, plus zero, minus zero, and zero without any sign indication all refer to the same integer. Nevertheless, it is sometimes desirable to retain the sign of zero in a problem to indicate from which direction the computations proceeded in arriving at the result of zero. For commercial applications, it is customary to consider zero as a positive quantity always; the red ink is not used unless the balance is less than zero. Although they offer no problems with paper-and-pencil computations, the details concerning the sign of zero frequently are a source of considerable annoyance in the design of computing machinery.

A question which arises at this point involves the necessity or desirability of requiring that all coefficients in the expression for a number be positive or all be negative. This requirement is not necessary, although the advantages to be gained by omitting it are not obvious. One result that is obtained by allowing the coefficients to be independent of one another with regard to sign is that a given integer then has no unique representation. For example, another decimal representation for the integer, 7, would be a 1 in the tens order and a -3 in the units order. The representation can be made unique, if desired, by restricting the range of the integers to only ten different values, such as from -4 to 5, and it turns out that there are some practical applications of this idea in connection with decimal multiplication and division.

Another system with positive and negative coefficients which has been studied with at least moderate thoroughness is the ternary system. Instead of using 0, 1, and 2 for coefficients, the coefficients which are used are -1, 0, and $+1$, abbreviated to $-$, 0, and $+$. The nature of the system may be illustrated by listing a few of the integers.

−3	0 − 0	+4	0 + +
−2	0 − +	+5	+ − −
−1	0 0 −	+6	+ − 0
0	0 0 0	+7	+ − +
+1	0 0 +	+8	+ 0 −
+2	0 + −	+9	+ 0 0
+3	0 + 0		

As can be seen from the brief listing, the sign of the number is contained in the digits making up the number, but since a given nonzero digit always represents a number which is larger in magnitude than the sum of all less significant digits, the sign of the number may be quickly determined from the sign of the most significant nonzero digit. The procedure for inverting the sign of a number while not changing the magnitude is to change all +'s to −'s and all −'s to +'s and to leave the 0's unchanged. Addition and multiplication tables for this system may be built up without difficulty. The multiplication table is particularly simple; and, because of it, the study of the system can be a source of great fascination. Further, it is intriguing to visualize a computer which uses positive electrical pulses to represent +'s, negative pulses for −'s, and no pulses for 0's. However, it takes more than a simple multiplication table and a bare idea about pulses to design a computer. When the difficulties which are encountered in the design of a ternary computer are combined with the dearth of ternary computer components and with the difficulties in adapting the system to applications where the decimal system is already entrenched, it appears that the disadvantages of the ternary system with positive and negative coefficients substantially outweigh the advantages.

There are cases, however, where the simple medium of plus and minus signs is not the most convenient means of indicating negative quantities. Consider a computer that is performing only the function of counting, and assume that it has started with some positive number and is counting downwards or in the direction of smaller numbers. The units counter wheel (or other counting device) proceeds from digit to digit in the sequence of ··· 2, 1, 0, 9, 8 ··· as it counts, and each time it passes from 0 to 9 it causes the tens counterwheel to move one position and indicate the next lower digit. This process should continue until the counters of all orders reach zero. If further counts are recorded, the sign indicating device should be actuated to indicate a negative balance; and for succeeding counts, the counter wheels should be caused to move in the opposite direction with digits appearing in the sequence ··· 8, 9, 0, 1, 2 ··· and with counts being sent from one order to the next higher order as the corresponding counter wheel passes from 9 to 0. It is possible to design a counting mechanism which will perform a function such as this, but the requirements that the system be able to sense when the counters of all orders are at zero and that the counters be able to operate in either direction cause undesirable complexities in the mechanism.

If negative numbers were represented according to the pattern,

$$
\begin{array}{rl}
+2 & 0002 \\
+1 & 0001 \\
0 & 0000 \\
-1 & 9999 \\
-2 & 9998
\end{array}
$$

it would be possible to avoid the zero sensing device and to use counter wheels which will function in one direction only. With the illustrated system for portraying negative numbers, it is not necessary to sense zeros to determine when the balance changes from positive to negative, because it is necessary only to detect when the thousands order counter moves from 0 to 9. Also in counting numbers beyond zero on the negative side, the counter wheels may function in exactly the same manner as for positive numbers. Another feature of this method of representing negative numbers is that the highest order counter wheel may be used to indicate the sign of the balance at the expense of the capacity of the counter. For example, a 9 indication in the highest order may be taken to indicate a negative balance with any other digit in this order indicating a positive balance. In this case, the capacity of the counter is from +8999 to −1000. If an 8 or a 9 in the highest order is used for a negative indication, the capacity is shifted to the range +7999 to −2000. The term used to describe this scheme for negative number representation is "10's complement," although the term is not to be interpreted to mean that each individual digit is a 10's complement. Actually, only the least significant nonzero digit is a 10's complement of the true digits; higher-order digits are 9's complements. For example, the 10's complement of 4680 is 5320. A more descriptive term would be "ten-thousand's complement," but this is clumsy.

Frequently it is desirable to employ a system for negative numbers similar to that just described in the counter itself but to convert the representation to that shown in the left-hand column when the result is recorded. For this purpose a slight but important modification is useful.

$$
\begin{array}{rl}
+2 & 0002 \\
+1 & 0001 \\
0 & 0000 \text{ or } 9999 \\
-1 & 9998 \\
-2 & 9997
\end{array}
$$

With this method of representation for negative numbers, the change to the commonly used system is made very conveniently by subtracting each individual digit from 9, and for this reason the representation is known as the 9's complement. The 9's complement may be generated when the counter goes from a positive to negative balance by using the signal obtained from the highest-order counter wheel as it passes from 0 to 9 to cause one additional count called "end-around borrow," to be registered in the units order. When counting in the positive direction from a negative balance, the counter will arrive at 9999 instead of 0000 for a zero indication. Then, when the next count is received, the signal which is obtained from the highest-order counter wheel may be used as an "end-around carry" to advance the units order counter from 0 to 1. From this point on, the counter will proceed in the usual manner and yield a true indication for positive balances. The balance sign indicator may be a separate device operated by the highest-order counter wheel, or, as before, the highest-order counter wheel itself may be used; but in this case the capacity for negative balances is reduced by 1, such as from $+8999$ to -999, when compared with the previous system.

The differences between true and complement notation become of increased importance when operations of addition and subtraction, other than by simple counting, are considered. On the other hand, for multiplication, the complement system frequently introduces more problems than it solves.

Similar ideas involving complement notation may be employed for the binary system or system of any other radix.

Nonintegral Quantities. There are two types of nonintegral quantities —those which may be represented as the ratio of two integers and are called rational (the integers themselves are rational), and those which cannot be represented as the ratio of two integers and are called irrational.

If it is desired to represent exactly a rational quantity, commonly called a fraction, it is usually done by recording the two integers involved, each with the same notation as used previously. The fact that the two integers are related is indicated on paper by writing one above the other with a line drawn between the two. It is conceivable that a computer could be designed whereby the position of the number in a storage unit is indicative of its function in a fraction, although the incorporation of a physical device to represent the line between the numbers appears to be somewhat superfluous. The advantages of a computer built along these lines would be realized only in certain special cases; and, in those cases where fractions must be dealt with in an exact manner, it has been found more practical to handle separately and independently in the computer each of the two integers involved. The functional relationship between the two integers may be maintained through the programming of the sequence of arithmetic and other operations to be performed.

Usually it is not necessary, and sometimes it is not even desirable, that fractions be represented exactly. By extending the number system to include terms involving the negative powers of the radix, such as $d_{-1}R^{-1}$, $d_{-2}R^{-2}$, etc., any fraction may be represented to any degree of accuracy. With this extension,

$$N = \cdots d_3d_2d_1d_0 \cdot d_{-1}d_{-2} \cdots$$

The period or point between d_0 and d_{-1} is used to signify the location of the units order, and the locations of all other orders are automatically specified. This point, called the decimal point in the decimal system, the binary point in a binary system, etc., is necessary when writing on paper because the digits corresponding to positive and negative powers of the radix are otherwise indistinguishable; but in a computer the orders may be assigned certain specific locations in the storage unit and are operated upon accordingly. Therefore, there is no need to provide an additional physical device in the computer for recording a counterpart of the dot (point) on a piece of paper. The assignment of the locations may change from problem to problem or even from step to step within a problem, but such changes are usually noted and recorded in the program. In general, it is possible to give an exact representation of a fraction by this scheme if the denominator of the fraction contains no prime factors which are not factors of the radix. An example is one eighth, which is 0.125 in the decimal system. The denominator of the fraction, one seventh, for example, contains a prime factor, seven, which is not a factor of ten. Therefore, one seventh cannot be represented exactly by this scheme, although by employing enough orders (0.1428571 $\cdots$) the difference between the indicated value and the exact value may be made as small as desired.

Some irrational numbers may be represented by integers with appropriate positional significance. For example, the integers 1, 2, and 3, if placed in the manner, $2^{1/3}$, represent the cube root of two. Much more exercise of the imagination is required to employ integers in the representation of irrational numbers derived from limits, trigonometric functions, and other sources. But, as in the case of fractions, an exact representation is not usually required anyway, and the customary procedure is to employ the same extension of the number system to terms involving negative powers of the radix in order to gain an approximate representation to any desired degree of accuracy.

Integral and Fractional Computers. Some computers are assumed to handle only integers and are therefore called integral computers, whereas in other computers the numbers are all assumed to have a magnitude less than unity, and these computers are called fractional. Although the difference between integral and fractional representation is of considerable importance when preparing a problem for solution by a computer, this difference is largely a figment of the imagination when considering the actual physical construction of the computer. But one physical difference worth mentioning lies in the disposition of the product after a multiplication. If a computer is built to handle numbers of a certain size, say four digits, the product of two of these numbers may contain eight significant digits. In an integral computer, if a number is to be added to the product, it should be added to the right-hand four digits, which are the ones of lesser significance. For the points to be lined up in a fractional machine, the addition should be to the left-hand, or most significant, digits. Sample computations of the kind $AB + C$ for the two types of computers are shown below.

3023.	A	.3023	A
$\times$ 6104.	B	$\times$ .6104	B
18452392.	AB	.18452392	AB
+ 4116.	C	+ .4116	C
18456508.	$AB + C$	.59612392	$AB + C$
Integral		Fractional	

Integral computers are most useful for problems which are essentially integral in nature; and many money calculations, for example, are of this type. With an integral computer, a quantity such as $109.30 would be considered to be 10930, and the problem would be solved in cents instead of dollars and hundredths of dollars. At the conclusion of the problem, appropriate reconversions would be made.

The value of a fractional machine is realized for those problems where the data are not of an integral nature and where results of extreme accuracy either cannot or need not be obtained. Although the product of two four-significant-digit numbers may contain eight digits, it can be shown that only the four higher-order digits in the product are significant if the original factors were approximations and not exact representations. Actually, to say that a number has four significant digits implies that there is some doubt in the accuracy of the fourth digit; the extent of this doubt combined with certain fine points which may be included in the definition of significance may indicate that the product has only three or as many as five significant digits, but in general the number of significant digits in the product is equal to the least number of significant digits in any one of its factors. In the above fractional example, the digits 2392 in the product AB are not significant and may be dropped. A subsequent addition should, therefore, be made to the left-hand four digits, as shown. If the factor C to be added were 0.004116, the last two digits may as well be dropped, because, even though they are significant in the factor C itself, they would not increase the number of significant digits in the result to any more than four when added to a product such as AB.

In an integral computer, therefore, the disposition of the product is such that subsequent additions are automatically made to the lowest orders, and special steps must be taken to handle any overflow into the higher orders. But in a fractional computer, the additions are automatically made to the highest-order digits of a product and the low-order digits are dropped unless special steps are taken to preserve them. In all but the most modest of computers it is possible to shift the digits in a number to lower or higher orders and thereby make additions of a number into any desired orders of a product, although the means for shifting vary greatly in convenience of operation and in required time in machines of different designs. Because of the ability to shift numbers, it is possible to perform fractional-type calculations on an integral machine and integral calculations on a fractional machine.

If the factors A and B in the fractional example had been 0.1342 and 0.1041, respectively, the product would be 0.01397022 with the four significant digits appearing in the second to the fifth positions to the right of the decimal point instead of the first to the fourth positions. For this and other reasons, frequent shifting is required for some problems; and, in general, the more shifting that is required for miscellaneous reasons, the less difference it makes whether the problem is solved on an integral or a fractional machine. Some computers are designed so that the orders into which a number is added must be specified for each addition. With computers of this type, either integral or fractional calculations may be performed with equal ease (or equal difficulty).

Floating-point Computers. A floating-point computer produces the effect of indicating the location of the point in a number, but the effect is accomplished through a means quite different from a physical indication between the digits. A number may be indicated by a series of digits multiplied by a power of the radix, where the point in the series of digits is understood to be always in the same place, such as to the left of the highest-order nonzero digit. The number, therefore, may be determined by the digits and the power, or exponent, of the radix. Some examples in the decimal system are listed below:

Customary Notation		Floating-point Notation	
8076000.	$= 0.8076 \times 10^7$	8076	$+07$
80.76	$= 0.8076 \times 10^2$	8076	$+02$
0.8076	$= 0.8076 \times 10^0$	8076	$+00$
0.0008076	$= 0.8076 \times 10^{-3}$	8076	-03

This floating-point type of notation is particularly useful for computations involving many multiplications and divisions where the magnitudes of the quantities involved are likely to vary widely and where only crude predictions can be made of the amount of variation. In multiplication, for example, the digits are multiplied in the usual manner, and the exponents are added. The main advantage of the system is derived from the ability to store very large or very small numbers by storing only the significant digits and the exponent; whereas, in a fixed-point machine, either integral or fractional, it is necessary to include all the zeros between the significant digits and the point or else keep track of the point through the programming of the problem.

In the examples shown above, the sign of the exponent is also of importance and must be recorded. The necessity of recording the sign can be avoided by assuming the point to be several orders to the left of the most significant digit. If it is fifty orders to the left, 0.8076, for example, would be thought of as $0.00 \cdots 008076 \times 10^{50}$ and would be recorded as 807650 with the last two digits indicating the exponent of the multiplier. Of course, the range of exponents is halved by the dropping of the sign.

The floating-point system has an important disadvantage beyond the obvious fact that increased complexities are required to handle both significant digits and exponents in multiplication. Addition and subtraction, which are normally relatively simple operations, become much more difficult and time consuming than in fixed-point machines because of the necessity of shifting to match exponents before two numbers can be added together or subtracted one from the other. Also, overflows become more frequent. For example, the sum of two four-digit numbers can produce a five-digit number and require a shift to the right of one order and an increase by one in the exponent. Further, products and quotients must be tested for zeros to the left of the most significant digits and appropriate shifts executed when zeros are detected; otherwise there may be a gradual loss of significant digits as the computations proceed, which will be in addition to any losses caused by the mathematical nature of the problem.

With most large "general-purpose" fixed-point computers, it is possible to perform computations in a floating-point manner by special techniques in the programming of the problems.

Mixed Radices. So far, it has been assumed that the radix of each term in a number is the same as the radix of all other terms. As might be expected, it is not necessary to impose a restriction such as this; and, in fact, in some fields of application, different radices are commonly used for different terms, especially for terms to the right of the point in comparison with the terms to the left of the point.

Although the decimal system is well adapted to the finger counting of integers, it is not so well adapted to the division of a quantity into parts. Anyone who has tried to cut an object into ten equal parts knows that it is not easy; whereas the cutting of the object into halves, then to fourths and eighths and so on, may be accomplished readily with reasonable accuracy. The cutting into thirds is also an awkward operation, but it is nevertheless a particularly frequent requirement. It is probably for reasons of this nature that in India the counting of rupees is done in the decimal system with the rupee divided into 16 annas, the anna divided into 4 pice, and the pice divided into 3 pie. The same reasons might have figured in the adoption by the English of 20 shillings to the pound, 12 pennies to the shilling, and 4 farthings to the penny, or in the adoption of the English system of weights and measures, which is badly scrambled with an assortment of radices. The linear measuring system, involving inches, feet, yards, rods, furlongs, and miles, is particularly confusing. The New York Stock Exchange employs the decimal system for dollars and a substantially binary system for parts of dollars in the representation of the price of stocks, even though the amount of money involved in any transaction is always indicated in dollars and cents. A possible justification for this practice is that a buyer and a seller can more readily establish a compromise price which is halfway between the bid and asked prices.

By using special codings for each digit in the conventional decimal system, another set of systems (including, notably, the biquinary system) may be derived; and some of these systems are often considered to be of the mixed radices type. However, it has been decided to omit these systems from the present discussion and to include them in the subject of decimal codes, because in almost every case the purpose of the coding is to make the decimal system more adaptable to computing machinery and because the mixed radices properties are usually incidental.

It is of interest to note that, in many cases where a mixed radices system has been established, it has been subsequently abandoned in favor of a pure decimal system. An example is surveying, where it is frequently found desirable to replace inches with tenths of a foot. For mechanical machine work and other applications where small or accurate dimensions are involved, the practice of subdividing the inch into eighths, sixty-fourths, etc., has been largely replaced by the employment of the decimal system for fractional parts with the unit being the mil, or 0.001 of an inch. The division of pounds (weight) and gallons into tenths, instead of ounces and quarts, respectively, is frequent practice. The use of the decimal system for fractional parts in disregard of the established units is done for simplicity of notation and ease of computation and is evidence that any advantages which may be advanced in support of the mixed radices system cannot be very strong.

It is possible to design a special computer which will handle any one of the mixed radices systems fairly well, and in some simple applications a computer of this type is probably the best solution to the problem of performing computations once the system is established. An example is an adding machine for English or for Indian money, but a special adding machine would be useful only for the special application for which it was designed. A second solution to the problem is feasible when a more elaborate computer is employed, because then the computer itself can be used to execute conversions to pennies or annas, as the case may be, even though the machine operates with a number system of uniform radix. After the desired computations are completed, the computer can then reconvert the results into the desired units. Neither of these solutions is particularly satisfactory, however; and there is little doubt that the uniform radix systems are superior. As machine computations come into increased use, the reasons for abandoning the mixed radices systems become more compelling.

It should be pointed out that the mixed radices systems which have been mentioned employ the same decimal digits in every case instead of special digits as might be expected. For example, three thirty-seconds in a stock quotation is written $\frac{3}{32}$, and not 0.00011; also, thirteen shillings is written 13 where the 1 and the 3 together may be considered to be a new symbol, but it is more customary to view the digits with their usual decimal meaning. Details such as this, although of no fundamental importance, must be taken into consideration in the design of computing machinery.

Complex Numbers, Matrices, and Tensors. A complex number is customarily written as $A + jB$, where A and B are numbers according to previously described number systems, and j is the square root of minus one. As in the case of fractions, it is conceivable that a computer could be designed whereby the position of a number in a storage unit would indicate its function in a complex number and that addition, multiplication, and other operations on complex numbers would be handled in the proper fashion automatically. For some classes of problems, particularly in communications and power engineering work, practically all quantities involved are most conveniently represented by complex numbers. For these problems a complex number machine has advantages, and at least one organization (Bell Telephone Laboratories) has constructed complex number machines. However, because a complex number computer would be inefficient when applied to other types of computations, and since the two parts, A and B, of a complex number are so easily handled separately with all individual arithmetic steps programmed, the usefulness of a machine designed especially for complex numbers appears to be of limited importance.

Similar remarks could be made with regard to matrices, tensors, and other forms of mathematical symbols, but the over-all desirability of a machine built to handle such quantities automatically seems to be even less because of the great complications which would be necessary in the machine and because of the more limited application of the symbols.

Conclusions with Regard to Symbols. Although the advantages and disadvantages of the various systems of symbols can be pointed out, it does not appear possible to prove that any one system is better than all other systems.

It is a fact, however, that the systems employing the principle of position and a uniform radix are the only ones that have received wide acceptance; and if there is a system more adaptable to computers, it is probably one which has not yet been invented.

The important decision to be made is the choice of radix. Radix two is most attractive if machine simplicity is of prime importance, but the choice of radix ten is frequently dictated because of the desirability of using the computer in applications where the decimal system is already in general use. With large-scale high-speed computers, it is sometimes practical to employ the binary system internally in the computer and to use the computer itself to perform the necessary conversions between the decimal and binary systems in those cases where the use of the decimal system is required. The use of a binary computer with special conversion equipment to allow the use of the decimal system for data and solutions is also practical in some cases.

If the decimal system were not already so well established for general use, the choice might not fall on either the decimal or binary systems. In the choice of a radix, a compromise has to be made between the number of digits necessary to write a number and the number of different digits which it is necessary to employ. For the binary system only two different digits are required, but for any given number, over three times as many digits are required for recording the value of the number, when compared with the decimal system. On the other end of the scale, to decrease the number of required digits by a factor of two, it is necessary to employ a radix of one hundred, which means that one hundred different digits would be required. Although radix ten appears to be a good compromise, radices eight and sixteen are also good compromises, and most of the advantages of the binary system can be realized with the octonary or sexadecimal systems.

The advantages of radix twelve are not derived from any particular adaptability of this radix to machine computations, and the advantage of radix three is slight at best and is found to be no advantage at all when the true nature of practically all currently available computer components is considered.

Chapter 2

BOOLEAN ALGEBRA APPLIED TO COMPUTER COMPONENTS

Boolean algebra derives its name from George Boole, who first introduced it in 1847 in a paper on the mathematical analysis of logic. The adaptability of this form of algebra to telephone and computer switching circuits appears to have been first pointed out by C. E. Shannon some ninety years later (1938) in the *Transactions* of the American Institute of Electrical Engineers. Since 1938 the interest in Boolean algebra and the extent of its use have grown rapidly with its growth closely paralleling the rapid development of complex switching networks as found in automatic telephone dialing systems and in large digital computers.

Boolean algebra is very different from ordinary algebra at first glance, and for this reason it may seem confusing or even a little ridiculous. Actually, it is an extremely simple algebra and, as will be shown, is of great value in the design of switching networks. However, one point should be understood from the start: it does not lead directly to the "best" circuit (usually the circuit with the least number of components, although sometimes other criteria are more important) in the same sense that, for example, calculus can be used to find minima in a function. What the algebra does provide is a convenient means of representing a switching circuit without drawing the circuit. Also, and probably more important, is the fact that it provides a means for quickly finding a multitude of different circuits that will perform any desired switching function. With a little practice, the circuit designer thereby has a powerful tool to aid him in finding a "good" circuit, even though it may not be the "best" one.

Basic Principles of Boolean Algebra. In Boolean algebra, there are only two different quantities or values which come into consideration, and these quantities are 0 and 1. Arithmetic operations in Boolean algebra with "numbers" which can be only 0 or 1 bear little resemblance in meaning to the arithmetic operations in ordinary algebra, although in many instances the rules for performing the operations are the same. In particular, addition will be assigned the meaning of "or," and multiplication has the meaning of "and." The results obtained when "adding" and "multiplying" the various combinations of 0's and 1's are as follows:

$$0 + 0 = 0 \qquad 0 \times 0 = 0$$

$$0 + 1 = 1 \qquad 0 \times 1 = 0$$

$$1 + 1 = 1 \qquad 1 \times 1 = 1$$

The first equation involving "addition" has the meaning, "0 or 0 is equal to 0." The second equation has the meaning "0 or 1 is equal to 1," because the "or" function, as indicated by the plus sign, serves to signify that the resultant quantity is 1 if either of the given quantities is 1. This interpretation of the "or" function includes the case where both of the given quantities are 1; therefore, "1 or 1 is equal to 1." Since there is no such quantity as 2 in Boolean algebra, the latter equation is, of necessity, different from anything found in ordinary algebra. A simple example of the Boolean algebra "or" function would be a fire-alarm device which may be actuated by signals from two different sources. The signal from each source may be represented by a 1, and the absence of a signal may be represented by a 0. The signal lines from the two sources should be combined so that the alarm will sound whenever a signal is received from either source. In other words, a signal is sent to the alarm when a signal is received from one source "or" the other source. Of course, if signals are received from both sources simultaneously, the alarm will sound in this case also, but not with twice the amplitude.

The equations involving "multiplication" have corresponding meanings, but with the word "and" substituted for "or." The "and" signifies that the resultant quantity is 1 only when both of the given quantities are 1. The last equation, which states that "1 and 1 is equal to 1," should not be confused with addition in ordinary algebra. An elementary example of an "and" function would be the firing of an explosive charge through the use of two signals where, in the interest of safety, it is required that both signals be present simultaneously in order to cause the charge to explode. The charge will explode only when a signal is received from one source "and" the other source also.

As in ordinary algebra, symbols may be used to represent "unknowns" or "variables," although the range of variation is limited to one or the other of the two discrete quantities, 0 and 1. The symbolic equation

$C = A + B$, for example, means that C is 1 if A "or" B is 1 (or if both are 1); otherwise, C is 0. Similarly, the equation $C = AB$ means that C is 1 only if both A "and" B are 1; otherwise, C is 0.

From the above definitions, the following relationships may be obtained directly:

$$A + 0 = A$$

$$A + 1 = 1$$

$$A + A = A$$

$$A0 = 0$$

$$A1 = A$$

$$AA = A$$

The meaning of these equations may be readily understood by substituting for A each of the two possible values it may have.

Both the "or" and "and" functions are commutative and associative.

$$A + B = B + A$$

$$AB = BA$$

$$(A + B) + C = A + (B + C)$$

$$(AB)C = A(BC)$$

Also, each function is distributive with respect to the other.

$$AB + AC = A(B + C)$$

$$A + BC = (A + B)(A + C)$$

These equations are not definitions, but are natural consequences of the nature of the "or" and "and" functions. For example, if A "and" B is 1 or if A "and" C is 1, it must be that A is 1 "and" that B "or" C is 1. The last two equations above are not independent of one another as may be observed by multiplying out $(A + B)(A + C)$ and simplifying according to the rules of the preceding equations.

$$
\begin{aligned}
(A + B)(A + C) &= (A + B)A + (A + B)C \\
&= A + BA + AC + BC \\
&= A(1 + B + C) + BC \\
&= A + BC
\end{aligned}
$$

With the above set of basic rules it is possible to solve a wide variety of Boolean algebra problems. A simple but illustrative example is proving that $A(A + B) = A$. The steps in one form of the proof are as follows:

$$A(A + B) = AA + AB = A + AB = A(1 + B) = A1 = A$$

A fundamental concept which is found in Boolean algebra and which has no counterpart in ordinary algebra is the "not" function, as indicated by a line over a symbol. In particular, $\bar{0}$ means "not 0" and has the value of 1 because, if it is not 0, the only other value it can have is 1. Similarly, $\bar{1}$ has the value of 0. From this definition it follows that, if a variable, A, is 0, then $\bar{A}$ (called "not A") is 1; but, if A is 1, then $\bar{A}$ is 0. From this definition and the nature of the "or" and "and" functions, the following equations may be obtained.

$$A + \bar{A} = 1$$

$$A\bar{A} = 0$$

$$\bar{\bar{A}} = A$$

Two other important equations are

$$\overline{ABC} = \bar{A} + \bar{B} + \bar{C}$$

and

$$\overline{A + B + C} = \bar{A}\bar{B}\bar{C}$$

where the line over a group of symbols means that the "not" function applies to the entire expression under the line. These equations are shown for three variables, although analogous equations exist for any number of variables. The validity of the equations may be established easily by allowing the variables to take on the two possible values, 0 and 1, in all possible combinations. To obtain a better visualization of the meanings of the equations, it may be observed that the left-hand side of the first equation is 1 when the quantity ABC is 0, and ABC will be 0 whenever any of the individual variables are 0, which is exactly the same condition that will cause the right-hand side of the equation to be 1. For the second equation, a corresponding observation may be made.

It is now possible to prove, for example, that

$$\overline{AB + BC + CA} = \bar{A}\bar{B} + \bar{B}\bar{C} + \bar{C}\bar{A}$$

which is an equation arising in the study of binary adders. One way to establish the equality is to apply the equations given above according to the method outlined on the next page.

$$\overline{AB + BC + CA} = \overline{(AB)}\ \overline{(BC)}\ \overline{(CA)}$$
$$= (\bar{A} + \bar{B})(\bar{B} + \bar{C})(\bar{C} + \bar{A})$$
$$= (\bar{A}\bar{B} + \bar{A}\bar{C} + \bar{B})(\bar{C} + \bar{A})$$
$$= \bar{A}\bar{B} + \bar{B}\bar{C} + \bar{C}\bar{A}$$

The operations of subtraction and division have no parallel in this system of Boolean algebra. Division, in particular, is to be avoided; quantities cannot be "divided out" according to the familiar rules used in ordinary algebra. An example is the equation,

$$(A\bar{B} + B\bar{C} + C\bar{A})(\bar{A}B + \bar{B}C + \bar{C}A) = (A + B + C)(\bar{A}B + \bar{B}C + \bar{C}A)$$

where the quantity, $\bar{A}B + \bar{B}C + \bar{C}A$, cannot be divided out because

$$A\bar{B} + B\bar{C} + C\bar{A} \neq A + B + C$$

It is instructive to prove by means of the relationships already discussed, first, that the equation is correct and, second, that the inequality is correct. A more obvious example is the equation, $A(A + B) = A$, where the factor, A, cannot be divided out because $A + B$ is not necessarily equal to 1.

The subject may be extended far beyond the elementary points presented here, but the definitions and relationships which have been given should be sufficient to take care of all of the problems and applications to be presented. However, as an indication of the direction in which further development of Boolean algebra proceeds, the following equations are presented without proof.

$$f(A, B, C) = Af(A, B, C)_{A=1} + \bar{A}f(A, B, C)_{A=0}$$
$$f(A, B, C) = [A + f(A, B, C)_{A=0}][A + f(A, B, C)_{A=1}]$$

Here the notation, $f(A, B, C)_{A=1}$, for example, means any arbitrary function of A, B, and C but with the value, 1, substituted for A and the value, 0, substituted for $\bar{A}$.

It should not be construed that the system of Boolean algebra notation used here is universally accepted. In fact, several different types of symbols have been employed by various writers to indicate the "and" and "or" functions. Also, the "not" function may be represented in a number of different ways, some of which differ by more than just the choice of a symbol. However, the system of notation which has been described is well suited for the application, algebraic manipulations are straightforward, the symbols are easily learned and remembered, and the confusion with the ordinary algebraic functions which might be expected has not been found to exist in practice.

An important variation in the notation may be obtained by interchanging the "product" and "sum" indications with respect to the "and" and "or" operations. It happens that all of the basic relationships are correct with either convention. Whichever convention is chosen, it is occasionally desirable in the design of computer circuits to apply the opposite convention to the solution of a problem. In this way it is sometimes possible to discover quickly certain circuit arrangements which might otherwise be overlooked. Since the use of both conventions does involve a certain amount of confusion, the procedure will not be described further.

Application to Computer Components. The bare rules of Boolean algebra, as described in the previous section, probably seem somewhat

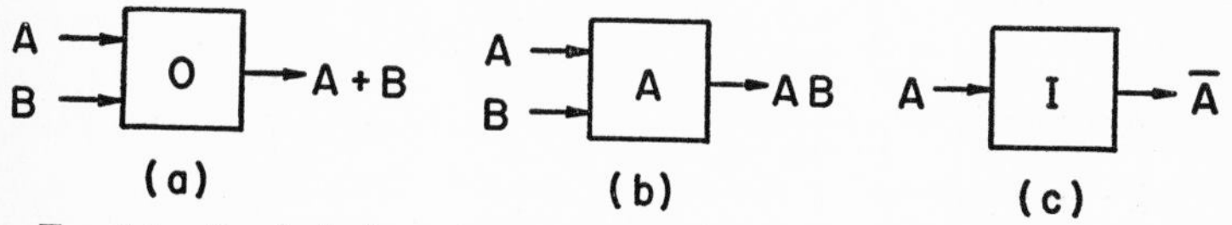

Fig. 2-1. Symbols for components that perform the basic functions.

artificial and pointless when considered by themselves, but their meaning and application should become more understandable when the correlation between the functions and computer components is described in more detail.

A simple "or" switch will be symbolized by a block labeled with the letter O. The "or" switch may have any number of inputs, and each input will be indicated by a separate line with an arrow pointing in the direction of the block. The output from the switch correspondingly will be represented by a line with an arrow pointing away from the block, as indicated in Fig. 2-1(a). If the input signals to a two-input "or" switch are represented by the variables, A and B, and the output by C, the functional relationship between the output and the inputs may be designated by the equation, $C = A + B$. Of course, the input variables are always the independent variables, with the output being dependent upon the inputs. Again, each variable is either 1 or 0, according to the presence or absence of a signal on its corresponding line. The equation, therefore, has the meaning that a signal will be present on line C if a signal is present on line A "or" on line B (or both).

With practical circuits and components, the nature of the signal on a line may assume any of a wide variety of forms. A frequently used form of signal is a positive voltage to represent a 1 and a negative voltage to represent a 0, where "positive" and "negative" are potentials relative to each other and not necessarily relative to ground potential. Another form of signal could be a transient pulse of voltage of either polarity. Further, the signal need not even be electrical; mechanical motions of various descriptions may be used.

A simple "and" switch will be symbolized, correspondingly, by a block labeled with the letter A, as shown with two inputs in Fig. 2-1(b). In the case of the "and" switch, the functional dependence of the output, C, expressed in terms of the inputs, A and B, may be represented by the equation, $C = AB$. The meaning of the equation is that C is 1 only when both A "and" B are 1.

The "not" operation, or inversion, is symbolized by a block labeled with the letter I. If the input to an inverter is A, the output is $\bar{A}$.

Diodes. Because of the wide application of the diode switch, a brief description of this particular form of switch will be given. With the

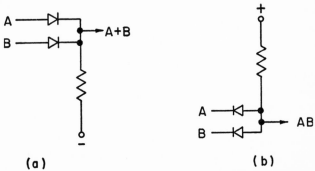

(a)   (b)

Fig. 2-2. Diode "or" and "and" circuits (1 and 0 are represented by positive and negative voltages, respectively).

assumption that 0's and 1's are represented by relatively negative and positive potentials, respectively, the diode "or" circuit is shown in Fig. 2-2(a). The diodes are connected to a common load resistor, which in turn is connected to source of relative negative voltage. Each diode will pass current freely in the direction of the "arrow," but offers a high impedance to the flow of current in the other direction (electron flow is against the arrow). Then, when both input lines indicate 0, the output line will also indicate 0 because the diode resistance to current flow in this direction is assumed to be negligible compared to the resistance of the load resistor. If either one of the input lines is raised in potential to indicate a 1, the output line will indicate a 1, since an increased amount of current will be caused to flow in the load resistor. In other words, the output line will still be connected through a relatively low impedance to the input line with a 1-signal, and the diode corresponding to the input line with a 0-signal will not pass current because the potentials on its terminals will be in the high-impedance direction of this particular diode. Therefore, the output will be positive if one input line "or" the other (or both) is positive.

The diode circuit for forming an "and" switch is indicated in Fig. 2-2(b). The circuit is similar to the "or" switch except that the connections of the diodes are inverted and the load resistor is connected to source of relatively positive potential. With the "and" switch, if both of the input lines are held at a relatively negative potential to represent 0's, the output line will also be at the same relatively negative potential because the voltage drop from the positive supply will appear across the resistor and not the diodes. When the potential of one of the input lines is raised to indicate a 1, the corresponding diode will have a voltage impressed across it which is in the reverse, or high-impedance direction, and the potential of the output line will be unaffected. Only when 1's appear on both input lines will potential on the output line become relatively positive as is required for a 1 indication. In other words, the output line will become positive only when one input line "and" the other line also become positive.

It should be noticed that the roles of the circuits in Fig. 2-2 become interchanged when a 1 is represented by a negative instead of a positive potential. For example, in Fig. 2-2(a) the output becomes negative when both of the input lines are negative, and in (b) the output becomes negative when either input line is negative. For this reason, in identifying "or" and "and" circuits, it is necessary to specify the polarity of signals which are in use.

The importance and usefulness of Boolean algebra notation arise from the fact that each algebraic expression represents a different physical circuit, even when the expressions are mathematically equivalent. As an example of this property of the relationship between the notation and the circuits, consider a switching network with four input lines, A, B, C, and D, and with an output line, E, which is 1 when A "and" B are 1 or when C "and" D are 1. The Boolean algebra expression is $E = AB + CD$, and the switching network which will perform this function is shown in Fig. 2-3(a). However, it is possible to write down the desired switching function in other ways. One other way is indicated by the following equation.

$$AB + CD = (A + C)(A + D)(B + C)(B + D)$$

The expression on the right-hand side of the equation describes the switching arrangement shown in Fig. 2-3(b). The correctness of the equation may be established either by multiplying out the terms in the right-hand side or by factoring the left-hand side and arriving at the expression,

$(A + CD)(B + CD)$, as a first step. That the arrangement in Fig. 2-3(b) yields the desired switching function may be understood by observing that both A and B must be 1, or both C and D must be 1 in order to cause signals to be present on all four input lines of the "and" switch, which is the necessary condition for a 1 to appear on the output line.

In spite of the functional equivalence of the two arrangements in Fig. 2-3, the physical difference in the two circuits is by no means trivial.

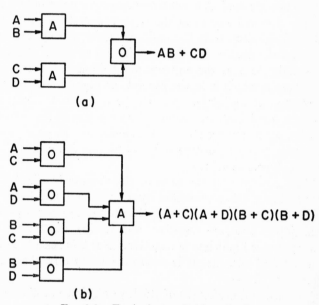

(a)

(b)

Fig. 2-3.　Equivalent switching circuits.

With the diode switching circuits which have been described, the number of diodes in any "or" or "and" switch is equal to the number of inputs to the switch. Therefore, a total of 6 diodes is required to form the circuit in (a), but 12 diodes are required in (b). If the switching circuit given in (b) had been given first, a reduction in the required number of diodes could have been achieved merely by performing algebraic manipulations without any consideration to the switching circuits themselves. Unfortunately, it is not always possible to arrive in a direct manner at the switching network which gives the desired switching function with the minimum number of components. However, the important point is that each manipulation of a Boolean algebra expression represents a physical change in the switching network without a change in the switching function, that is, without a change in the relationship between the output and input signals. Therefore, Boolean algebra provides not only a convenient notation for recording switching networks without drawing them out in detail, but also a means for making changes in the network configuration in the search for the most desirable network for any given switching function. Numerous practical examples of the notation employed for this purpose will be found in subsequent chapters.

The Vacuum Tube. The vacuum tube is another frequently used component in computers although its application to "or" and "and" switching functions is not quite as straightforward as in the case of diodes. The fundamental triode vacuum-tube circuit is shown in Fig. 2-4(a). The input voltage, which for the purpose at hand is assumed to be taken from the anode of another vacuum-tube circuit, is applied to a voltage divider comprised of resistors R_1 and R_2. The circuit is so designed and the supply voltages are so chosen that the potential of the grid will be maintained either below cut-off value or slightly above ground potential. The output potential, which is developed across the anode load resistor, R_3, is positive when the input is negative and is negative when the input is positive. "Positive" and "negative" potential here are relative to each other and not relative to ground. Because of the nature of this triode circuit, it is an inverter; that is, if a signal, A, is applied to its input, the signal appearing on the output line is $\bar{A}$. The functional properties of the simple triode may be represented by a block labeled "I" with one input and one output line as in Fig. 2-4(b). Sometimes a triode circuit is more conveniently indicated by a symbol, such as shown in Fig. 2-4(c), with the input grid connection in the lower-left corner and the output anode connection in the upper-right corner.

When two triode circuits are connected with a common anode load resistor, as shown in Fig. 2-4(d), the functional result depends upon the convention used in the assignment of polarities. If a positive signal represents a 1 and a negative signal represents a 0, the function is equivalent to two inverters feeding an "and" circuit. This function may be visualized by noting that the output will be positive only when both of the inputs are negative. The function is the same as that of an "or" circuit feeding an inverter because, as has been pointed out, $\overline{AB} = \bar{A} + \bar{B}$. The corresponding functional block diagrams for two triodes with their anodes connected together are given in Fig. 2-4(e). If the opposite convention with respect to polarities had been assumed, the "and" and "or" functions would be interchanged. When the symbols for two or more triodes (or multigrid tubes) are shown with the output terminals connected together as in Fig. 2-4(f), it is implied that there is only one anode load resistor in the circuit and that the value of its resistance is substantially the same as would be used for one tube alone.

CIRCUIT   FUNCTION   SYMBOL

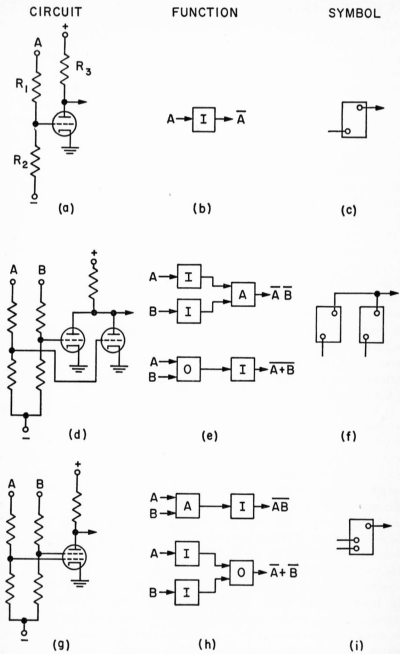

Fig. 2-4.   Vacuum-tube functions.

A circuit employing a tube with two control grids is shown in Fig. 2-4(g). The functional nature of this circuit may be represented by an "and" circuit feeding an inverter as can be determined by noting that the output will be negative only when both input signals are positive. An equivalent functional arrangement is two inverters feeding an "or" circuit. As in the case of the two triodes, the functional properties of the multigrid tube depend upon the assumption made concerning the polarities of the signals. It has been assumed that a positive signal represents a 1; if a negative signal represents a 1, the "and" and "or" operations would be interchanged. The symbol which will be used for the two-grid tube is the same as for the triode except that two input terminals are placed in the lower-left corner of the rectangle. Tubes with three or more control grids can be constructed; however, they are generally considered to be impractical not only because they would involve a more complicated and possibly inefficient electrode arrangement, but also because conventional triodes and two-grid tubes can be adapted to any functional operation and their large volume of production causes them to be less expensive.

For simplicity, certain important, although nonessential, components have been omitted from the circuits in Fig. 2-4. Among the omissions are devices for suppressing parasitic oscillations (usually low-value resistances in series with the grids), condensers across the upper resistances in the voltage dividers for increasing the speed of the circuits, and various screen and suppressor grids which may be desirable particularly in the two-grid tube.

It is possible to assemble vacuum-tube circuits to yield any desired switching function. For example, the elementary "or" and "and" switches may be formed with nothing but triodes, as indicated in Fig. 2-5. With these two "components" together with the single triode used as an inverter, the assembly of any switching function may proceed in a straightforward manner, but the circuit so obtained will, in general, contain many more tubes than necessary. The problem of arriving at the circuit composed of the least possible number on tubes is a formidable one. In the text, *Synthesis of Electronic Computing and Control Circuits*, by members of the staff of the Harvard Computation Laboratory (Harvard University Press, 1951), a system is presented for arriving at economical circuits when a limited number of input signals and one output signal are involved. Also, some special cases involving multiple output switching circuits are included. However, since the system has its complications and limitations, and since engineering details often dictate numerous special considerations, it is usually necessary to resort to "cut-and-try" methods in order to obtain the most desirable circuit.

Boolean algebra is nevertheless a useful tool in the design of vacuum-tube switching circuits, because it provides a means for quickly and accurately analyzing the switching arrangement obtained at each stage of the development. To determine the relationship between the output signals and input signals in any switching circuit, it is sufficient to write down the output of each tube or set of tubes with common anode connec-

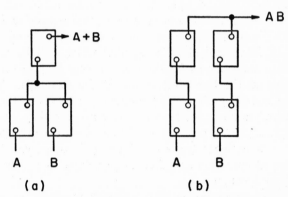

FIG. 2-5. Triode "or" and "and" circuits.

tions in terms of the signals on the corresponding grids in accordance with the functions shown in Fig. 2-4(b), (e), and (h). The case where multigrid tubes have their anodes connected in common with the anodes of other tubes may be handled conveniently by visualizing each multigrid array as constituting an "and" switch, the tube itself as constituting an inverter, and the common anode connection as constituting another "and" switch. An example of this sort is shown in Fig. 2-6. After proceeding

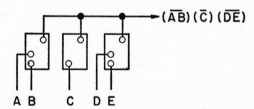

FIG. 2-6. Multi-grid tubes with common anode connection.

through all tubes from the input lines to the output lines, the resulting expressions for the output signals may, of course, be rearranged as desired when they are not immediately in suitable form.

Gate Tubes. The two-grid tube discussed in the previous section is sometimes used in such a different manner that it is worthy of special mention. Through the use of a two-grid tube, a pulse-type signal may be "gated" by the presence or absence of another signal, which may be either a steady-state type of signal or another pulse. The distinguishing feature of a tube used in this manner is that the output is always a pulse, and therefore a transformer may be placed in series with the anode to obtain an output pulse which has the same polarity as the pulse being gated. Functionally, a gate-tube circuit of this sort is a simple "and" switch.

A conventional pentode may be used as a gate tube, in which case it is customary to apply the pulse input to the control grid and the gating signal to the suppressor grid. The opposite connection is not used because a steady-state signal applied to the control grid would cause excessive current to the screen grid in the absence of a signal on the suppressor.

Relays. The basic "or," "and," and "not" circuits as performed with relays are shown in Fig. 2-7. The input signals are applied to the coils

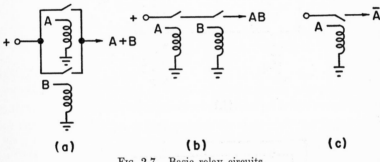

FIG. 2-7. Basic relay circuits.

of the relays, and when a coil is energized it attracts the armature toward it. In the case of the "or" and "and" circuits, the effect is to close contacts which are normally open; but for the "not," or inverter, function, a normally closed contact is opened by the action of the coil. In the figure, the symbol for the relay armature is drawn so that its normal state may be determined by noting whether motion toward the coil would tend to close or open the contact. It will be assumed that positive polarity voltages are used to actuate the coils and to provide the signals through the contacts, although negative voltages could be used just as well. The "or" switch is simply a parallel connection; a signal applied to one relay "or" the other will cause a signal to appear on the output line. The "and" switch is a series connection where one relay "and" the other must be energized to yield an output signal. In the "not" circuit, an output signal appears except when an input signal is applied, which causes the contact to open.

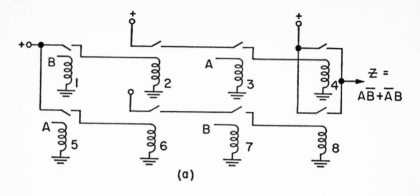

(a)

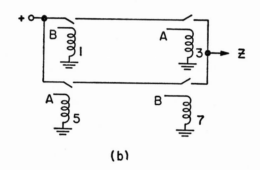

(b)

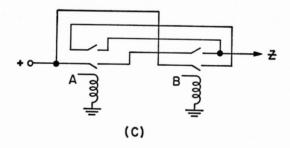

(C)

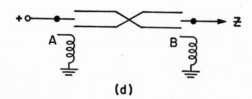

(d)

FIG. 2-8.   Relay circuits for $A\overline{B} + \overline{A}B$.

Boolean Algebra 41

Any desired switching function may be assembled through the use of the three basic circuits by following exactly the same procedures that would be used to assemble switching arrangements composed of diodes and vacuum-tube inverters. However, the circuits so obtained would be wasteful of relays and contacts because there are several ways by which relay switching networks may be simplified which are not applicable to other types of components. As an example, consider the switching function $Z = A\bar{B} + \bar{A}B$. The "straightforward" way to form such a switching function would be to invert X and Y, then apply the signals to relay "and" circuits each composed of two relays, and finally apply the outputs of the "and" circuits to a two-relay "or" circuit. This configuration is shown in Fig. 2-8(a).

One fact that may be used to reduce the number of relays appearing in Fig. 2-8(a) is that no relays at all are required to form an "or" circuit when the inputs to the "or" circuit are from the contacts of other relays. Therefore, relays numbered 4 and 8 may be eliminated simply by connecting together the contacts on relays numbered 3 and 7. Further, it is not always necessary to use two relays to perform an "and" function; an "and" circuit may be made by applying one signal to the contact and the other signal to the coil of a single relay. By this means, relays numbered 2 and 6 may be eliminated. The resulting circuit is given in Fig. 2-8(b). Since it is not necessary that each contact have its own separate actuating coil, the number of relay coils may be reduced by mounting all contacts operated by the A signal on one relay and all contacts operated by the B signal on a second relay, as shown in Fig. 2-8(c).

By the use of transfer points, another reduction in circuit complexity may be achieved. A transfer point corresponds to the "double-throw" switch used in electrical power work. The moving point makes a contact at each end of its motion. That transfer points may be used in the switching function presented in Fig. 2-8 is not exactly obvious, but it may be determined readily when it is observed that in an "and" circuit the order or sequence of the contacts makes no difference and that the connections to an individual contact may be reversed if desired. When these steps are taken, the circuit given in Fig. 2-8(d) can be derived. The derivation can probably be visualized more easily through study of (b) than (c); in (b) if relays 1 and 3 are interchanged and if the connections to the contacts on the relays actuated by B are reversed, the circuit in (d) follows almost directly.

The switching function, $Z = A\bar{B} + \bar{A}B$, may be generated by other relay circuits involving interesting variations if the expression is factored according to the following steps:

$$A\bar{B} + \bar{A}B = (A + \bar{A}B)(\bar{B} + \bar{A}B)$$
$$= (A + \bar{A})(A + B)(\bar{B} + \bar{A})(\bar{B} + B)$$
$$= (A + B)(\bar{A} + \bar{B})$$

The "straightforward" relay circuit for providing the switching function according to this expression is shown in Fig. 2-9(a). $A + B$ is formed by relays 1 and 2; relays 5 and 6 combine $\bar{A}$ with $\bar{B}$ to form $\bar{A} + \bar{B}$; and relays 7 and 8 perform the final "and" operation. Since the inputs to relays 5 and 6 come from other relays, this "or" function may be accomplished simply by connecting the outputs of relays 3 and 4 together. Also, it is possible to eliminate relays 7 and 8 by connecting the two "or" circuits in series instead of applying the outputs of the "or" circuits to separate relays which have their contacts in series. The resulting arrangement is given in Fig. 2-9(b). As before, all contacts actuated by the signal may be combined on one relay, and in this case the circuit of Fig. 2-9(c) is obtained. By reversing the connections to the contacts on relays 1 and 2 in Fig. 2-9(b), it is possible to make use of transfer points as shown in Fig. 2-9(d). Note that each of the circuits in Fig. 2-9 is different from the circuits in Fig. 2-8; yet the switching function is the same in every case.

It is necessary to be cautious when using the simplifications described in the previous paragraphs because of the possibility of getting undesirable "back circuits" in the system. Two examples of situations where back circuits can arise are shown in Fig. 2-10 (coils not shown). In (a) the desired switching function is $(AB + CD) E + (CD)F$. The term, CD, is generated by a series connection of contacts on relays operated by the C and D signals. If this term is combined with AB in an "or" function by merely connecting the wires together instead of using separate relays for the "or" function, it cannot be combined with F with nothing but another series connection. The reason is that a path from the supply voltage to the output line would be closed when $ABF = 1$, which is not desired. By placing a diode, as indicated, current flow through that particular wire is limited to one direction, and the undesired connection is eliminated. In (b) the switching function is $(AB + D) C + AE$, but without the diode the term DBE would be included also since the contacts can pass current in either direction. If the use of diodes is objectionable, the difficulty may be avoided without employing individual relays for every "or," "and," and "not" function by using duplicate contacts for certain input signals. In Fig. 2-10(a), back circuits could have been avoided by using duplicate contacts for C and D; in (b) a duplicate contact for A would be sufficient.

An alternative method of eliminating back circuits in the switching

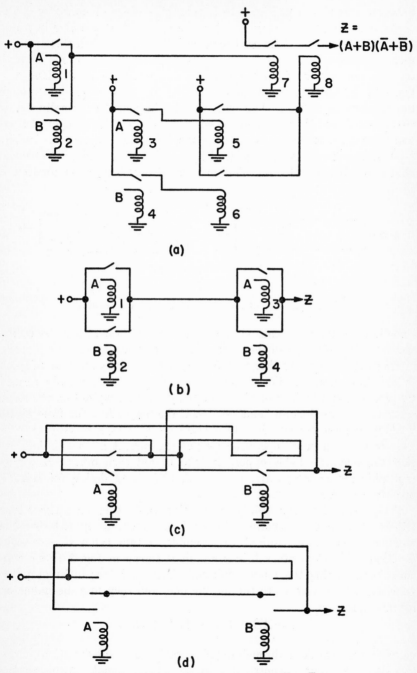

FIG. 2-9. Relay circuits for $(A + B)(\overline{A} + \overline{B})$.

44   Arithmetic Operations in Digital Computers

arrangements shown in Fig. 2-10 is through the use of normally closed
contacts as found on a relay inverter. In Fig. 2-10(a) a normally closed
contact on relay F may be used to replace the diode. With this arrangement, if relays A, B, and F are operated, there will be no closed path
through the contacts from the supply voltage to the output. However,
when C, D, and E are operated there will be a closed circuit through
the contacts as desired. The path will be through the normally closed
contact on F and then through the contact on E if F is not operated but
will be through the normally open contact on F if F is operated. In Fig.
2-10(b) the diode may be replaced by a normally closed contact operated either by D or by E. This method of back circuit elimination is

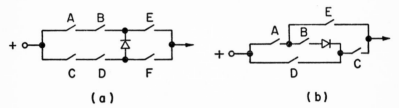

Fig. 2-10. Use of diodes to eliminate back circuits.

sometimes preferable because it is possible to make use of transfer points
which utilize both ends of the motion of the relay armature.

There are several further methods by which relays may be adapted
to switching circuits. For example, an "or" function is readily formed
by placing two windings on the same relay. Two windings on the same
relay may be used as an "and" switch if the magnetic force from either
winding alone is not sufficient to operate the armature, or they may be
used to create a "not" operation by passing current in the windings so
that the magnetic fields oppose instead of aid each other. However,
multiple-winding relays are, in general, difficult to design for reliable
operation as "and" or "not" elements.

Bridge Circuits. The ability of a relay contact to pass current in
either direction can sometimes be used to advantage in reducing the
number of contacts required to assemble certain types of switching
functions. An elementary bridge circuit is shown in Fig. 2-11(a) with
coils for actuating the relays omitted. There are four different paths
from the supply voltage to the output line, and they may be indicated
by the expression,

$$Z = AB + CD + AED + CEB$$

where the current flows through the E contact in opposite directions in the
two situations that it contributes to the output signal. Although the

analysis of switching circuits containing bridge connections is usually not difficult, the finding of a bridge connection to satisfy a given switching function is mostly a matter of cut-and-try, and the practical cases where any bridge connections at all can be used are not particularly numerous.

Other types of switching components, such as the diode switches which have been described, are "one-way" devices, and bridge circuits cannot

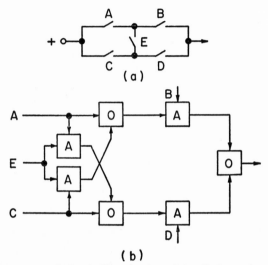

FIG. 2-11.   Relay bridge circuit and its diode analogy.

be formed with devices of this type.   Of course, it is possible to simulate a bridge circuit as indicated in Fig. 2-11(b), but this particular arrangement could easily be found by writing the switching function as follows:

$$Z = B(A + CE) + D(C + AE)$$

The visualization of this arrangement as a bridge circuit is somewhat artificial; also, it has no advantages as in the case of a relay bridge circuit.

Although the bridge circuit itself is not of outstanding importance as a switching scheme, it is illustrative of a fundamental difference between switching components which involve the controlled opening and closing of "two-way" current paths and those which have the property that signals appearing on the output line from other sources cannot react back on the input lines.   Many of the basic principles are the same, but the details of the procedure for determining the most desirable arrangements are quite different in the two cases.

46   Arithmetic Operations in Digital Computers

Inhibitors. Signals on certain input lines will inhibit the passage of signals applied to other input lines by means of a device called an inhibitor. The symbol for an inhibitor is shown in Fig. 2-12, where the use of a semicircle instead of an arrow indicates the inhibitor input. A signal will be present on the output line when a signal is applied to input line, A, unless there is a signal present on B to inhibit it. The output of the inhibitor is therefore $A\bar{B}$. If $A = 1$, that is, if there is always a signal present on A, the function of an inhibitor is no different from that of an inverter.

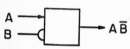

FIG. 2-12. Symbol for inhibitor.

A considerable variety of functions can be built into inhibitors with more than two input lines. For example, two or more "ordinary" input lines can be made to operate as an "or" function where the output will be inhibited by a signal on any one of several inhibitor inputs. Similarly, either the "ordinary" or the inhibitor inputs, or both, can be made to operate in an "and" fashion.

The distinction between inhibitors and inverters is sometimes little more than a matter of viewpoint, although usually there is also a physical difference in the components. Inhibitors are most adaptable to applications where transient pulse-type signals are employed; inverters are more convenient for steady-state signals. In the functional organization of any arithmetic or switching operation, the two types of components are substantially interchangeable. Inverters will be used in the following chapters because, for the most part, steady-state signals will be assumed. Where it is desired to adapt any of the arrangements to pulse-type signals, inhibitors may be substituted in a relatively straightforward manner provided proper precautions are taken with regard to any delays that may be encountered by the signals in passing through the various components. With pulse-type signals it is frequently necessary to introduce compensating delays at appropriate points in a switching network to insure that all input signals arrive simultaneously at any given "and" switch or inhibitor.

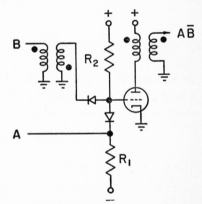

FIG. 2-13. Inhibitor circuit.

A typical inhibitor circuit is shown in Fig. 2-13. Resistors R_1 and R_2 are so chosen that the tube is normally cut off. A positive pulse on input, A, will cause the tube to conduct and create a positive pulse on the output line unless the action is inhibited by a positive pulse on input, B. The transformers are used principally for polarity inversion, although they also serve the useful purpose of shifting the voltage levels of the signals in order that the output from the plate circuit may be used to drive the grid circuit of other tubes.

Feedback Connections. In some cases, useful results may be obtained by feeding the output lines of a switching network back to one or more of the input lines. The most outstanding use of such connections is in the formation of multistable circuits. As an example, consider the circuit

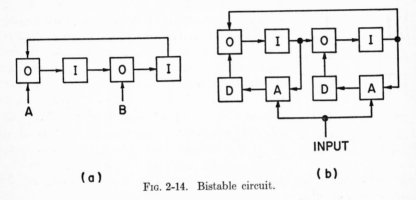

(a)   (b)

Fig. 2-14. Bistable circuit.

in Fig. 2-14(a) comprised of two inverters and two "or" switches connected so that there is a closed loop in the circuit. Assume that signals are not present on either of the input lines, A and B. If no signal, that is, a 0, is present at the input to the first inverter, a signal (1) will appear at the output of this inverter and will pass through the "or" switch to be applied to the input of the second inverter. The output of the second inverter will therefore be 0. This 0 will be applied to the "or" switch connected in the input circuit of the first inverter and, since a 0 was assumed to be applied to input, A, the circuit will remain in this state indefinitely. When a signal is applied to input, A, even temporarily, the 1 appearing at the input of the first inverter will cause the input to the second inverter to be 0. The output of the second inverter, which will now be 1, will be applied through the "or" switch to the first inverter and will cause the circuit to change to this state. In an analogous manner, a signal applied to input, B, will cause the circuit to transfer back to its original state. Commonly used names for a bistable arrangement of this nature are "trigger" and "flip-flop."

By connecting the two input lines it is possible to form a circuit which will alternate from one stable state to the other upon reception of a series of pulses applied to the resulting common input line. However, provision must be made to insure that an input pulse will reach only the desired "or" switch. One configuration which will achieve this result is shown in Fig. 2-14(b). Assume that the arrangement is in the state indicated by the 1's and 0's in the figure and that a signal is applied temporarily at the input. The input signal will pass through the right-hand "and" switch and then through the right-hand delay unit (indicated by a block labeled D) to the corresponding "or" switch. If the input signal is terminated by the time the delayed signal arrives at this "or" switch, the input signal will not reach the left-hand "or" switch, and the circuit will change to its other stable state. A subsequent application of a temporary input signal will cause a transfer back to the original state by a similar process. A flip-flop connected in this manner can be used as a binary counter in ways that will be described in more detail in other chapters. Actually, in many practical binary counter circuits (for example, the familiar twin-triode flip-flop), separate components are not needed for all of the various "and," "or," and delay functions; but an analysis of the circuit operation will reveal that each of the required functions is being performed by some means or other.

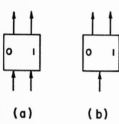

(a)   **(b)**

Fig. 2-15.   Symbols for bistable devices.

The bistable arrangement of Fig. 2-14 is so frequently used that it is convenient to adopt a special symbol for it, as given in Fig. 2-15. The two stable states can be represented by a 0 and a 1; that is, the device is capable of storing a binary digit. In Fig. 2-15(a) a signal applied to the input line of the left-hand side will cause the bistable device to transfer to the state representing 0 if it is not already in this state. Similarly, a signal applied to the right-hand input line, even temporarily, will initiate a transfer to the state representing 1. The output lines, which are taken from the outputs of the inverters, are used to indicate the state of the device. A signal is always present on one or the other, but not both, of the output lines; and the state is 0 or 1 according to whether the signal is on the left- or right-hand output line, respectively. The symbol given in Fig. 2-15(b) corresponds to the configuration shown in Fig. 2-14(b); a temporary signal applied to the common input line will cause the flip-flop to change to its opposite state regardless of which state it was in originally.

The arrangement shown in Fig. 2-16(a) has three stable states; and the circuit can be caused to exist in any one of the three states by the temporary application of signals to inputs, A, B, or C, respectively. A variation is shown in (b). Much more elaborate feedback loops are possible; but, since none are used in the arithmetic circuits to be described in subsequent chapters, the subject will not be discussed further.

It is plausible to apply Boolean algebra to feedback loops including the loops found in individual triggers. Since triggers can be thought of as

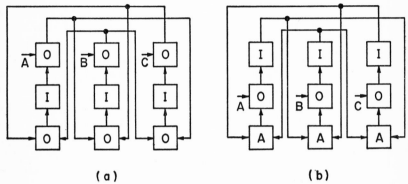

(a)   (b)

Fig. 2-16. Arrangements with three stable states.

being comprised of elements of switching circuits, it is even conceivable that Boolean algebra techniques could be extended to the point where a whole computer could be represented by a single algebraic expression. However, such an extension does not appear practical, and the use of Boolean algebra will be confined to isolated switching networks without feedback connections.

One other important feedback loop is employed in the formation of a bistable element when pulse-type instead of steady-state signals are used. The arrangement is shown in Fig. 2-17. A pulse applied to the input line, marked 1, will pass through the "or" switch to a delay device (1D) which delays the pulse approximately one "cycle" or the time between the "clock pulses," which are a continuous series of pulses at a uniform repetition rate applied to the "and" switch as shown. The

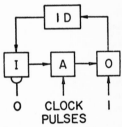

Fig. 2-17. Bistable arrangement employing pulse-type signals.

initial pulse must be applied at a time relative to the clock pulses such that the delayed pulse arrives at the "and" switch simultaneously with the next clock pulse. The output of the "and" switch then circulates through the loop in the same manner as the initial pulse.

The purpose of matching the circulating pulse in an "and" switch is to insure that the pulse circulation occurs in step with the remainder of the machine of which this circuit is a part. Although it is not shown, the loop must also contain an amplifier which will prevent the deterioration of the amplitude and shape of the pulse. In order to terminate the circulation of a pulse in the loop, a pulse is applied at the proper time on the input line marked 0, which is connected to the inhibiting input of an inhibitor. One stable state is therefore represented by the existence of a pulse circulating in the loop, and the other stable state is represented by the nonexistence of a circulating pulse. The output signal may be taken from any point in the loop. Variations in the configuration may be obtained by rearranging the four components in any sequence without affecting the bistable properties.

Other Components. There are many types of components other than diodes, vacuum tubes, and relays which may be adapted to switching circuits. For example, a conducting path between two electrodes in a gaseous tube can be established by applying a high-frequency signal to an electrode which is external to the tube. The input signal turns on or off an oscillator that generates the high-frequency signal, which in turn causes the gas in the tube to be ionized and allow a flow of electrons. Such a device would be a direct analogy to an electromechanical relay except that transfer points would not be possible.

Transistors and magnetic cores are components which are adaptable to computer circuits and with which it is possible to perform switching operations. However, their major application seems to be in amplifiers and storage, respectively; and their role in switching circuits does not appear to be as straightforward as in the case of diodes, tubes, or relays.

The arrangements for performing the various arithmetic operations, as discussed in subsequent chapters, are substantially independent of the components that are used to perform the various switching and storage operations. Some types of components can be made to fit directly in the block diagrams, whereas appropriate modifications in the block diagrams will have to be made for other components; but the principles of operation of the arrangements can remain unchanged.

Chapter 3

SWITCHING NETWORKS

Before proceeding to the arithmetic operations specifically, this chapter will be devoted to switching networks in general. As will be illustrated in subsequent chapters, arithmetic operations are performed in computers largely through the assembling of the computer components to form switching networks of various descriptions. Also, switching networks have application in parts of a computer other than the part which does the actual adding, multiplying, and other operations. In particular, the control portion of a computer is comprised almost entirely of switching networks. Further, switching networks are of interest in many machines and devices such as elevator controls, telephone switchboards, code and cipher machines, and railway signaling systems, which are not computers in the usual sense of the word at all.

In broad terms, a switching network is any digital device to which input signals may be applied and from which output signals may be obtained that are some prescribed function of the input signals. In the examples to be described, it will be assumed that the signals are all two-valued; that is, on a given signal line, a signal either will be present or will not be present. In other words, a signal can be considered as having the value 1 or 0, according to whether it is in existence or not. There is no inherent reason why multivalued signals could not be used, but very little practical use has been made of them because of the difficulties in designing suitable physical components. Reference will be made both to steady-state and pulse-type signals. In most cases either type of signals may be assumed; those instances which require one kind of signal or the other will be apparent from the text or from the nature of the switching network.

Some of the most elementary networks were discussed in the previous chapter. More complicated, in fact even very complicated, switching networks usually may be quite easily assembled in a straightforward manner. The difficult part of the task is finding an arrangement which has the minimum or a reasonable number of components or which meets some other requirement such as speed of operation. Frequently, further complications are introduced that might not be apparent from the functional block diagrams containing only the switching elements. One such complication is encountered when diodes are used. When a signal passes through a succession of alternate "and" and "or" switches, its amplitude rapidly diminishes. If the circuits are properly designed, simple cathode follower circuits may be used at intermediate points to produce the required current gain. With a large number of stages, voltage amplification as well as current amplification will be required. Of course, the signal amplification equipment must be considered as well as switching elements themselves. Even with components that require no separate amplifiers, two or more different types of components may be used; and then it is necessary to find the lowest possible "weighted count" in the various possible switching configurations, because the different types may have variations in cost or desirability.

In spite of the virtual impossibility of finding a general solution to network problems which must include engineering considerations, a few aids and tricks are known. Some of the more useful procedures for finding suitable switching networks will be pointed out.

Elemental Form of Network. Any switching function involving a single output signal which is a function of a set of simultaneously applied input signals may be reduced to an "elemental form." Here, the term, elemental form, means a Boolean algebra expression (or the equivalent physical circuit) where the desired result is obtained by a set of "and" terms combined by an "or" relationship, where each "and" term contains all of the variables. It is possible to find this form in any given instance merely by noting those combinations of input signals for which an output signal is desired.

For example, with three input signals, A, B, and C, there are eight and only eight possible input combinations. Each input combination may be represented by an "and" term such as $\bar{A}B\bar{C}$, which has the meaning that a signal is applied to input B but not to inputs A or C. Any given switching function may be specified by a listing of the combinations of input signals which will produce an output signal. Since the listing implies an "or" relationship, it follows that any switching function may be represented by an expression of the form,

$$\bar{A}\bar{B}\bar{C} + \bar{A}BC + \bar{A}B\bar{C} + \cdots$$

where only those terms which are to yield an output signal are included. Of course, when a switching function is encountered in a practical problem, it may not appear in this elemental form, but through Boolean algebra manipulations it is not difficult to alter the representation to fit this form. For instance, the elemental form of the function $\overline{(AB + \overline{C})}$ may be found by proceeding through the following steps:

$$\overline{(AB + \overline{C})} = \overline{AB}C$$

$$= (\overline{A} + \overline{B})C$$

$$= \overline{A}BC + A\overline{B}C + \overline{A}\overline{B}C$$

Through a study of the elemental forms of switching networks, the total number of different switching functions may be determined. In the case of only one input variable, the networks are all trivial; nevertheless, there are four of them as represented by the expressions, 0, A, $\overline{A}$ and $A + \overline{A}$. The first is an open circuit, the second is a straight connection between the input and output, the third is an inverter, and the last is a steady output signal independent of the input. With two input variables, there are sixteen different switching functions as follows:

0	$\overline{A}\overline{B} + \overline{A}B + A\overline{B}$
$\overline{A}\overline{B}$	$\overline{A}\overline{B} + \overline{A}B + AB$
$\overline{A}B$	$\overline{A}\overline{B} + A\overline{B} + AB$
$A\overline{B}$	$\overline{A}B + A\overline{B} + AB$
AB	$\overline{A}\overline{B} + \overline{A}B + A\overline{B} + AB$
$\overline{A}\overline{B} + \overline{A}B$	
$\overline{A}\overline{B} + A\overline{B}$	
$\overline{A}\overline{B} + AB$	
$\overline{A}B + A\overline{B}$	
$\overline{A}B + AB$	
$A\overline{B} + AB$	

As will be explained shortly, most of these expressions can be simplified considerably. With three input variables, a total of 256 different switching functions are possible, although many of them are merely rearrangements of the variables.

In general, the number of switching functions may be found by noting that the total number of different input combinations is equal to 2^N, where N is the number of input variables. It may be desired to have an output signal for any set of input combinations. Therefore, each of the sets can be represented by a binary number of 2^N digits with a 1 or a 0 in the number, meaning that the corresponding input combination causes or does not cause, respectively, an output signal. Since there is a one-to-one correspondence between the sets and the binary numbers, the total number of switching combinations is equal to 2 raised to the 2^Nth power.

Simplifying the Elemental Form. The elemental form of representation of a switching function does not, of course, necessarily yield a representation of the physical switching circuit which is most economical in terms of the number of components required. In fact, in the wide majority of instances, the circuit may be simplified. In this section only those circuit configurations which involve a set of "and" switches combined by an "or" switch will be considered.

When hunting for unnecessary components to remove from an "and-to-or" switching circuit (such as a circuit in its elemental form), a good way to start is to look for combinations of variables in any of the forms, $X\overline{Y} + XY$, $X + XY$, or $X + \overline{X}Y$, because each of these expressions can be reduced as follows:

$$X\overline{Y} + XY = X(\overline{Y} + Y) = X$$

$$X + XY = X(1 + Y) = X$$

$$X + \overline{X}Y = (X + \overline{X})(X + Y) = X + Y$$

As an illustration of the use of these relationships, consider the switching function, $\overline{A}\overline{B} + \overline{A}B + A\overline{B}$, which is found in the list of the sixteen two-input functions. The first two of the three terms in the expression are of the type represented by the first equation above, and the function may therefore be reduced to $\overline{A} + A\overline{B}$, which, in turn, may be reduced to $\overline{A} + \overline{B}$ as determined by the third equation. Through the use of the three equations, it may be found quickly that the entire list of sixteen two-input switching functions may be reduced to the following list of relatively simple expressions.

$$0$$
$$\overline{A}\overline{B} \qquad\qquad \overline{A} + \overline{B}$$
$$\overline{A}B \qquad\qquad \overline{A} + B$$
$$A\overline{B} \qquad\qquad A + \overline{B}$$
$$AB \qquad\qquad A + B$$
$$\overline{A}$$
$$\overline{B}$$
$$\overline{A}\overline{B} + AB$$
$$\overline{A}B + A\overline{B}$$
$$B$$
$$A$$

When working with switching functions involving three or more input variables, the three equations presented in the previous paragraph can be represented in a more general manner.

Switching Networks 55

$$f(X_n)\overline{g(Y_m)} + f(X_n)g(Y_m) = f(X_n)$$

$$f(X_n) + f(X_n)g(Y_m) = f(X_n)$$

$$f(X_n) + \overline{f(X_n)}g(Y_m) = f(X_n) + g(Y_m)$$

Here, X_n signifies a set, X, of n variables; and Y_m signifies a set, Y, of m variables. It is not a requirement that any given variable appear in only one set; it may appear in both sets. A notation such as $f(X_n)$ means any Boolean algebra function of X_n. In this section most of the functions are limited to simple "and" combinations of the variables, but it should be understood that this limitation is not general.

As another example of the procedure, consider the function,

$$ABC + A\bar{B}C + AB\bar{C}D$$

If the first two terms of the expression are examined, it will be observed that AC is common to both of them and may be taken as a single variable or function. Therefore, the expression reduces to $AC + AB\bar{C}D$. Further simplification cannot be achieved through direct application of any of the three equations; but, if the common variable, A, is factored to yield $A(C + B\bar{C}D)$, then BD may be taken as a single variable. The resulting expression is $A(C + BD) = AC + ABD$. In this, as in most other examples, several different sequences of steps could have been used to achieve the same result.

Sometimes when simplifying a switching function it is easier, at least from the standpoint of visualization, to use a given term more than once in the process. For example,

$$\bar{A}B\bar{C} + A\bar{B}\bar{C} + AB\bar{C} = \bar{A}B\bar{C} + A\bar{B}\bar{C} + AB\bar{C} + AB\bar{C}$$

The third term in the left-hand side of the equation is recorded twice in the right-hand side (possible because $X = X + X$). Then, by considering the first and third terms together and the second and fourth terms together, it is found that the expression is equivalent to $B\bar{C} + A\bar{C}$.

A more striking example of the power of the three generalized simplifying equations is illustrated in the following example.

$$(AB + C) + \overline{(AB + C)}(CD + A) = (AB + C) + (CD + A)$$
$$= A + C$$

The simplified form is found very quickly by considering the expressions within the brackets as individual variables. Without the generalized equations, a process somewhat as follows would be necessary:

$$(AB + C) + \overline{(AB + C)}(CD + A) = (AB + C) + \overline{AB}\overline{C}(CD + A)$$
$$= (AB + C) + (\overline{A} + \overline{B})\overline{C}(CD + A)$$
$$= (AB + C) + A\overline{B}\overline{C}$$
$$= A(B + \overline{B}\overline{C}) + C$$
$$= A(B + \overline{C}) + C$$
$$= AB + A\overline{C} + C$$
$$= AB + A + C$$
$$= A + C$$

A Difficulty and Its Solution. Occasionally, switching functions of the simple "and-to-or" variety contain superfluous terms which cannot be detected by the methods described in the previous section. An example is $AB + \overline{B}\overline{C} + A\overline{C}$, where the third term, $A\overline{C}$, is superfluous and may be dropped without altering the value of the function.

One way to show that the term is superfluous is through multiplying it by $B + \overline{B}$, which is equal to 1 and therefore does not change its value.

$$AB + \overline{B}\overline{C} + A\overline{C} = AB + \overline{B}\overline{C} + A\overline{C}(B + \overline{B})$$
$$= AB + \overline{B}\overline{C} + AB\overline{C} + A\overline{B}\overline{C}$$
$$= AB(1 + \overline{C}) + (1 + A)\overline{B}\overline{C}$$
$$= AB + \overline{B}\overline{C}$$

Although the steps illustrated here may seem perfectly straightforward, it is sometimes quite puzzling to find the proper steps when an example of this type is encountered for the first time. Experience and practice are a great help in knowing which steps of the multitude that are possible are most likely to be fruitful in finding simplifications in the switching function. A study of the following additional three examples will aid in discerning patterns that are likely to signify superfluous terms.

$$A\overline{B} + BC + AC = A\overline{B} + BC$$
$$\overline{A}B + B\overline{C} + \overline{A}\overline{C} = \overline{A}B + B\overline{C}$$
$$\overline{A}B + \overline{B}C + \overline{A}C = \overline{A}B + \overline{B}C$$

By using a "testing" process, superfluous terms can be detected in·a positive manner. To test a given term, the values of the input variables are observed which cause an output signal because of the term being tested. These values of the variables are then inserted in all of the other terms; and if it is found that an output signal is always created through at least one other term, it is known that the term being tested is superfluous. The process will be illustrated by testing the term $A\bar{C}$ in the previous example of $AB + \bar{B}\bar{C} + A\bar{C}$. For $A\bar{C}$ to cause an output signal (that is, to cause the value of the switching function to be 1), it must be that $A = 1$ and $C = 0$. In this case, however, the first two terms yield $(1)B + \bar{B}(1)$, which is always equal to 1. Therefore, the $A\bar{C}$ is superfluous. By applying this test to all terms in an "and-to-or" switching function, it is possible to find with certainty any that may be superfluous.

Another illustrative example is the switching function,

$$A\bar{B} + B\bar{C} + C\bar{A} + \bar{A}B + \bar{B}C + \bar{C}A$$

A test on any one of the six terms will indicate that it is superfluous. The result of testing the first term (set $A = 1$ and $B = 0$) is

$$0 + 0 + 0 + (1)C + \bar{C}(1) = 1$$

and analogous results are obtained from tests of any one of the other terms. However, it should not be concluded that all terms are superfluous and that the function is equivalent to 0. After testing one term and finding that it is superfluous, it should be eliminated before testing another. In particular after eliminating the first term, the second or third terms will be found superfluous, but the last three will not be superfluous. It happens that in this example the switching function may be simplified to any one of two equivalent functions which are:

$$A\bar{B} + B\bar{C} + C\bar{A} = \bar{A}B + \bar{B}C + \bar{C}A$$

Although individual variables that are superfluous can usually be found by methods described previously, the testing procedure may be used for them also. A slight modification in the procedure is required. For example, in the switching function, $AB + A\bar{B}C$, the appearance of $\bar{B}$ in the second term is superfluous. To test this particular appearance of the variable, it must be observed that it will contribute to the output only when $A = 1$ and $C = 1$. But then the expression is equivalent to $(1)(B) + (1)\bar{B}(1) = 1$. Since the first term causes the expression to be equal to 1 when $B = 1$ and since the variables other than B would cause the second term to be equal to 1 when $B = 0$, the value of the expression is never dependent upon the $\bar{B}$ factor in the second term. Therefore, the $\bar{B}$ factor in the second term is superfluous and may be eliminated.

As another example, consider the switching function, $AB + A\bar{B}C + \bar{A}\bar{B}$. The appearance of A in the second term or the appearance of $\bar{B}$ in the second term, but not both, is superfluous as may be determined by testing. The test for A in the second term is to note that $B = 0$ and $C = 1$ when this term contributes to the output. Since, in this case, the switching function is $0 + A(1)(1) + \bar{A}(1)$, which is always 1, it follows that the A in the second term is not needed. The same result could have been found with previously described methods by factoring $\bar{B}$ out of the second and third terms as a first step. By similar procedures it may be shown that $\bar{B}$ in the second term could be eliminated instead of A.

Another Difficulty and Its Solution. In all of the examples described previously the simplifications were accomplished through eliminating unnecessary variables or terms in the expression. Occasionally, when applying the methods which have been described, it is possible to proceed into a "trap." The trap is a situation where an expression is found which contains no superfluous variables or terms, as can be proved by testing, but yet is not the simplest "and-to-or" expression which represents the desired switching function.

An example is the following switching function which, when represented in its elemental form, is

$$A\bar{B}\bar{C} + \bar{A}B\bar{C} + \bar{A}\bar{B}C + \bar{A}BC + A\bar{B}C + AB\bar{C}$$

By grouping first and fifth, the second and fourth, the first and sixth, and the third and fourth terms in pairs, the function may be simplified to:

$$A\bar{B} + \bar{A}B + A\bar{C} + \bar{A}C$$

which contains no superfluous variables or terms. Yet it is possible to form the function with less terms than this. If the terms in the original expression had been grouped with the first and fifth, the second and sixth, and the third and fourth terms in pairs, the result would have been

$$A\bar{B} + B\bar{C} + C\bar{A}$$

Although a criterion for simplicity is sometimes difficult to define, by almost any conceivable standards this expression is simpler than the previous one. It may be recognized that this example is substantially the same as a previous one; by a different grouping of the original terms the different, but equivalent, expression

$$\bar{A}B + \bar{B}C + \bar{C}A$$

could have been obtained.

What is needed in avoiding traps of the type just described is a systematic way of finding all possible combinations of simplified forms so that the most desirable one may be selected. One such system involves expanding the function to its elemental form (if it is not already in its elemental form). Then, through repeated applications of the formula, $X\bar{Y} + XY = X$, in a systematic manner, all "basic" terms in the expression may be found, where a basic term is any correct term which contains no superfluous variables. In the previous example, a total of six basic terms ($A\bar{B}$, etc.) is found by pairing the terms of the elemental form in various ways. Actually, it is not known that these terms are basic until each of them has been compared with all others and it has been determined that further reductions cannot be made. After finding all basic terms, a table is made that indicates which of them are contained in each term in the elemental form. For the example cited, the table is shown in Table 3-I, where an X indicates that the basic term listed in the corresponding row is contained in the elemental term at the top of the corresponding column.

TABLE 3-I. TABLE FOR SIMPLIFYING $A\bar{B} + \bar{A}B + A\bar{C} + \bar{A}C$

	$A\bar{B}\bar{C}$	$\bar{A}B\bar{C}$	$\bar{A}\bar{B}C$	$\bar{A}BC$	$A\bar{B}C$	$AB\bar{C}$
$A\bar{B}$	X				X	
$\bar{A}B$		X		X		
$B\bar{C}$		X				X
$\bar{B}C$			X		X	
$C\bar{A}$			X	X		
$\bar{C}A$	X					X

Through inspection of the table and a systematic selection of the basic terms, all possible combinations of basic terms which will be equivalent to the original expression can be found. The basic terms must, of course, be selected such that each term in the elemental form is represented at least once (that is, such that the selected terms will represent at least one X in each column).

As another example, it may be shown by similar procedures that the following four-term expression is a trap in that it contains no superfluous terms or variables and that it may be reduced to either of two different three-term expressions.

$$ACD + A\bar{B}C + \bar{A}BC + \bar{A}C\bar{D} = ACD + \bar{A}BC + \bar{B}C\bar{D}$$
$$= A\bar{B}C + \bar{A}C\bar{D} + BCD$$

The systematic procedure for analyzing switching functions is sometimes useful even when no simplifications can be achieved. As an example of this case, consider the switching function, $ABC + A\bar{B}D + B\bar{D}$. When this expression is expanded to its elemental form by multiplying individual terms by expressions of the form $X + \bar{X}$, it is found that the elemental terms shown at the top of Table 3-II are present after duplicates have been eliminated.

When the terms of the elemental form are grouped by two's in all possible combinations, a set of three-variable terms is found as follows: ABC, ACD, $AB\bar{D}$, $BC\bar{D}$, $A\bar{B}D$, $B\bar{C}\bar{D}$, and $\bar{A}B\bar{D}$. Of these, the third and seventh and also the fourth and sixth may be paired, with each pair yielding the

TABLE 3-II.   ANALYSIS OF $ABC + A\bar{B}D + B\bar{D}$

	$ABCD$	$ABC\bar{D}$	$A\bar{B}CD$	$AB\bar{C}\bar{D}$	$\bar{A}BC\bar{D}$	$\bar{A}B\bar{C}\bar{D}$	$A\bar{B}\bar{C}D$
ABC	X	X					
ACD	X		X				
$B\bar{D}$		X		X	X	X	
$A\bar{B}D$			X				X

term, $B\bar{D}$. The basic terms of the expression are, therefore, ABC, ACD, $B\bar{D}$, and $A\bar{B}D$. In this example, it happens that three of the basic terms were in the original expression, but one new one has been found. From Table 3-II it is easily determined that $B\bar{D}$ is a necessary basic term because it is the only one appearing in the columns for $AB\bar{C}\bar{D}$ and two other elemental terms. For a similar reason, $A\bar{B}D$ is necessary. Since both of these terms must appear in any simplified form of the switching expression, the only elemental term not accounted for is $ABCD$. Either ABC or ACD may be chosen, and the other one becomes superfluous. Although no reductions in the number of terms or variables have been achieved, it has been found that $ACD + B\bar{D} + A\bar{B}D$ is an alternate expression; this expression would have been extremely difficult to find in any haphazard way. One possible value of the alternate expression could arise from physical characteristics of the circuits supplying the input signals. If it happened that the circuit supplying B were capable of operating only one "and" switch while the circuit supplying D could operate two, the alternate would be preferable.

Separation of Variables. If it is possible to group the terms in an expression so that none of the variables appearing in any one group appears in any other group, the network simplifying procedures that have been described can be applied to the individual groups instead of to the entire expression, with a considerable saving in effort. Consider the switching expression,

$$A\bar{B} + BC + AC\bar{D} + D + A\bar{B}E + \bar{E}$$

To analyze this expression thoroughly by expanding it to its elemental form would be laborious, but by procedures described previously it may be quickly simplified to:

$$(A\bar{B} + BC + AC + A\bar{B}) + (D + \bar{E}) = A\bar{B} + BC + D + \bar{E}$$

Note that the terms in the first set of parentheses contain only A, B, and C; and the terms in the second set contain only D and E. Although a formal proof is somewhat involved, it can be shown that the expression obtained from simplifying the groups separately is the same as would be obtained by handling all of the original terms together.

Factoring. When it is not a requirement that the switching function remain of the "and-to-or" type, a reduction in the number of components can be achieved frequently through the use of simple factoring. An example is $AB + AC$, where the A may be factored out to yield $A(B + C)$. If diode switching is employed where the number of diodes in the circuit is equal to the number of input signals to each "and" and "or" switch, a total of six diodes is required for a circuit conforming to the original expression, but only four are required for the factored form.

Factoring does not always yield a simplification; in fact, in some instances more components are required and other disadvantages are introduced. Consider the switching function, $ABC + ADE + F$, which requires nine diodes. If the A is factored to yield $A(BC + DE) + F$, a total of ten diodes becomes necessary. Furthermore, some of the input signals, B for instance, must proceed through an "and-to-or-to-and-to-or" switching sequence. Multiple level switching such as this is accomplished only with difficulty when diodes or some other types of switching components are used.

Converting to an "Or-to-and" Type of Circuit. Through repeated applications of the formula, $X + YZ = (X + Y)(X + Z)$, any switching function in "and-to-or" form may be converted to "or-to-and" form. In the previous chapter, this procedure was used to develop the following equality:

$$AB + CD = (A + C)(A + D)(B + C)(B + D)$$

In this case, no simplification is obtained; instead, the expression becomes more complex. However, if the original expression had been $AC + AD + BC + BD$, it could be shown by the same procedure (or by simple factoring in this case) that it is equivalent to $(A + B)(C + D)$, which corresponds to a substantially simpler circuit.

From the above example it might be expected that the probability of finding a more complex or a simpler circuit is the same. For random switching functions this situation is true because there is a one-to-one correspondence between the set of all possible "and-to-or" circuits and all possible "or-to-and" circuits, which of course includes all possible circuits. For the switching functions encountered in practical applications, there is considerable question about their randomness. Although no conclusive data are known, some rough surveys have indicated that the "and-to-or" type, which becomes more complex upon conversion, is the more prevalent.

Factors other than the number of components frequently contribute to the "simplicity" of a circuit. One such factor is standardization. It is sometimes desirable, for reasons of standardization, to use only "and-to-or" circuits or only "or-to-and" circuits. In other cases, it may be that switching components are chosen which function much more satisfactorily in one type of circuit than the other. Since conversion is possible, either type may be used regardless of the nature of the switching functions. If it happens that the type most suited to the components requires a larger number of components than the other type, this disadvantage may be avoided in some machines by redefining the representation of a "signal" and "no signal." For example, if a signal is normally represented by a relatively positive voltage, changing to a relatively negative voltage for a signal representation will cause all "and" and "or" functions to be interchanged.

The significance of the "or-to-and" form of switching networks is of interest from the standpoint of mental visualization. In some cases the "or-to-and" form is a distinct aid in visualizing the true nature of a switching function, but in most cases it seems to be only an artificial sort of representation. In particular, the elemental "and-to-or" form specifies in an easily visualized manner those combinations of input signals which create an output signal. Elemental "or-to-and" functions can be worked out, but their usefulness, if any, is difficult to imagine. For example, the elemental "or-to-and" form for $(A + B)(\bar{B} + C)$ would be

$$(A + B + C)(A + B + \bar{C})(A + \bar{B} + C)(\bar{A} + \bar{B} + C)$$

which seems to obscure the true nature of the function.

One example where the "or-to-and" form might be useful for visualization purposes is

$$A\bar{B} + B\bar{C} + C\bar{A} = (A + B)(A + \bar{C})(\bar{B} + \bar{C}) + C\bar{A}$$

$$= (A + B + C)(\bar{A} + \bar{B} + \bar{C})$$

From the "or-to-and" form, it may be observed readily that the function causes an output signal to be generated in any situation where at least one of the three input variables, A, B, and C, is 1 and at the same time at least one of the variables is 0. This visualization of the function is not so clearly observable from the "and-to-or" form.

Two reasons for the selection of the particular Boolean algebra notation which is being used here can now be explained. One reason is related to the fact that the majority of switching functions encountered in practical applications yield a less complex switching circuit when in the "and-to-or" form. The other pertains to the fact that the "and-to-or" form is usually more useful for mental visualization of the function. For both reasons the use of $+$ signs and parentheses is the lesser when the "and" and "or" function notations are made to correspond to sums and products, respectively. In applications where the "or-to-and" form is known to predominate, the opposite convention may be used in order to decrease the incidence of $+$ signs and parentheses.

A peculiar property of the conversion process is that, if the factors in the "or-to-and" expression which is obtained after a conversion are arbitrarily altered to form terms in a new "and-to-or" expression, the new expression will frequently contain superfluous terms which cannot be removed by the more elementary procedures. For example, the expression, $AB + \bar{B}D + C\bar{D}$, when converted to "or-to-and" form is equal to

$$(A + \bar{B} + C)(A + \bar{B} + D)(A + C + D)(B + C + D)$$

When the variables in the factors are arbitrarily grouped to generate a new "and-to-or" expression, the following switching function is obtained:

$$A\bar{B}C + A\bar{B}D + ACD + BCD$$

Either the first or the third term, but not both, is superfluous, as may be proved by testing or by analyzing the expression more completely through use of methods which have been described. By inverting the new expression, it is found to be equal to

$$(A + B)(A + C)(A + D)(\bar{B} + C)(\bar{B} + D)(C + \bar{D})$$

which may be arbitrarily altered to

$$AB + AC + AD + \bar{B}C + \bar{B}D + C\bar{D}$$

It can be shown that the second, third, and fourth terms are all superfluous in this "and-to-or" expression. Note that it is equivalent to the expression used at the start of the example. It is always true that, after two conversions with arbitrary alterations of this type, the result will be equivalent to the original expression.

The conversion property described in the previous paragraph has academic usefulness in that it may be used to find new examples and problems for students. Also, incidentally, through mere rearrangement of terms and inversions of variables, many of the examples given in this chapter can be rendered substantially unrecognizable and can then be used as problems. Three miscellaneous examples which provide good practice in Boolean algebra manipulations and which were originally discovered through selecting random functions and running them through two successive conversions are listed below.

$$A\bar{B} + AC + A\bar{D} + \bar{B}D = ABC + \bar{B}D + A\bar{D}$$

$$= AC + A\bar{D} + \bar{B}D$$

$$ABC + A\bar{B}D + ACD + \bar{A}\bar{C} + \bar{B}\bar{C}D = ABC + ACD + \bar{A}\bar{C} + \bar{B}\bar{C}D$$

$$= ABC + A\bar{B}D + \bar{A}\bar{C}$$

$$ABC + ACD + \bar{A}\bar{B}C + \bar{A}C\bar{D} + BC\bar{D} + \bar{B}D$$

$$= ACD + \bar{A}C\bar{D} + BC\bar{D} + \bar{B}D$$

$$= ACD + \bar{A}\bar{B}C + BC\bar{D} + \bar{B}D$$

$$= ABC + \bar{A}\bar{B}C + BC\bar{D} + \bar{B}D$$

$$= ABC + \bar{A}C\bar{D} + \bar{B}D$$

When performing conversions, if relationships of the type

$$(W + X + Y + Z)(W + X) = W + X$$

are kept well in mind and used where possible, much work can be avoided by simplifying the expressions obtained at intermediate steps in the process. The correctness of this relationship can be established readily through methods described previously.

An alternative method of finding the "or-to-and" form of a switching function is to list all of the elemental terms for which the function is zero. When these terms are combined by an "or" relationship and inverted, an equivalent form of the initial function is obtained. Another way of viewing the situation is to observe that a function is equal to "not" any of those conditions which are not in the function. The expression in this form may then be altered easily to yield an "or-to-and" expression. For example, consider a function which in its elemental form is $ABC + AB\bar{C} + \bar{A}\bar{B}C$. By listing all other elemental terms, the following equation can be obtained:

$$ABC + AB\bar{C} + \bar{A}\bar{B}C = \overline{\bar{A}BC + A\bar{B}C + A\bar{B}\bar{C} + \bar{A}B\bar{C} + \bar{A}\bar{B}\bar{C}}$$

The "and-to-or" expression under the "not" sign in the right-hand side of the equation may be simplified by the methods which have already been described. When this simplification is made, the conversion of the original function to "or-to-and" form proceeds according to the following steps:

$$ABC + AB\bar{C} + \bar{A}\bar{B}C = \overline{\bar{A}B + A\bar{B} + \bar{B}\bar{C}}$$

$$= \overline{(\bar{A}B)}\ \overline{(A\bar{B})}\ \overline{(\bar{B}\bar{C})}$$

$$= (A + \bar{B})(\bar{A} + B)(B + C)$$

Situations Where Some Combinations of Input Variables Will Not Exist. In all previous examples it was assumed that input signals might be applied in any possible combination. In many applications encountered in computers and other machines which use switching networks, it may be discovered upon detailed examination of the problem that certain combinations of input signals will never exist. When this situation is found, it is frequently possible to find a circuit which uses less components or is otherwise simpler than one which must respond properly to all possible combinations of input signals.

In other instances it may be, for one reason or another, that the existence or nonexistence of an output signal is immaterial for certain combinations of input signals. From the standpoint of switching network design, this situation is exactly the same as the previous one; in either case the response of the network to input signal combinations in question may be disregarded.

As an example, consider a switching network where the desired output signal in terms of the input signals may be represented by the expression, $\bar{A}B + A\bar{B}\bar{C}$, and assume that the combination of input signals represented by the elemental term, $A\bar{B}C$, will never be applied. For purposes of circuit simplification, a good way to visualize the problem is to imagine that, if the combination were applied, an output signal would be caused. The representation of the switching function would then be $\bar{A}B + A\bar{B}\bar{C} + A\bar{B}C$, which can be reduced to $\bar{A}B + A\bar{B}$. The fact that this particular expression is not a correct representation of the desired switching function is of no consequence because it has been assumed that the combinations of input signals which would cause a discrepancy will never occur. As a variation in the example, assume that it is the combination, ABC, which is never applied to the input lines. In this case, the expression which may be used is $\bar{A}B + A\bar{B}\bar{C} + ABC$. Although the A in the third term is superfluous, the expression is more complex than the original one; therefore the fact that ABC is never applied is of no help in this example.

As a further variation in the above example, assume that the input combination, AC, is never applied. This specification is the same as stating that neither $A\bar{B}C$ nor ABC will be applied. It may be imagined that, if AC were a valid input combination, an output signal would be generated. The resulting switching expression would then be

$$\bar{A}B + A\bar{B}\bar{C} + AC = \bar{A}B + A\bar{B} + AC$$

In applications where three-input "and" switches are highly undesirable, it is conceivable that this form of the switching network would be chosen in preference to the original form, which was $\bar{A}B + A\bar{B}\bar{C}$. However, in most applications the original form would probably be preferable.

From the nature of the above example it is apparent that, when making use of nonexistent input combinations for finding network simplifications, they must be considered in all possible ways. More specifically, the non-existent input combinations must be expanded to their elemental form. Then attempts must be made to simplify the network by making use of each one combination in turn, each two input combinations, each three, and so on. In the above example, the greatest simplification would be achieved when making use of the fact that $A\bar{B}C$ was nonexistent even in the case when both $A\bar{B}C$ and ABC are nonexistent. If, when represented in their elemental form, there are N nonexistent input combinations, a total of 2^N different switching expressions must be studied in order to find the most desirable one. Although the task can be laborious when many input variables are involved, an experienced circuit designer can frequently eliminate many of the possibilities "by inspection."

A slightly more illustrative example is the switching function $\bar{A}B\bar{C}\bar{D} + A\bar{B}CD$ with the input combinations, $AC\bar{D}$ and $BC\bar{D}$, nonexistent. If the switching network is altered so that it would produce an output in the presence of one or the other, or both, of these combinations, no simplification can be achieved (by most standards). However, when the nonexistent terms are expanded to their elemental form, three different terms are found: $ABC\bar{D}$, $A\bar{B}C\bar{D}$, and $\bar{A}BC\bar{D}$. When the second and third of these terms, but not the first, are used, the switching function can be simplified to $\bar{A}B\bar{D} + A\bar{B}C$.

A Diagram Method of Finding Suitable Switching Arrangements. For cases where the number of input variables is no greater than four, there is a diagram method of finding suitable switching arrangements which is convenient because it by-passes much of the clerical work required with previously described methods. As will be explained later, the method can be extended to problems involving more than four variables, but the difficulties in visualizing the various patterns increase rapidly as the number of variables is increased.

For four variables, the diagram consists of a square divided into sixteen smaller squares as shown in Fig. 3-1(a). To assist in the explanation of the method, the squares are numbered from 1 to 16, although normally the numbers are neither required nor used. The top half of the large square (small square numbers 1 through 8) corresponds to A, that is, to cases where A is 1; and the bottom half, to the cases where A is 0 (that is, where $\bar{A}$ is 1). Similarly, the left or right half of the large square corresponds to the cases where B is 1 or 0, respectively. The two center rows (numbers 5 through 12) correspond to cases where C is equal to 1, with the top and bottom rows for C equal to 0. For D, it is the center and outside columns, respectively. With these assignments, each small square represents one of the sixteen possible combinations of the input variables.

Switching Networks

67

For examples, square number 2 represents $AB\bar{C}D$, number 9 represents $\bar{A}BC\bar{D}$, and number 16 represents $\bar{A}\bar{B}\bar{C}\bar{D}$.

To indicate any given switching function, its Boolean algebra notation is expanded to elemental form, and for each elemental term in the result, a 1 is written in the corresponding square in the diagram. As an example, the diagram representation for $ABCD + A\bar{B}C\bar{D} + \bar{A}B\bar{C}\bar{D}$ is given in Fig. 3-1(b).

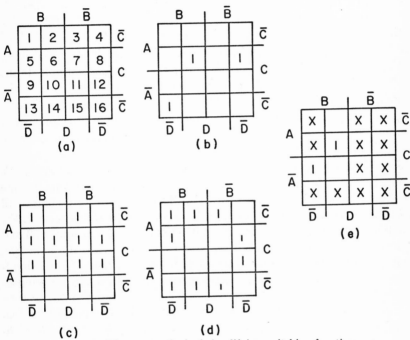

Fig. 3-1. Diagram method of simplifying switching functions.

The usefulness of the diagram is derived from the fact that patterns of 1's which will yield the simplest terms can be easily and quickly observed by inspection (after a little practice). If any two 1's are located in adjacent squares or at opposite ends of any row or column, it may be observed that three of the input variables will be the same in the two corresponding elemental terms, and the status of the fourth variable will be irrelevant. These two elemental terms may then be combined into one three-variable term. If any row or column or squares, any block of four squares, the four end squares of any two adjacent rows or columns, or the four corner squares are filled with 1's, it will be found that two of the input variables are the same in each of the corresponding elemental terms and that the other two variables will be encountered in all possible combinations. Therefore, the four terms can be combined into one two-variable term containing the two common variables. Further, if any two adjacent rows or columns, the top and bottom rows, or the right and left columns are completely filled with 1's, the corresponding terms can be represented by a single variable.

When using the diagram, a search is first made for any possible one-variable terms that can be used in an expression for the desired switching function. Then, if no such terms can be found or if there are some 1's not accounted for, a search is made for patterns of these 1's (in combination with the 1's that are already accounted for, if necessary) which can be represented by two-variable terms. The search is continued in an analogous manner for three-variable and then for four-variable terms until all of the 1's in the diagram are contained in at least one of the terms. The selection of the terms to yield the simplest "and-to-or" form of the function is made in a manner which is the same in principle as the method described previously. The value of the diagram is in the ease with which the selections can be made.

For an illustration of the use of the diagram, refer to the pattern of 1's shown in Fig. 3-1(c). It may be observed that the two center rows (square numbers 5 through 12) are filled with 1's. These squares correspond to all of the cases where C is equal to 1, with the result that C is a term in the simplified expression for the switching function. The 1's in squares 3 and 15 may be grouped with those in squares 7 and 11 to yield the term $\bar{B}D$, since this column contains all of the cases for which $\bar{B}$ and D are 1 simultaneously. In similar fashion, the 1's in squares 1 and 5 may be grouped to yield $AB\bar{D}$. The function in its simplest "and-to-or" form is then $C + \bar{B}D + AB\bar{D}$. As another illustration, consider the pattern in Fig. 3-1(d). Here, the 1's in squares 1, 2, 13, and 14 may be grouped to yield $B\bar{C}$, and those in squares 2, 3, 14, and 15 may be grouped for $\bar{C}D$. The 1 in square 12 can be grouped only with the 1 in square 8 to produce $\bar{B}C\bar{D}$, but the 1 in square 5 may be grouped with either the 1 in square 8 or in square 1 to yield $AC\bar{D}$ or $AB\bar{D}$, respectively. The resulting expression is then either $B\bar{C} + \bar{C}D + \bar{B}C\bar{D} + AC\bar{D}$ or the same with the last term replaced by $AB\bar{D}$.

The diagram is particularly convenient for finding simplest "and-to-or" expressions for problems where certain combinations of the input variables will not exist (or, which amounts to the same thing, where the output is irrelevant for certain combinations of the input variables). An X is placed in the squares which correspond to the nonexistent input combinations. When searching for simplest terms, any square containing an X may be included in a grouping if it simplifies the result, or it may be disregarded. For example, assume that it is desired to find the simplest switching network that will yield the function, $ABCD + \bar{A}BC\bar{D}$, under conditions where the only other combinations of input signals that will ever be applied are $\bar{A}BCD + AB\bar{C}D$. The resulting pattern of 1's and X's is given in Fig. 3-1(e). The right-hand half of the diagram is filled with X's which would be an indication for $\bar{B}$; but, since all of the X's may be disregarded, this term need not be used. Each of the two 1's must, however, be included; and the 1 in square 9 can be included in the one-variable term, $\bar{D}$, since both the left and right columns are completely filled. The term AC can be used for the 1 in square 6, because all of the squares in the second row are filled. The switching function may therefore be reduced to $\bar{D} + AC$.

Equivalent "or-to-and" networks may be found easily by means of the diagram. The procedure is exactly the same except that the empty squares instead of the filled squares are considered, and the resulting expression is "inverted." Inversion here implies the interchange of all the "and" and "or" functions as well as the inversion of all of the individual variables. For example, in Fig. 3-1(d), the empty squares yield $CD + \bar{A}BC + \bar{B}C\bar{D}$, which upon inversion produces $(\bar{C} + \bar{D})(A + \bar{B} + \bar{C})(B + C + D)$. That this expression is equivalent to the original "and-to-or" form may be checked by multiplying the factors and simplifying.

When the problem includes nonexistent input combinations, all empty squares must be accounted for, and squares containing X's may or may not be included when forming the "or-to-and" circuit. In the example of Fig. 3-1(e), square 2 can be combined with the remainder of the top and bottom rows to obtain the term, $\bar{C}$; and square 10 may be combined with squares 11, 14, and 15 to obtain $A\bar{D}$. The expression, $\bar{C} + \bar{A}D$, is then inverted to yield $C(A + \bar{D})$. Of course, $C(A + \bar{D})$ is not equal to the previously obtained expression, $\bar{D} + AC$, but in this instance it does not matter because the combinations of input signals which will show up the discrepancy have been assumed to be nonexistent.

One way of extending this diagram system to handle more than four input variables is to subdivide the individual squares. Then for a fifth variable, E, the left half of each square might correspond to E and the right half to $\bar{E}$. To aid in determining at a glance which half of a square a given mark is in, it may be preferable to divide the squares diagonally with the upper-right and lower-left halves representing E and $\bar{E}$, respectively. Another idea is to build a three-dimensional array using transparent planes so that all squares can be seen. With three dimensions, two more variables, for a total of six, may be added with substantially the same system as used for four variables in two dimensions. In all of the schemes, the rules for grouping the squares are extensions of the rules described previously, although visualization of the patterns becomes more difficult.

Miscellaneous Forms. In the general problem there is, of course, no requirement that the final solution be of the pure "and-to-or" or "or-to-and" variety. When multilevel switching networks are permissible, it is frequently possible to find a more desirable arrangement through some miscellaneous form of network. As mentioned in a previous section, simple factoring of one or more of the variables will occasionally produce desirable results. In more complicated cases, significant improvements in the switching circuits can usually be achieved only through exercising considerable ingenuity; no general methods are known.

For an example, consider the switching function,

$$AB + A\bar{C}D + BC + BDE + \bar{A}DE + \bar{C}DE$$

It is easy enough to show that this expression is equivalent to

$$(A + BC + DE)(B + \bar{A}E + \bar{C}D)$$

once this latter configuration has been found, but the finding of it is indeed a puzzle. Frequently, clues to arrangements of this type can be observed through a searching for similarities of variables in the various factors of the pure "or-to-and" form. Even then, a certain amount of cleverness and skill on the part of the circuit designer seems to be required.

Inverted Inputs Not Readily Available. It has been implied in all of the previous examples that the inverse of each variable has been available as an input signal when required. When the signals are generated by flip-flop type of circuits, it is true that the inverse of any variable may be obtained merely by making a connection to the opposite side of the flip-flop. However, frequently more than just a connection may be required. In electronic circuits particularly, it may be necessary to install a power amplifier between the flip-flop and the switching network. When the signals must be transmitted a substantial distance, the fact that two wires are needed for each signal with its inverse may be an important disadvantage. Furthermore, in a computer, signals may be obtained from many types of circuits other than flip-flops, and in these cases the inverted signals must usually be obtained through the use of inverters of some sort.

When inverters or other extra equipment must be used to obtain inverted signals, it becomes desirable to design switching networks with the minimization of inverters an objective, as well as the minimization of "and" and "or" switches. Here, the general problem becomes very complex, because the most desirable network configuration in any given instance is dependent upon the relative importance of eliminating an inverter or other components. Also, the more subtle points, such as number of levels of switching, the driving power of the input signals, switching speed, and possible nonexistence of certain combinations of input signals must be taken into consideration.

Again, ingenuity on the part of the circuit designer is the primary requirement for finding the most desirable circuit. As an example, the switching function

$$\bar{A}\bar{B}DE + \bar{A}\bar{B}C + \bar{A}\bar{C}DE + AB$$

requires that three of the input variables be available in inverse form. Although it is difficult to find, the expression

$$\overline{A + BC}(DE + C) + AB$$

represents the same function, and only one inverter is required.

Multiple-output Switching Networks. Multiple-output networks are, in general, even more remote from the cases for which systematic procedures are known for finding the most desirable arrangements. Of course, if each output signal may be generated by a separate network, all of the remarks made previously can apply. Also, when the networks are limited to pure "and-to-or" or "or-to-and" forms, obvious extensions of the previously described rules and procedures may be used as aids. The rules will help in finding terms or factors which may appear in the expressions for two or more of the output signals and which need not be duplicated in the physical circuitry.

A few practical examples of multiple-output networks are worked out in subsequent chapters. In particular, the full adders described in Chapter 4 on binary addition and subtraction are examples of networks with three input signals and two output signals. In the chapter on decimal addition and subtraction, a decimal adder operating in the 8,4,2,1 code and involving nine inputs and five outputs is worked out in some detail. The method of analysis for this example was also used for deriving the 8,4,2,1 doubler and quintupler described in the chapter on decimal multiplication and division. Since these and other examples meeting various specialized requirements can be found elsewhere in the text, none will be presented here.

Matrices. A certain category of multiple-output circuits deserve special mention because of their wide application. The circuits are known as "matrices" because they are sometimes drawn on paper (or occasionally even constructed physically) in an array of rows and columns which vaguely resemble mathematical matrices. A switching matrix is a switching network which has an output line corresponding to each possible combination of input variables; that is, an output signal appears on a separate wire for each elemental term composed of the input variables.

When only two variables are involved, the matrix as shown in Fig. 3-2 is almost trivial. An output signal is obtained on one of four sepa-

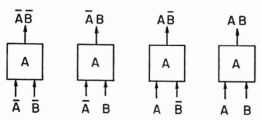

Fig. 3-2. Two-variable matrix.

rate output lines according to the four possible combinations of input variables. When $A = 0$ and $B = 1$, for example, a signal will be present on the line yielding AB, but none of the others.

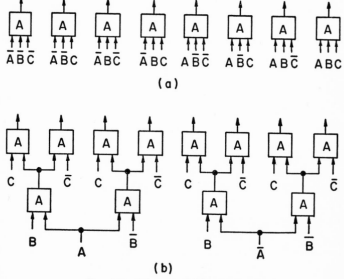

Fig. 3-3. Three-variable matrices.

With three variables, either of the arrangements shown in Fig. 3-3 may be used. In (a) eight 3-input "and" switches are required, whereas in (b) twelve 2-input "and" switches are required. With diode switching of the type described, it happens that a total of 24 diodes is necessary in either case, although when other types of switching components are employed one or the other of the arrangements may be preferable. The arrangement in (b) is sometimes called a "tree" or a "pyramid." Note that C appears as an input to a relatively large number of "and" switches when compared with B or A. This unequal loading of the input signals may be a disadvantage. The loading may be equalized somewhat by interchanging the B and C inputs in either the right-hand half or the

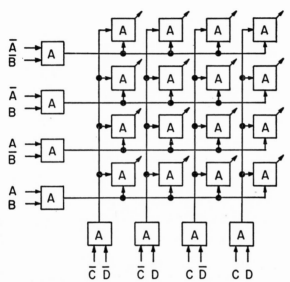

Fig. 3-4. One form of four-variable matrix.

left-hand half of the figure; it happens that this change does not affect the output functions.

For four or more input variables, obvious extensions of Fig. 3-3 may be made, but the number of diodes required for the two arrangements are no longer the same. With n input variables, $n2^n$ diodes are required when the first type of arrangement is used, and $2^3 + 2^4 + \cdots + 2^{n+1}$ diodes are required for the "tree." The type of matrix which is most conservative in components, at least when diodes are used, is shown for four variables in Fig. 3-4. The variables are divided into two groups with one group including A and B and the other group including C and D. Four intermediate signal lines are derived from each group, and then these are combined in a set of sixteen two-input "and" switches which will yield a signal on one of sixteen output lines.

With five input variables, an analogous array is used to minimize the number of components. In this case one group would contain two vari-

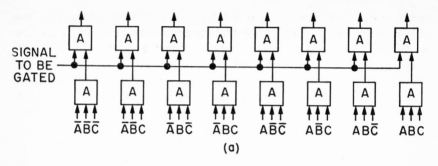

(a)

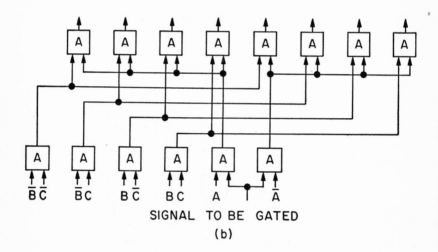

SIGNAL TO BE GATED

(b)

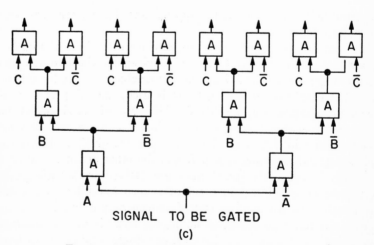

SIGNAL TO BE GATED

(c)

Fig. 3-5. Three-variable "gating" matrices.

ables; the other would contain three with eight intermediate lines formed according to either of the arrangements shown in Fig. 3-3. The thirty-two output lines would then be obtained with a four-by-eight array of two-input "and" switches.

In general, with n input variables, the variables are divided into two groups with $n/2$ variables in each group when n is even and with $(n + 1)/2$ and $(n - 1)/2$ variables, respectively, when n is odd. Each group is divided into subgroups in a similar manner, and the subdividing is continued until all subgroups contain either 2 or 3 variables. The 2-variable and 3-variable subgroups are applied to switching networks of the types shown in Figs. 3-2 and 3-3, respectively. The subgroups are then combined with appropriate arrays of 2-input "and" switches.

In some applications the output signals from a matrix are used directly as implied in the preceding discussion. In other applications the matrix is used to "gate" an external signal (such as series of pulses) onto one of a multiplicity of signal lines. For three input variables, probably the most obvious way of accomplishing the desired result is shown in Fig. 3-5(a). Since the signal to be gated may be considered as another input to the switching network as a whole, a number of variations in the matrix are possible. Two variations are shown in Fig. 3-4(b) and (c). Either of these arrangements requires less components than (a), but they have the disadvantage that the signal to be gated must pass through more "and" switches in succession, and with some types of components the delay might be excessive.

When a matrix involving four or more variables is necessary for the gating of the signal, extensions of the schemes shown in Fig. 3-5 may be readily worked out. One arrangement with four matrix variables, which combines the features of Figs. 3-4 and 3-5(c), is given in Fig. 3-6. When choosing the most desirable arrangement for any given application, it should be noted that in some arrangements certain of the "and" switch inputs must pass the signal being gated, whereas others need to respond only to the matrix switching signals. It may be that an "and" switch which must pass the gated signal is much more expensive than the other "and" switches. For this reason, the simple minimization of "and" switches is not necessarily the best criterion for judging the various possible network configurations.

Another important application of matrices is the selection of a signal from one on several different lines and applying this signal to a single output line. In this case the multi-output features of matrices substantially disappear, and the notation used earlier in the chapter for single output circuits may be applied directly. For selecting one of eight sig-

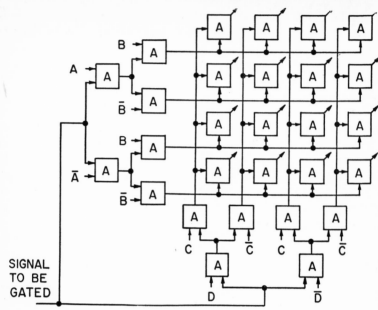

SIGNAL
TO BE
GATED

Fɪɢ. 3-6.   One form of four-variable "gating" matrix.

nals, S_1 to S_8, by means of a matrix using three control signals, A, B, and C, the output may be expressed as

$$S = S_1ABC + S_2\bar{A}BC + S_3A\bar{B}C + S_4\bar{A}\bar{B}C + S_5AB\bar{C}$$
$$+ S_6\bar{A}B\bar{C} + S_7A\bar{B}\bar{C} + S_8\bar{A}\bar{B}\bar{C}$$

This expression may be rearranged and factored in a number of different ways to produce new circuits.   An example is

$$S = [(S_1A + S_2\bar{A})B + (S_3A + S_4\bar{A})\bar{B}]C$$
$$+ [(S_5A + S_6\bar{A})B + (S_1A + S_8\bar{A})\bar{B}]\bar{C}$$

When four or more control signals are involved, the principle illustrated in Fig. 3-4 may be applied.   If one of sixteen signals is to be selected, the signals may be entered as third inputs to the four-by-four array of "and" switches, and the sixteen outputs are then combined in an "or" switch.

In all of the matrix examples, when the number of outputs involved is not exactly 2^n, where n is some integer, it is necessary of course to choose a number, n, of control signals such that 2^n will be greater than the number of outputs.   In these instances, special arrangements can sometimes be found which will require less components than will be required through eliminating unused "and" and "or" switches in the more straightforward configurations.

Sequenced Signals. In some applications the sequence in which the various input signals are applied to a switching network is of consequence in the formation of the desired output signal. To make a switching network sensitive to the sequence of the applied signals it it necessary to employ feedback paths (storage).

As a simple example, consider two pulse-type signals, A and B, where it is desired that A not appear on the output and that B appear on the output line only in the event that A is applied prior to B. If it is known

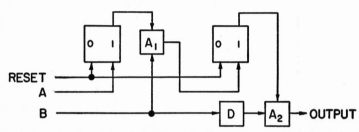

Fɪɢ. 3-7. Example of circuit responsive to sequence of signals.

that A and B will never be applied very close together in time, it is sufficient to have A flip a flip-flop, the output of which is applied to an "and" switch that will control the passage of B. In the general case when the input signals may appear at substantially random times, a more refined switching circuit is necessary. The difficulty arises from the fact that, when A and B are applied close together in time, the flip-flop may be changing when B appears at the "and" switch. The amplitude of the output pulse might then be reduced by an unknown amount where it would be desired to have zero output or a full-sized pulse.

An arrangement which produces the desired result, except for a delay, is shown in Fig. 3-7. A flip-flop and an "and" switch are used as described in the previous paragraph, but the output of the "and" switch is used to flip a second flip-flop. The output of this second flip-flop is then combined in a second "and" switch with the delayed B signal. With this arrangement, the second flip-flop will either flip or not (no intermediate state is possible), regardless of the strength of the output from the first "and" switch. Consequently, the output pulse will be either full-sized or zero.

Several variations in the switching arrangement are possible which have various advantages and disadvantages, depending upon the detailed requirements of the application. One type of variation worth noting is derived from the fact that, of the four possible combinations of stable states of the two flip-flops, one combination never exists. Specifically, the second flip-flop is never in the "1" state at the same time that the first flip-flop is in the "0" state. As a consequence, the two flip-flops may be replaced by a single configuration which has three stable states. The resulting arrangement is shown in Fig. 3-8. After a pulse is applied to the "reset" line, a signal appears at the output of the first inverter, but no signals appear on the output lines from the second or third inverters.

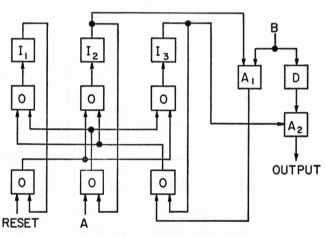

FIG. 3-8. A variation of Fig. 3-6.

If the B input pulse is applied prior to A, it will not pass either "and" switch. If A is applied prior to B, a signal will be caused to appear at the output of the second inverter. The B signal will then pass the first "and" switch and cause the array to exist in its third stable state. The second "and" switch will now be opened, and the delayed B pulse will appear on the output line. As before, the output pulse will be either zero or full-sized.

A requirement frequently encountered in the control portion of a computer involves the starting and stopping of a uniform series of pulses by start and stop pulses which may be random in time. The basic problem involved, which is the causing of all output pulses to be either zero or full-sized, is substantially the same as when designing switching networks to respond to sequenced signals.

Three solutions to the problem are shown in Fig. 3-9. All are similar in their use of bistable storage elements, but the differences in the placement of the delay device create important differences in circuit operation as illustrated by the timing chart in the figure. In (a), all pulses occurring after the start pulse and before the stop pulse will appear on the output line. However, they will be delayed because they must pass through the delay device. The amount of delay should be short relative to the time between successive pulses, but should be longer than the time required for the bistable device to change its state. In (b) the output pulses will not be delayed at all, although the first pulse after

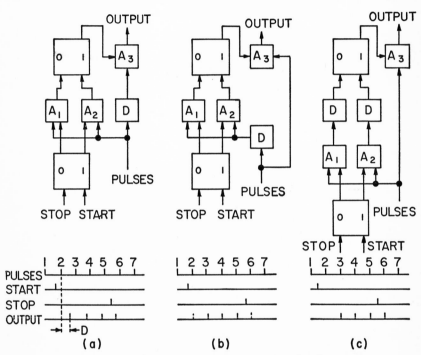

FIG. 3-9. Starting and stopping a series of pulses.

the start pulse (the 2 pulse in the timing chart) may not appear on the output line. For the 2 pulse to appear, the start pulse must be applied at a time prior to the appearance of the 1 pulse at the A_1 and A_2 "and" switches. Similarly, the 6 pulse may or may not appear on the output in accordance with whether or not the 5 pulse arrives at the "and" switches prior to the application of the stop pulse. With the arrangement in (c), the first pulse to pass is the second one after the start pulse, and the last one will be the first one after the stop pulse. In all three arrangements, any given pulse will either not pass at all or will pass with full amplitude, regardless of the timing relative to the starting and stopping signals.

80   Arithmetic Operations in Digital Computers

The time of application of signals of the steady-state type can be of consequence as well as when pulse signals are used. Flip-flops or other multistable configurations are employed in the same general manner. Because the problems that arise in practice are usually so "miscellaneous" in nature and because no organized methods of solution are known, the subject will not be discussed further.

Chapter 4

BINARY ADDITION AND SUBTRACTION

Addition and subtraction of numbers of any radix can be accomplished by a process of simple counting; that is, by adding "counts" to one number while at the same time subtracting "counts" from another number, the sum of the two numbers will be obtained when the second number is reduced to zero. However, it is much faster and generally more satisfactory to add and subtract digits of corresponding orders separately and to adjust the results of the individual digit sums according to rules of carrying and borrowing to be described. With pencil-and-paper arithmetic it is customary to add three or more numbers together as a simultaneous process whenever such a sum is required. In every known example it has been found more practical for machine computations to handle numbers only two at a time. Then, three numbers would be added by adding the third to the sum of the first two. Pencil-and-paper subtraction methods usually involve only two numbers at a time so, for subtraction, machine arithmetic involves no new ideas in this respect.

In most instances, explanations of arithmetic operations will be made through the use of functional block diagrams instead of actual components and circuits. When making an attempt to reduce the functional block diagrams to circuits which may be used, it is found that in some cases the reduction is straightforward, but in other cases substantial modifications in the functional arrangements must be made, with the difference depending upon the characteristics of the computer components which have been chosen for use. Diode rectifier switching circuits, for example, fit many of the functional diagrams very well. On the other hand, vacuum tubes are commonly used components which often require substantial modifications in the functional diagrams for switching, and a few circuits employing vacuum tubes are presented to illustrate this point. Transistors and magnetic cores are components which

81

also require modifications in functional arrangements in some cases. However, the principles involved in the arithmetic operations to be described are independent of the nature of the physical components.

Comparison of Parallel and Serial Operation. Addition and subtraction are executed in parallel or serially, according to the manner in which the numbers are transmitted; and there are two different methods by which binary numbers may be transmitted from one place to another in a computer. One method involves the use of a separate channel or wire for each digit of the number, and all digits are transmitted simultaneously "in parallel." With the other method, only one channel or wire is used and the digits are transmitted one at a time "serially" on this channel. For parallel operation it is required that separate devices be used for addition and subtraction in each order of the numbers involved, whereas for serial operation only one such device is necessary because it is possible to process the orders one at a time and thereby use the same device for all orders.

The advantage of parallel operation is that higher computation speeds are possible, and the advantage of serial operations is that less equipment is required. The evaluation of these advantages is, however, quite difficult. For example, if n orders are involved, it is not true that a parallel machine is n times as fast as a serial machine; neither is it true that the parallel machine requires n times as much equipment. In making such comparisons, it must of course be assumed that similar types of components and engineering techniques are used.

It does not appear possible to make a definite statement about the factor in speed that can be gained through parallel operation. In any case, the factor is seldom as great as n because, for one reason, parallel operation does not necessarily imply that the addition or subtraction of all orders of two numbers is accomplished simultaneously. The result of the addition or subtraction in the lowest order may affect the result in the next order, and the result there may affect the next higher order. This process may continue through all orders, and with most parallel systems a finite amount of time is required for it. With serial operation, the required time is automatically available through the nature of serial transmission; therefore, no additional time need be allotted. Also, in a computer, time is required for operations other than the fundamental arithmetic operations. For example, with most computer designs, time is required to send numbers to and from the number storage unit in the computer, and this time is not available for computations.

It is similarly difficult to make a reasonable statement about the factor by which the amount of equipment is increased through the use of parallel operation. Nevertheless, the factor is clearly less than n, because there is much more to a computer than the wires for transmitting numbers and the device which adds and subtracts. In particular, the device for the storage of numbers in the computer would be roughly the same size for the two methods of operation, where it is assumed that the same amount of storage is provided and that similar types of storage elements are used in the two cases.

The choice between parallel and serial operation is probably affected by the type of number storage device which has been selected for use as much as by speed and equipment considerations. Any type of number storage device can be adapted to either serial or parallel operation; but some types are more conveniently adapted to parallel operation, whereas others lend themselves better to serial operation.

Both parallel and serial binary computers have been built, and there is as yet no conclusive evidence that one mode of operation has a net advantage over the other.

Parallel Operation. In general, when the sum of two digits in corresponding orders of two numbers to be added is equal to or greater than the radix of the system in use, the sum digit of the next higher order must be increased by one. The rules for the binary addition of digits are most easily expressed by the use of a simple table such as Table 4-I, where the augend digit is the digit to which the addend digit is being

TABLE 4-I. BINARY ADDITION

Augend Digit	0	1	0	1
Addend Digit	0	0	1	1
Sum Digit	0	1	1	0
Carry	0	0	0	1

added. A device which will accept two signals representing the augend and addend digits and produce output signals representing the sum and carry in accordance with Table 4-I is known as a "half adder." The reason that the term "half" is employed is that it is yet necessary to add the carry signal from the next lower order so as to obtain the correct sum digit in the number representing the sum of the augend and addend. The rules for adding the carry are exactly the same as the rules in Table 4-I for the addition of the augend and addend digits, and therefore a second half adder may be used for this purpose. Except for the lowest order, two half adders per order are required for the addition of two numbers. Actually, slightly more equipment than two half adders per order is required, because a carry signal may be received from either of the half adders, and provision must be made for transmittal of either one of these two carries to the next higher order. A block diagram of the equipment necessary for the addition of two binary numbers by this process is shown in Fig. 4-1. The two numbers to be added are $X = \cdots X_3 X_2 X_1$ and $Y = \cdots Y_3 Y_2 Y_1$ to produce a sum, $S = \cdots S_3 S_2 S_1$. The half adders are so labeled, and the "or" switches for "mixing" the

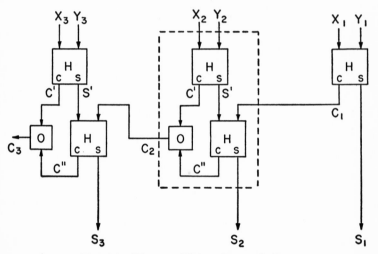

FIG. 4-1. Binary addition, first variation.

carries are indicated by blocks labeled O. The sum output of the first half adder of each order is designated as S' to distinguish it from the correct sum, S, which is the sum output from the second half adder. The carry outputs from the first and second half adders are similarly labeled C' and C''. Note that from the rules of binary addition it is impossible to have carry signals simultaneously from both half adders in an order. This statement can be understood by observing that, for C' to be 1, it is necessary that the corresponding digits of both X and Y be 1, in which case S' is 0 and therefore C'' will be 0. The carry which is sent to the next higher order is therefore comprised of C' or C''. The "or" function is executed so ingeniously in some circuits and devices that its existence can easily escape notice, but in the design of a binary adding device it must not be forgotten.

A variation in the method of binary addition may be obtained by adding the carry to the digit of one of the numbers and then adding the digit of the other number to the resulting sum. A block diagram of this method is shown in Fig. 4-2. As before, the carry to be transmitted to the next higher order is C' or C''. Mathematically, the difference between the arrangements shown in Figs. 4-1 and 4-2 is trivial, but from an engineering viewpoint there is an important difference which occurs in the speed with which a carry may be propagated through the orders. Consider the example where $X = 00001$ and $Y = 01111$. A carry will occur in the lowest order, which, when added to the second order, will produce a carry there; the carry in the second order will produce

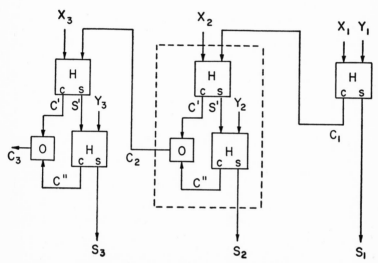

FIG. 4-2. Binary addition, second variation.

a carry in the third order, and so on. With the arrangement shown in Fig. 4-1, the carry must proceed through only one half adder per order, but in Fig. 4-2 it must proceed through both half adders in each order and is therefore slower. Since there are no particular advantages for the arrangement shown in Fig. 4-2, it will not be discussed in any further detail.

Half Adder. From Table 4-I it may be deduced that the Boolean algebra expressions for simple binary addition (the function performed by a half adder) are

$$\text{Sum} = X\bar{Y} + \bar{X}Y \qquad \textit{Exclusive-OR}$$

$$\text{Carry} = XY$$

where X and Y are the input signals of a given order in the augend and addend. The subscripts on X and Y are omitted for simplicity of notation. The determination of these expressions from the table is straightforward; it is necessary only to note the cases for which the sum or carry is 1 and to write down the corresponding conditions on X and Y. A functional block diagram of a half adder operating in this straightforward manner is shown in Fig. 4-3(a). With some types of computer equipment, the signals and their inverses are both available, in which case the inverters in the half adder may be omitted; in this case the half adder takes its simplest form.

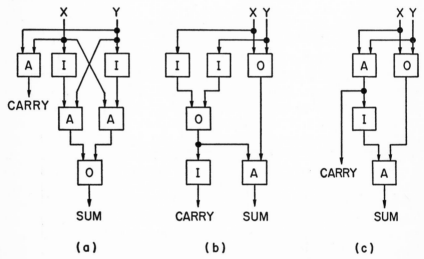

Fig. 4-3. Three functional diagrams for a half adder.

The expressions for the sum and carry may be factored and rearranged in a number of ways, and each different expression for the sum or carry represents a physically different way of forming a half adder. For example, the sum and carry could be written

$$\text{Sum} = (X + Y)(\overline{X} + \overline{Y})$$

$$\text{Carry} = \overline{\overline{X} + \overline{Y}}$$

and a functional block diagram for a half adder built in this way is shown in Fig. 4-3(b). The derivation of these expressions may be accomplished either by an examination of Table 4-I or by algebraic manipulations of the expressions obtained previously. The determination of these expressions from the table is probably not as straightforward as for the previous form, but it is not difficult. The sum would be thought of as "at least one 1 in X or Y while at the same time at least one 0 in X or Y." The carry would be thought of as "not a 0 in either X or Y."

If the inverses of the input digits are not available directly, a reduction in the amount of required equipment, particularly inverters, may be obtained by factoring the expression for the sum in the following manner.

$$\text{Sum} = (X + Y)\overline{(XY)}$$

$$\text{Carry} = XY$$

"Exclusive OR" (+) (handwritten annotation)

It is clear from Table 4-I that "the sum is 1 when X or when Y is 1, but not when both X and Y are 1," which is a word picture of this expression for the sum. The functional block diagram for this arrangement is shown in Fig. 4-3(c).

For some applications it may be desirable to develop an output to represent "not sum" and "not carry." This may be accomplished for each of the arrangements shown in Fig. 4-3 by the addition of inverters on the sum and carry output lines. The purpose of generating the inverted outputs may be to provide a means for checking the operation of the half adder; that is, for example, if both the sum and its inverse were 1 or both 0, an error would be indicated. For this application it would be necessary to generate the inverted outputs separately to insure that a malfunctioning of the adder would produce an output which could be distinguished as an error. A simple inverter would not be sufficient, because an error would occur in the "not sum" also, and the conditions for an indication of an error would not be satisfied. Functional arrangements for the generation of the inverted outputs may be designed from the expressions for the inverted outputs, and the procedure is substantially the same as previously described.

$$\overline{\text{Sum}} = \overline{X}\overline{Y} + \overline{X}Y = XY + \overline{X}\overline{Y} = (X + \overline{Y})(\overline{X} + Y) = XY + \overline{(X + Y)}$$

$$\overline{\text{Carry}} = \overline{XY} = \overline{X} + \overline{Y} = \overline{X}\overline{Y} + X\overline{Y} + \overline{X}Y$$

Application of Vacuum Tubes to the Half Adder. It is clear from the description of vacuum tubes in the previous chapter that the functional properties of vacuum tubes are such that vacuum tubes cannot be adapted to the functional arrangements for a half adder shown in Fig. 4-3. Additional rearrangements of the half adder are required. No straightforward method is known whereby vacuum-tube half-adder circuits can be determined. Through a "cut-and-try" process it has been found that, if the expressions

$$\text{Sum} = \overline{\overline{(XYX)}\ \overline{(XYY)}}$$

$$\text{Carry} = \overline{\overline{XY}}$$

are used, the resulting functional arrangement is one to which vacuum tubes may be adapted. The circuit is shown in Fig. 4-4(a). Note that the output of tube 2 would be $\overline{\overline{X}YX}$ and the output of tube 3 would be $\overline{\overline{X}YY}$, but, when the anodes of the two tubes are connected together, this intermediate output line becomes positive only when both tubes

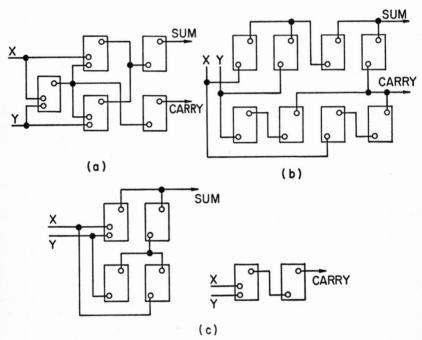

(a)

(b)

(c)

Fig. 4-4. Half adder circuits employing vacuum tubes.

are cut off so that an "and" operation is produced in the same manner as when the outputs of two triodes are connected together.

A circuit employing only triodes can be worked out when the sum and carry are expressed as follows:

$$\text{Sum} = \overline{(\overline{X}\overline{Y})}\ \overline{(\overline{\overline{X}}\ \overline{\overline{Y}})}$$

$$\text{Carry} = \overline{\overline{X}}\ \overline{\overline{Y}}$$

This circuit is shown in Fig. 4-4(b). Since two triodes can be built conveniently into one bulb, a rough estimate of the amount of equipment in use can be obtained by counting the grids. Eight grids are in use in each of the circuits shown in Fig. 4-4. In Fig. 4-4(b), the input to tube 4 is the carry; and if the carry is generated with a circuit like that of tubes 1 and 5 in Fig. 4-4(a), a reduction to seven required grids may be achieved.

Another eight-grid arrangement is shown in Fig. 4-4(c). Here, the sum and carry are generated independently. This arrangement is probably more straightforward and has the minor advantage that the input signals must pass through only two instead of three tubes to generate the sum.

Full Adder. The amount of equipment shown within the dotted lines in Figs. 4-1 and 4-2 is called a full adder. When the two half adders and the "or" circuit are considered as a unit, a number of different functional arrangements may be worked out whereby the individual half adders lose their identity. A full adder accepts signals, each of which may represent a 1 or a 0, from three different sources and adds them to yield 00, 01, 10, or 11 according to whether none, one, two, or all three of the input signals are 1's. The right-hand digit of the adder output is the sum digit, and the left-hand digit is the carry signal to be applied to the full adder corresponding to the next higher order. The rules of operation of a full adder are shown in Table 4-II, where X and Y are augend and addend digits, respectively, of a given order of two binary numbers to be added together, and C is the carry signal from the next lower order.

TABLE 4-II. BINARY ADDITION RULES FOR FULL ADDER

X	0	1	0	0	1	1	0	1
Y	0	0	1	0	1	0	1	1
C	0	0	0	1	0	1	1	1
Sum	0	1	1	1	0	0	0	1
Carry	0	0	0	0	1	1	1	1

By noting the conditions on X, Y, and C for which the sum and carry are 1, it is readily determined that

$$\text{Sum} = X\bar{Y}\bar{C} + \bar{X}Y\bar{C} + \bar{X}\bar{Y}C + XYC$$

$$\text{Carry} = XY\bar{C} + X\bar{Y}C + \bar{X}YC + XYC$$

This same result could have been determined from the half adders and the "or" circuit which may be used to form a full adder. From Fig. 4-1,

$$\text{Sum} = S'\bar{C} + \bar{S}'C = (X\bar{Y} + \bar{X}Y)\bar{C} + (XY + \bar{X}\bar{Y})C$$
$$= X\bar{Y}\bar{C} + \bar{X}Y\bar{C} + \bar{X}\bar{Y}C + XYC$$
$$\text{Carry} = C' + C'' = XY(C + \bar{C}) + (X\bar{Y} + \bar{X}Y)C$$
$$= XY\bar{C} + X\bar{Y}C + \bar{X}YC + XYC$$

A similar procedure may be followed through the use of the circuit shown in Fig. 4-2. The switching circuits for the generation of the sum and carry according to these expressions may be developed in a straightforward manner; in each case the requirements are four 3-input "and" circuits feeding a 4-input "or" circuit. The expression for carry may be simplified to

$$\text{Carry} = XY\bar{C} + X\bar{Y}C + \bar{X}YC + XYC + XYC + XYC$$
$$= XY(\bar{C} + C) + XC(\bar{Y} + Y) + YC(\bar{X} + X)$$
$$= XY + XC + YC$$

so that only three 2-input "and" circuits feeding a 3-input "or" circuit are required. The total number of inputs required for the various "and" and "or" circuits is therefore 25.

A reduction to 21 in the number of required inputs may be obtained by factoring the expressions for sum and carry in either of the following ways:

$$\text{Sum} = [(X\bar{Y} + \bar{X}Y) + C](XY + \bar{X}\bar{Y} + \bar{C})$$
$$\text{Carry} = (X\bar{Y} + \bar{X}Y)C + XY$$
$$\text{Sum} = [(X + Y)(\bar{X} + \bar{Y}) + C](XY + \bar{X}\bar{Y} + \bar{C})$$
$$\text{Carry} = [(X + Y)(\bar{X} + \bar{Y})]C + XY$$

The switching arrangements for these two variations in full adders are shown in Figs. 4-5(a) and 4-5(b), respectively. The X, Y, and C inputs may be interchanged, but the selections shown are preferred because the C input has then to pass through only one "and" and one "or" circuit to reach the "carry" output. As has already been mentioned, some problems require that the carry signal be propagated through two or more successive orders, and for purposes of high speed of carry propagation it is desirable to hold to a minimum the amount of equipment through which the carry signal must pass. It is not to be construed that the adder arrangements in Fig. 4-5 are necessarily practical; in fact, for most switching components it is generally found more satisfactory to employ a more straightforward switching arrangement even though the number of switching elements may be increased.

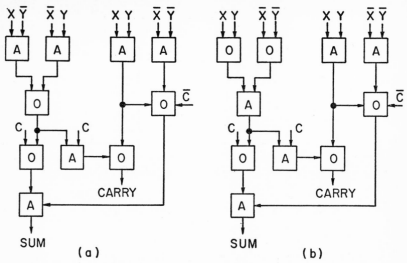

F IG. 4-5. Full adder arrangements, each employing 21 switching inputs.

Two other interesting although not very competitive ways of factoring the original expressions for sum and carry are:

$$\text{Sum} = (X\bar{Y} + \bar{X}C + Y\bar{C})(\bar{X}\bar{Y} + \bar{X}\bar{C} + \bar{Y}\bar{C}) + XYC$$

$$\text{Carry} = (X\bar{Y} + \bar{X}C + Y\bar{C})(XY + XC + YC) + XYC$$

$$\text{Sum} = (X + Y + C)(\bar{X}\bar{Y} + \bar{X}\bar{C} + \bar{Y}\bar{C}) + XYC$$

$$\text{Carry} = XY + XC + YC$$

By using the relationships presented in the section on Boolean algebra, the latter form may be used to derive a useful binary adder arrangement which does not require the inverse of any of the three input signals. One inverter is required; the equations are:

$$\text{Sum} = (X + Y + C)\overline{(XY + XC + YC)} + XYC$$

$$\text{Carry} = XY + XC + YC$$

It is not difficult to show that this may be modified to the following variation:

$$\text{Sum} = (X + Y + C)\overline{(XY + XC + YC + XYC)}$$

$$\text{Carry} = XY + XC + YC$$

The block diagram switching arrangements for these two variations are shown in Figs. 4-6(a) and 4-6(b). In addition to the inverter, 19 switching inputs are required in each case.

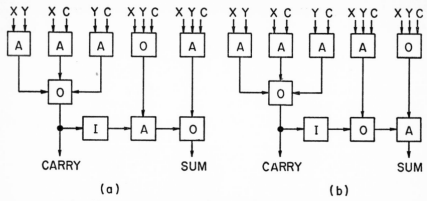

FIG. 4-6. Full adder arrangements, each employing one inverter but no inverted inputs.

The number of diodes can be reduced to 16 by appropriate factoring of the above equations for the 19-diode adders. Two variations may be represented as follows:

$$\text{Sum} = [(X + Y) + C][\overline{XY + (X + Y)C} + (XY)C]$$

$$\text{Carry} = XY + (X + Y)C$$

$$\text{Sum} = [(X + Y) + C]\overline{(X + Y)(XY + C)} + (XY)C$$

$$\text{Carry} = (X + Y)(XY + C)$$

The functional block diagrams of these two variations are shown in Fig. 4-7. Note that carry in passing from the C input to the carry output still has to pass through only one "and" switch and one "or" switch, with the result that the speed of carry propagation is not impaired. Further, it happens that in the design of diode switching circuits two successive "and" switches are only slightly more difficult to design than a single "and" switch; the difficult problems arise when signals pass through "and" and "or" switches alternately. Therefore, the fact that some signals must pass through four switches in the arrangements in Fig. 4-7 is not a serious disadvantage.

Application of Vacuum Tubes to the Full Adder. It is possible to form a full adder by employing two half adders as shown in Fig. 4-4 plus an "or" switch for the carry. A parallel inverter circuit, as shown in Fig. 2-4(b), may be used for the "or" switch, although an additional inverter is necessary to yield a carry output of the proper polarity. A full adder derived in this way is not the best that it is possible to obtain for two reasons. One reason is that the total number of tubes which would be used is greater than necessary; and the other reason is that the number of tubes through which the carry signal must pass when being propagated through a succession of orders is greater than necessary, and therefore the carry speed will be slow.

In Fig. 4-8(a) a circuit is shown for which the carry has to pass through only one tube, but in this circuit the inverse of the carry instead of the carry is obtained as an output. The obvious way to correct this situation is to use an inverter to obtain the true carry, but this would

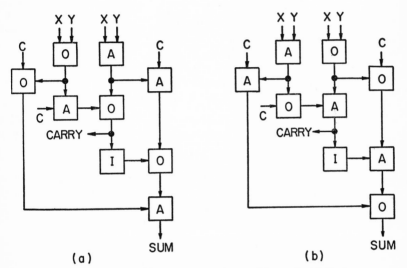

Fig. 4-7. Binary adder arrangements requiring only 16 diodes.

mean that the carry signal would have to pass through an extra tube per order. By designing the adder of the next higher order to accept inverted carry signals, the extra inverter may be avoided. An arrangement for an adder of this type is shown in Fig. 4-8(b). As with the arrangement shown in Fig. 4-8(a), the carry must pass through only one tube, but the true carry instead of its inverse is obtained. Therefore, by using the arrangements shown in Figs. 4-8(a) and 4-8(b) in alternate orders, the carry may propagate from order to order and pass through only one tube per order. For engineering reasons, it may be preferable that the one tube be a triode instead of a multigrid tube as in Figs. 4-8(a) and 4-8(b). The realization of this preference, at least in a straightforward manner, appears to be an impossibility, because, when a positive signal is applied to the grid of a triode, its plate potential becomes negative regardless of the remainder of the circuit. When a signal of either polarity is applied to one grid of a multigrid tube, the output potential may be either positive or negative, depending upon the nature of the remainder of the circuit and the conditions existing in the other parts of the circuit; and such a function is necessary in the generation of the carry signal from the C input from the next lower order.

As might be expected, the variety of full adder circuits which may be formed with vacuum tubes is extensive. The circuit shown in Fig.

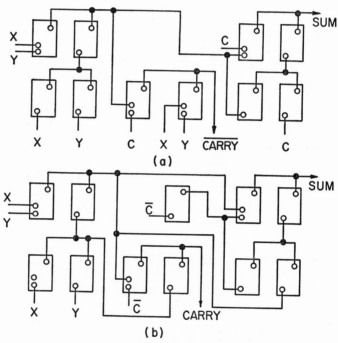

(a)

(b)

Fig. 4-8. Full adder employing vacuum tubes.

4-8 has been selected for presentation because, so far as is known, it employs less tubes than any other arrangement. A total of fourteen grids, or seven tubes, per order is required. A reduction of one grid per order may be obtained if the inverted X and Y inputs are available and if an inverted sum output from every other order can be used. If inverted inputs are available and carry propagation through two tubes per order is allowable, a reduction of two grids per order, or a total of twelve, may be obtained. With this arrangement, it so happens that the carry signal appears inverted between every order, but this is of no real consequence. The circuits are presented in Figs. 4-9 and 4-10, respectively.

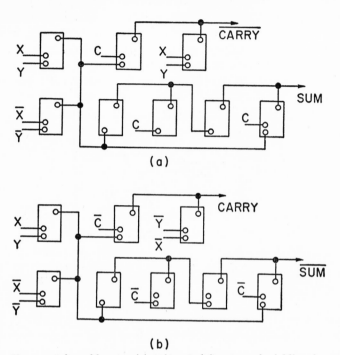

(a)

(b)

FIG. 4-9. Vacuum-tube adder requiring inverted inputs and yielding inverted sum output in alternate orders.

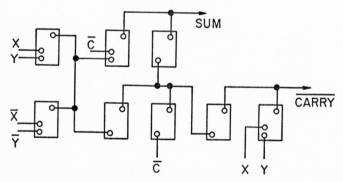

FIG. 4-10. Vacuum-tube adder requiring only twelve grids, but also requiring inverted inputs and two tubes per order for carry propagation.

Kirchhoff Adders. A different approach to the problem of binary addition may be obtained through the addition of some physical quantity, usually current or voltage. These adders are called Kirchhoff adders because of the application of Kirchhoff's laws to the design of the circuits. One form of Kirchhoff adder is shown in Fig. 4-11. The X, Y, and C inputs are positive or negative (relatively), according to whether the corresponding input signals are 1 or 0, respectively. The voltages in the grid circuit of triode, T_1, are so chosen that T_1 is cut off when none or only one of the input signals is positive, but is fully conductive

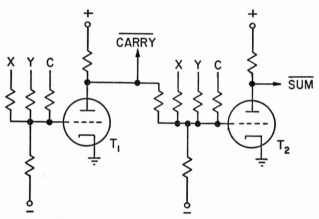

Fig. 4-11. One form of Kirchhoff adder.

when two or three of the inputs are positive. The components in the grid circuit of T_2 are so chosen that T_2 is cut off when all inputs are negative, but is fully conductive when only one input is positive. If two inputs are positive, the negative signal from T_1 again causes T_2 to be cut off. When all three inputs are positive, the amplitude of the signal from T_1 does not change and T_2 becomes conductive again. The output of T_1 is the inverse of the carry, and output of T_2 is the inverse of the sum. For the carry signal to be useful for the driving of the adder of the next higher order, it must of course be inverted unless tricks are used, such as designing the adder of every other order to handle negative signals.

Another type of Kirchhoff adder may be built up following the steps shown in Fig. 4-12. If three resistances each have one end connected to a common junction and the other end connected to a potential source of either 0 or E, as in 4-12(a), the potential of the junction will be 0, $\frac{1}{3}E$, $\frac{2}{3}E$, or E according to whether none, one, two, or three, respectively, of the supply potentials are E. This output potential is then applied to one end of two commonly connected resistances of values $2R_2$ and R_2. If a potential of 0 is applied to the other end when the first potential is 0 or $\frac{1}{3}E$, and a potential of $-\frac{1}{3}E$ is applied to the other end when the first potential is $\frac{2}{3}$ E or E, the potential of the junction will be 0 or $\frac{1}{9}E$. These two resistance networks may then be joined together to form an adder which utilizes the fact that the sum digit is equal to the sum of the three input digits minus twice the carry digit as can be determined from Table 4-II. Note that if none of the input

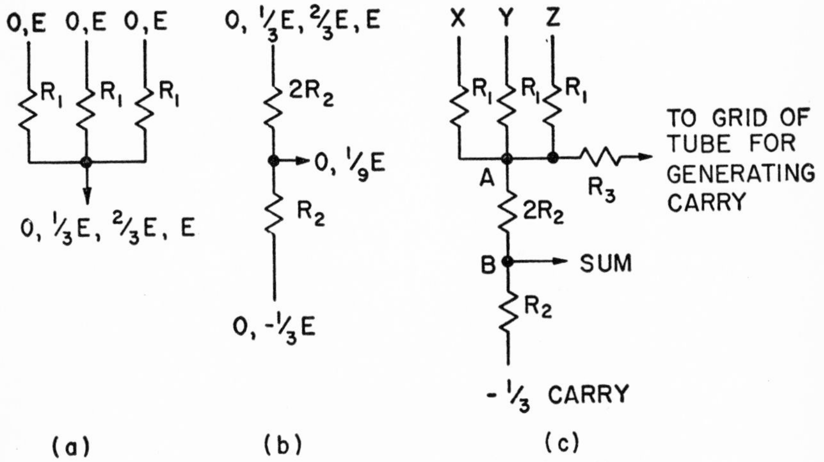

FIG. 4-12. Another form of Kirchhoff adder.

signals are 1, the carry and sum are both 0; if one of the input signals is 1, the carry is still zero and the sum is 1; if two of the input signals are 1, twice the carry subtracted from the sum of the input signals, 2, yields 0 for the correct sum digit; when all three of the input signals are 1, twice the carry subtracted from 3 yields 1, which is again the correct sum digit.

The combined circuit is shown in Fig. 4-12(c). The carry may be generated by applying the potential of point A to the grid of a tube through a resistor R_3, which should have a relatively high value of resistance in order to minimize the loading on point A. The tube is so biased that it is entirely cut off when none or one of the input signals is positive, but is fully conducting when two or three of the input signals are positive. The output (proper amplitude) of the carry tube is applied to the resistance network at the point shown, and a signal representing the sum is then available at point B. The value of R_2 should be large relative to R_1 so that the potential of point A will be substantially unaffected by application of the carry signal as described. Although the fundamentals of this type of adder are simple enough, the engineering details which must be taken into consideration in the design of a useful circuit cause the arrangement to be less attractive than may appear at first glance. By changing the $2R_2$ resistance to a value of $\frac{2}{3}R_2$ and by feeding back a full amplitude carry signal instead of $\frac{1}{3}$ amplitude, the amplitude of the sum output may be increased from $\frac{1}{9}$ to $\frac{1}{5}$ of the amplitude of the input signals, but this amplitude is still smaller than would be considered desirable.

Since Kirchhoff adders must be built of components with properties which must be accurately controlled and which are constant with time, proper functioning is more difficult to attain with them than it is with some of the other types of adder circuits. Nevertheless, circuit simplicity remains an important advantage of the Kirchhoff adders.

Accumulators. All of the adders described up to this point performed only an adding function; that is, signals representing the two binary numbers to be added were applied to appropriate input lines of the adder, and, after the transients in the adder circuits had died out, signals representing the sum of the two numbers appeared on the output lines. The output signals remained as long as the input signals were held operative. An "accumulator" executes addition through a different process.

The term, "accumulator," usually refers to a device which stores a number and, upon reception of another number, adds the two numbers and then stores the sum. An adder of any of the types described previously can be combined with a storage device to form an accumulator, but in this section only those forms of accumulators which employ "counters" will be taken into consideration. Unfortunately, at least two important variations in the definition of the term, counter, have come into use. A binary counter is here intended to mean a device having two stable states and which changes back and forth from one state to the other upon reception of pulse-type signals. That this function is counting in the binary system is apparent when it is observed that binary counting in any given order is merely a matter of alternating back and forth between zero and one. A counter in this sense is therefore one order of a binary counter which "counts" from zero to some relatively large number. When a number (the addend) is to be added to the number (the augend) already present in the accumulator, pulses representing the addend are sent in a parallel fashion to the appropriate order of the accumulator, which accepts them by a counting action in each order.

When the counter of any order passes from the state representing one to the state representing zero, an additional pulse (carry) is sent to the counter of the next higher order, and there is a variety of functional arrangements for handling these carries. After the carry signals have been recorded, the number in the accumulator is the sum of the number there previously and the number which has been sent to it. The number previously in the accumulator has been obliterated. Additional numbers may be sent to the accumulator, which will add them and indicate the accumulated sum, and it is from this function that the name is derived.

The relative advantages of adders and accumulators are difficult to assess when isolated units are considered. When an adder with a storage device is used, the function of shifting is, with some types of components, more easily accomplished than with an accumulator composed of counters. Shifting will be discussed in more detail in connection with multiplication. On the other hand, an accumulator can be assembled with fewer components.

Many different forms of accumulators may be designed if different types of components are used; but, even when a single given set of components is considered, there are several different functional arrangements which may be used, with the differences appearing mainly in the methods of handling the carry signals.

The most obvious way of handling the carries is to note, by some means or another, those orders in which carry signals have been generated and to send these signals to their corresponding next higher orders. The entry of the carry signals into the counters may produce additional carries. The next step is to sense if the entry of the carries has produced any new carries and to enter these into the next succeeding orders while at the same time making provision for the prevention of the entry of the original carries a second time. For example, the steps required to add 00011 to 01111 would be as follows.

$$01111$$
$$00011$$
$$\overline{}$$
$$01100$$
$$11$$
$$\overline{}$$
$$01010$$
$$1$$
$$\overline{}$$
$$00010$$
$$1$$
$$\overline{}$$
$$10010$$

Since a carry occurring in the lowest order may ultimately generate a carry to be entered into the highest order, the required steps to the process are equal in number to the number of orders in the accumulator. When several numbers are to be added together, the situation can be improved somewhat by alternately adding carries and numbers, although after adding the last number the carries must be added according to the procedure shown above. As an example, 00110 will be added to the two factors used above.

$$
\begin{array}{rr}
& 01111 \\
\text{Add number} & 00011 \\
\hline
& 01100 \\
\text{Add carries} & 11 \\
\hline
& 01010 \\
\text{Add number} & 00110 \\
\hline
& 01100 \\
\text{Add carries} & 11 \\
\hline
& 00000 \\
\text{Add carries} & 11 \\
\hline
& 11000 \\
\end{array}
$$

Note that when this procedure is followed it will never be necessary to add two carries into any given order in one operation.

When adding the last number with the above procedure, or when only two numbers are involved, it may still be necessary to add, one at a time, as many carries as there are orders in the numbers. If time is allowed for the addition of all the carries, regardless of the number of carries, actually occurring, the time required for addition may be undesirably long. If means are provided in the adding mechanism for sensing that all carries have been added, the time for addition may be materially reduced. The determination of the average number of successive carries that will occur in the addition of two numbers containing random digits is a difficult problem in probability. The addition of two forty-digit binary numbers will produce, on the average, 4.6 carries to be added in succession, according to *Preliminary Discussion of the Logical Design of an Electronic Computing Instrument*, by Burks, Goldstine, and von Neumann (Princeton University, 1947).

Although accumulators employing the step-by-step carry process have been designed, they are relatively slow in operation, and their use largely vitiates the speed advantage that parallel binary operation has when compared with serial operation. It is much faster and frequently more conserving of components to use a carry-handling method, whereby a carry signal is automatically passed along through higher orders in those situations which require it instead of using a step-by-step process. It is the automatic or "ripple through" processes which will be described.

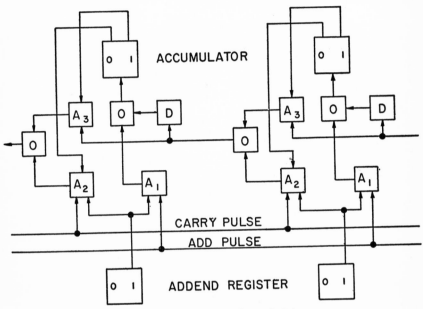

Fig. 4-13. Binary accumulator, first type.

One form of an accumulator is shown in Fig. 4-13. The upper row of blocks represents the binary storage devices or counters (usually called triggers or flip-flops when bistable twin-triode electronic circuits are used) of the accumulator register. Each binary counter has an input line on which the pulse-type signals to be counted are entered. Each binary storage device also has two output lines, one of which (the right-hand one labeled 1 in Fig. 4-13) maintains a steady-state signal when the storage device is in the state representing a 1, and the other (labeled 0) maintains a signal when a 0 is to be indicated. The lower row of blocks represents a storage register holding the addend. To add, a pulse is applied to the line marked "add pulse" which is connected to the "and" circuit marked No. 1 in each order. For those orders which hold a 1 in the addend register, the pulse is sent through to the corresponding counter in the accumulator to be counted.

Now, if in any given order there is a 0 in the accumulator and a 1 in the addend register, it must be that the counter changed from 1 to 0 and a carry is to be sent to the next higher order. Therefore the 0 signal from the counter and the 1 signal from the addend register are applied to two of the three inputs to the No. 2 "and" circuit. Subsequent to the entry of the addend digits into the accumulator, a carry pulse is applied to the third input of the No. 2 "and" circuits of all orders, and for those orders containing the conditions for a carry, this carry pulse is allowed to pass on through a delay device, indicated by a D, to the counter of the next higher order. If the counter of this next higher order contains a 1, this carry pulse should be transmitted on to the next order beyond. To provide for this rippling through of the carry, a No. 3 "and" circuit is provided for each order with one input to this "and" circuit being the carry from the next lower order and the other input being the 1 output from the counter. If several counters in consecutive orders in the accumulator indicate 1's and a carry pulse is received in the lowest order of the series, this carry pulse will then be sent through the switching circuits to all appropriate counters in one operation with the speed of operation limited only by the time required for the carry signal to pass through the series of switching circuits. The delay devices are necessary in principle to allow the applied carry pulse to die out before the counter changes state, because, if the counter changes state too rapidly, the carry may get through the switching circuits in cases when it should not. In practice, the counters are frequently slow enough in action to allow the delay device to be eliminated.

A still faster method of carry propagation is shown in Fig. 4-14. The entry of the addend into the accumulator is made through the No. 1 "and" circuit as before. The function of the No. 2 "and" circuit is somewhat different in that, if in a given order the counter indicates a zero and the addend storage unit indicates a 1, a steady-state signal is immediately sent on to the Nos. 3 and 4 "and" circuits of the next higher order. If the counter indicates a 1, a signal is applied to the other input of the No. 3 "and" circuit so that a signal arriving from the next lower order will be passed on to the next higher order. With this arrangement, the passage of signals through the successive orders is started immediately upon entry of the addend into the accumulator and before the carry pulse is applied. After allowing enough time for the signal to be sent through all orders of the adder (usually less time than this maximum will be required, but provision must be made for the worst case), a carry pulse is applied to the other input of the No. 4 "and" circuit, and for those orders for which a signal from the previous order is received, the carry pulse will be entered into the counters. In principle, a delay device is needed and may be placed in series with one of the input lines to the No. 3 "and" circuit, as shown, but the counters are frequently slow enough to allow the carry pulse to die out before the counter changes state.

With some computer designs it may be impossible, or at least very inconvenient, to obtain signals from the addend register for carry purposes after the entry of the addend has been made. To get around the diffi-

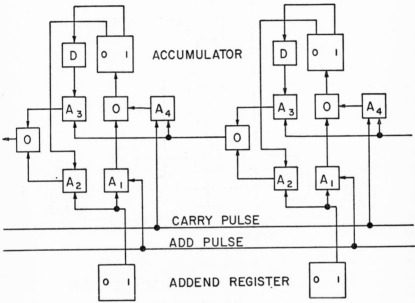

Fig. 4-14. Binary accumulator, second type.

culty, a carry-storage device may be used in each order. Figs. 4-15 and 4-16 each show one order of an accumulator with a carry-storage device which has its input connected to the 0 output of the accumulator-storage device. The connection is shown through a condenser to signify that a pulse-type signal is sent to the carry-storage device when the accumulator changes from the 1 state to the 0 state. At the beginning of an adding operation, the carry-storage device is off, or in the 0 state, so that a pulse from the accumulator-storage device always changes it to the 1 state (turns it on) to record a carry. Entry of the addend into the accumulator is indicated as being through the No. 1 "and" circuit in the same manner as in Figs. 4-13 and 4-14, but it should be understood that pulses representing the addend could arrive from any source without affecting the way in which the carries are handled. In Fig. 4-15, if in a given order, the carry-storage trigger is turned on, a signal is applied to one of the inputs of the No. 2 "and" circuit, and when the carry pulse is applied it will be transmitted to the next higher order. If the accumulator-storage device of a given order indicates a 1 and a carry pulse from a lower order arrives, the pulse will be transmitted to the next higher order through the action of the No. 3 "and" circuit. The ripple-through

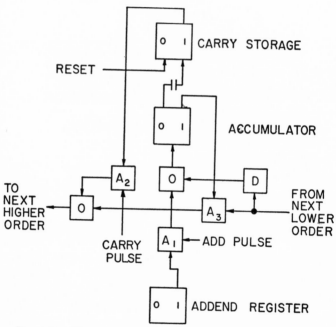

Fig. 4-15. Binary accumulator, first type with carry storage.

action of the carry pulse is substantially the same as in the arrangement shown in Fig. 4-13.

The arrangement shown in Fig. 4-16 is the same functional arrangement as that of Fig. 4-14 except for the addition of the carry-storage devices. Note that in Fig. 4-16, the No. 2 "and" circuit has been eliminated. As in Fig. 4-14, the signals on the switch circuits are applied and allowed to ripple through before the application of the carry pulse. The delay devices in Figs. 4-15 and 4-16 may be in series with the 1 outputs from the accumulator-storage devices instead of as shown. The locations of the delay devices in Figs. 4-13 and 4-14 are similarly interchangeable.

Another automatic carry propagation method for parallel accumulators is shown in Fig. 4-17. The entry of the addend is made through the

No. 1 "and" circuit and an add pulse, as before. Also, the carry-storage devices are turned on when the storage devices in the accumulator change from 1 to 0, as before. The 1 output from each carry-storage device is applied to one of the input lines to the No. 2 "and" circuit of the next higher order. After entry of the addend digits, a carry "gate" signal is applied to the other input of the No. 2 "and" circuit. The output of this

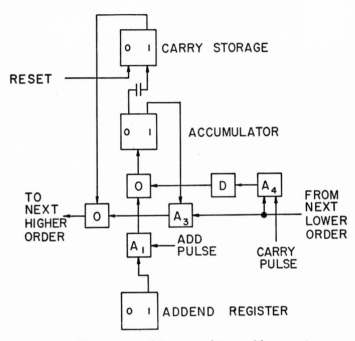

Fig. 4-16. Binary accumulator, second type with carry storage.

"and" circuit is applied through a condenser to generate a single pulse to be applied to the counter. Therefore, when the carry-gate signal is applied, a pulse will be entered into the counter of orders which should receive a carry. If a counter is holding a 1 when it receives a carry, it will change to 0 and at the same time turn on the corresponding carry-storage device. When this carry-storage device goes on, it will send a signal to the next higher order which already has the carry-gate signal applied and a pulse will be entered into the counter of this next higher order. In this manner the carries will be propagated through all appropriate orders, provided, of course, that the carry-gate signal is held operative for a sufficient length of time. This method of carry propagation is not, in general, as rapid as the previously described methods but can for some applications be made sufficiently rapid through the use of high-speed counters and carry-storage devices. It has the advantage that less components are required, and no delay devices are required, even in principle, because of the sequential nature of the carry propagation.

With all three of the accumulator arrangements employing carry-storage devices, it is necessary to reset these devices to 0 after each addition. The resetting is accomplished by means of a reset pulse applied to them after the carry propagation process has terminated.

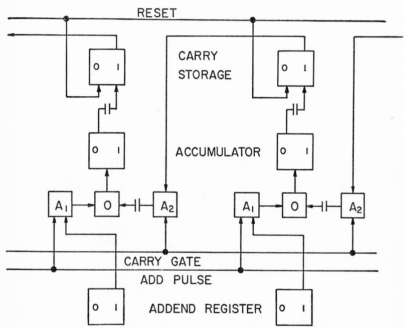

FIG. 4-17.   Another form of accumulator with carry storage.

The principles employed in Fig. 4-17 can be adapted to the carry propagation method given in Fig. 4-13 to gain an important advantage. The resulting functional arrangement is shown in Fig. 4-18. After entry of the addend in the usual manner through the No. 1 "and" switch, the carry-gate signal is applied. For those orders which contain a 0 in the accumulator and a 1 in the addend, a pulse is sent to the next higher order through the action of the No. 2 "and" circuit. If in a given order the accumulator contains a 1, and a pulse arrives from the next lower order, it will change to 0 and send a pulse to the No. 3 "and" circuit on which the carry-gate signal is now applied to the other input. This pulse will therefore be sent on to the next higher order. The advantage of this arrangement is that no pulse or steady-state signal has to pass through more than one order of switching circuits, and switches which attenuate the pulse may therefore be used without providing for amplification. For high-speed carry propagation it is necessary to use high-speed counters in the accumulator as well as high-speed switches.

With all of the accumulators so far described it has been necessary to apply a carry pulse or gate signal on a separate control line subsequent to the actual entry of the addend digits in order to initiate the propagation of the carries. A slow but simple form of accumulator re-

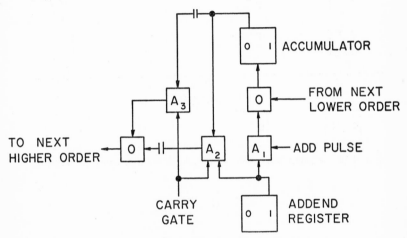

FIG. 4-18. Accumulator with carry signals passing through the switches of only one order.

quiring no carry pulse or gate is shown in Fig. 4-19. When any digit counter changes to 0, a pulse is sent through a delay device to the next higher order. Operation is slow because, for carry propagation, the delays are "in series."

A relatively fast carry propagation method requiring no separate carry pulse or gate signal is shown in Fig. 4-20. The method has obvious disadvantages, but is presented mainly to illustrate the nature of the problems involved. Upon entry of the addend into the counters of the accumulator register through the No. 1 "and" circuit, any counters which change from 1 to 0 will send a pulse through delay unit D_1 to the next higher order. Delay unit D_1 is necessary to allow the transients in the counter of the next higher order to die out because that counter may have at the same time received a pulse from the addend. The higher carry propagation speed is obtained in Fig. 4-20 by applying the 1 output of the counter through delay unit D_2 to one of the inputs of the No. 2 "and" circuit. If a carry pulse arrives from the next lower order and

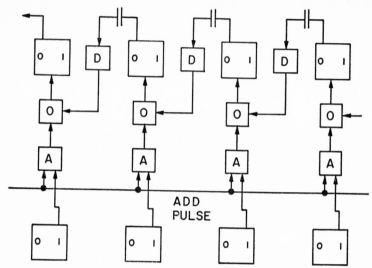

FIG. 4-19. Accumulator with slow, but automatic, carry propagation.

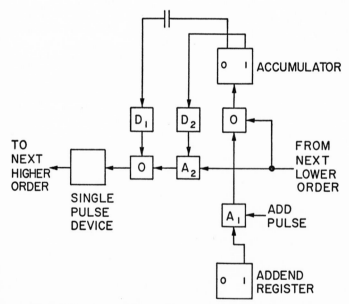

FIG. 4-20. Accumulator with automatic carry initiation.

the counter indicates 1, the carry will be sent directly on to the next higher order. Delay unit D_2 must provide enough delay to allow the carry pulse to die out in those cases where it causes the counter change from 0 to 1; otherwise, the carry will be sent on when it should not be. On the other hand, the delay should not be so great that the 1 signal from the counter is not applied to the No. 2 "and" circuit by the time the carry pulse from the next lower order arrives, which means that the

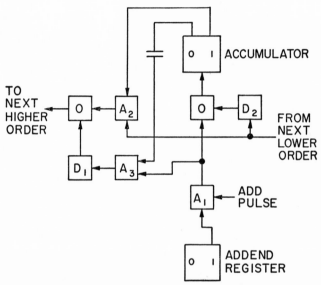

FIG. 4-21. Another accumulator arrangement with automatic carry initiation.

delay in the D_1 units must be greater than the delay in the D_2 units. When a counter changes from 1 to 0 upon receiving a carry pulse from the next lower order, it will send a pulse to the next high order in addition to the pulse propagated through the switching circuits. To eliminate this second pulse, a "single-pulse device" is shown in Fig. 4-20. The single-pulse device passes the first pulse but then becomes insensitive to pulses for a short period of time in order to block passage of the second one. A circuit known as a "one-shot multivibrator" may be used in the execution of this function.

Another accumulator arrangement with automatic carry initiation, which is probably more practical than the one shown in Fig. 4-20, is presented in Fig. 4-21. Here, the pulse, if any, which is entered into the accumulator from the addend register is combined with an output pulse from the accumulator in the A_3 "and" switch in those cases where the accumulator changes from 1 to 0. It is assumed that there is sub-

110 Arithmetic Operations in Digital Computers

stantially no delay in the action of the counter; if there is a delay, a compensating delay should be placed in the appropriate input line of the "and" switch. The output from A_3 is passed through a delay, D_1, and an "or" switch to the next higher order. D_1 must be great enough to allow the counter in the next higher order to recover from the entry of a pulse from the corresponding order of the addend register. In the event that a carry signal from the next lower order is received and the accumulator contains a 1, these two signals will be combined in A_2 and

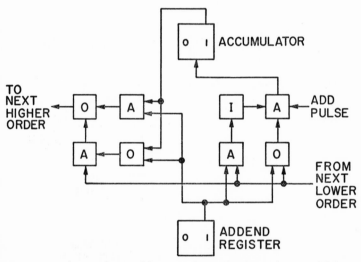

FIG. 4-22. Accumulator with carry determination prior to addition.

transmitted to the next higher order without delay. Note that an initial delay occurs in the D_1 of the order where the carry originates, but further delays in the ripple-through process are not required. If the accumulator counter changes from 1 to 0 upon receiving a carry from the next lower order, a second signal will not be transmitted through A_3 because the "add pulse" will have disappeared by this time. Delay D_2 is a short delay merely for the purpose of insuring that the carry pulse will be terminated before the signal from the counter to A_2 changes, and it may not be necessary if the counter action is slow relative to the duration of the pulse.

It is possible to generate the carry signals even before the entry of the addend into the accumulator is made, and Fig. 4-22 shows one method of accomplishing this result. The scheme has two advantages. One is that it may be somewhat faster to start generating carry signals as soon as the addend is entered into the addend register. A somewhat more important advantage occurs in the case of subtraction. As will be discussed in more detail later, the carry signal from the highest order may be used to determine whether the sign of the difference will be positive or negative. In some situations it may be desired to nullify the subtraction after the sign of the difference is known, and the nullification may be accomplished readily when the sign can be determined before the actual subtraction takes place. In Fig. 4-22 the carry is formed in a set of "and" and "or" switches according to the Boolean expression, $(X + Y)C + XY$, which has been discussed in connection with adders. In previously described accumulator circuits it was necessary for a counter to change its state twice in an addition where it happened to receive a pulse from both the addend register and the carry line from the next lower order. With this arrangement, the presence of both signals simultaneously can be sensed and both pulses may be eliminated. In other words, it is desired that a pulse be entered into a counter if a 1 is in the addend register or if a carry is received from the next lower order, but not when both of these conditions are present. A half-adder circuit may be used to perform this function. In the figure, the half-adder circuit follows the expression $(X + C)\overline{XC}$ with the "add pulse" applied as a third input to the final "and" switch.

Asynchronous Operation. When a computer is designed to operate in "asynchronous" fashion, each arithmetic or other operation is started when a signal is received which indicates that the previous operation has been completed. In all of the accumulators described in previous paragraphs, the carries could be initiated in any of the orders in the accumulator, and they would be propagated through as many higher orders as necessary; but no means was provided for determining when the carry propagation was complete. With many of the accumulator arrangements which have been described, it would be awkward and difficult to install means for indicating the completion of carry propagation, although in some cases it would be possible to use a multi-input "and" switch to sense the existence of a carry in any of the orders of the accumulator. This method of carry sensing would be more applicable to the step-by-step carry systems than the various "ripple-through" systems.

One accumulator arrangement with a ripple-through carry which yields a signal upon completion of the carry process is shown in Fig. 4-23. In each order of this accumulator there are two lines for the transmission of the carry from one order to the next. One line, C, has a signal when a carry is received from the next lower order and the other line, N, has a signal when no carry is to be entered into a given order. Note that, from the arrangement of the "and" and "or" switches forming the carry signals to the next higher order, a signal will not be produced on either

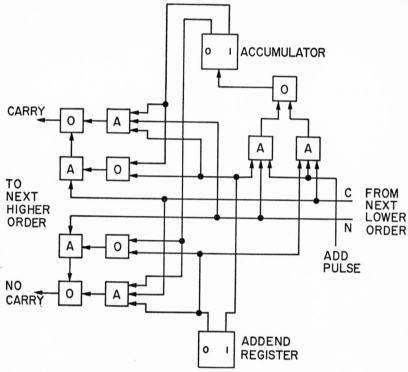

FIG. 4-23.   Accumulator for asynchronous operation.

of the carry-output lines until a signal is applied to one or the other of the carry-input lines. In Boolean algebra notation, the carry and no-carry signals may be expressed in the form:

$$\text{Carry} = (X + Y)C + XYN$$

$$\text{No carry} = (\overline{X} + \overline{Y})N + \overline{X}\,\overline{Y}C$$

To start the carry propagation process, a signal is applied to the N input of the lowest order. This signal then progresses through all orders, sometimes on the carry line between orders and sometimes on the no-carry line in accordance with the binary numbers being added; and it finally emerges from one of the output lines of the highest order. When the signal emerges from the highest order, it is known that carry propagation is complete. The entry of the sum into the accumulator may then be accomplished by applying a pulse to the "add pulse" line. This pulse causes each counter in the accumulator to be changed to its opposite state when the digit in the corresponding order of the addend register is

1, or when the signal from the next lower order is on the C line, but not when both of these conditions are present.

Many variations of the accumulator arrangement of Fig. 4-23 may be worked out. One variation will be described in connection with binary multiplication, where it is of particular interest.

Simultaneous Carry. In all the methods which have been described for handling the carries, either with adders or with accumulators, the carry was "propagated" from one order to the next in those cases where one carry created a carry in the next higher order. It is possible to add all carries simultaneously instead of one after another, and Fig. 4-24 shows the functional arrangement for accomplishing it. The scheme, as applied to an adder, is shown in Fig. 4-24(a). Consider the highest order, that is, the one on the left-hand side of the figure. A carry from this order to be sent to the next higher order can be generated in any one of three ways. First, the sum of the two digits X_3 and Y_3 may produce a carry; second, the sum of these two digits may be 1, and a carry from the next lower order may be present; and third, the sum may be 1, the sum of X_2 and Y_2 may also be 1, and a carry from the lowest order may be present. The "and" switches with two and three input lines and the extra input lines to the "or" switch provide for the generation of the carry when it arises from the conditions set forth in the second and third cases, respectively. Although a rather large amount of switching is required when more than a few orders are employed in the adder unit, carries which would otherwise have to be propagated will arrive substantially simultaneously at all appropriate orders.

One order (the 4th) of an accumulator employing simultaneous carry is shown in Fig. 4-24(b). A number is added into the accumulator by applying a pulse in the line marked "add pulse," and the carry, if any, to this order is entered by subsequent application of a pulse on the line marked "carry pulse." The amount of time required for the carry to be made ready for entry is independent of the order in which the carry originated.

Several other variations in the functional arrangements for simultaneous carry may be devised. Also, it may be worth while in some applications to employ simultaneous carry with the orders in groups of, say, three or four to increase carry propagation speed, whereas the amount of equipment required for simultaneous carry in all orders might be impractical.

Direct Subtraction. When subtracting two digits, one from the other, each digit of the minuend is decreased by the amount of the corresponding digit of the subtrahend, and if the minuend digit thereby becomes less than zero, the minuend digit of the next higher order must be re-

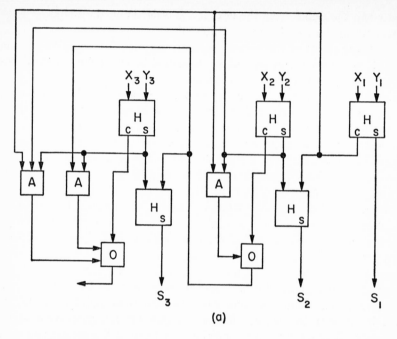

(a)

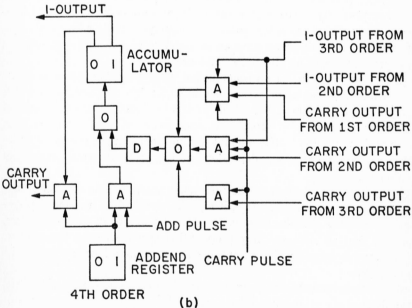

(b)

Fig. 4-24. Simultaneous carry as applied to an adder (a) and an accumulator (b).

duced by one; that is, a 1 must be "borrowed" from the next higher order. This procedure, which follows the paper-and-pencil method of subtraction, is referred to as direct subtraction and is in contrast to subtraction by means of complements, to be described later. The rules for binary subtraction are shown in Table 4-III.

TABLE 4-III. BINARY SUBTRACTION

Minuend Digit	0	1	0	1
Subtrahend Digit	0	0	1	1
Difference Digit	0	1	1	0
Borrow	0	0	1	0

A device which accepts minuend and subtrahend digits and produces a difference and borrow in accordance with Table 4-III is called a "half subtracter." A second half subtracter is required to subtract the borrow from the next higher order so that two half subtracters per order are required to execute binary subtraction. Actually, as in the case of addition, an extra "or" circuit per order is required also. Block diagrams of two arrangements by which the half subtracters may be connected are shown in Figs. 4-25 and 4-26, where X is assumed to be the minuend and Y the subtrahend. The two inputs of the half subtracter are not interchangeable as in the case of the half adder, and the input which is marked with a plus sign receives the digit from which another digit is being subtracted, and this other digit, which is beng subtracted, is applied to the input indicated by a minus sign.

In Fig. 4-25 the borrow, indicated by B, is subtracted from the appropriate digit of the minuend, and the subtrahend digit is then subtracted from the difference. The resulting difference is then the desired digit of the difference of X and Y. Note that the borrow signals from the two half subtractors cannot both be 1 simultaneously, for if the borrow B' from the first half subtracter is 1, the difference D' is also 1, and B'' will be 0 regardless of the digit from Y. A borrow signal from either half subtracter must be transmitted to the next higher order, and this is done through the "or" circuit. In Fig. 4-26, the borrow is subtracted from the difference of the minuend and subtrahend digits. Although this procedure probably does not follow the mental steps usually taken when subtracting by the pencil-and-paper methods, it has the advantage that the borrow signal must pass through only one instead of two half subtracters. This feature is important for fast operation, because borrow propagation through a series of orders may be required in a

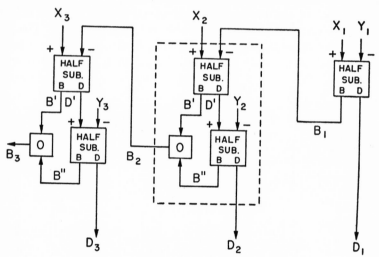

FIG. 4-25. Binary subtraction, first variation.

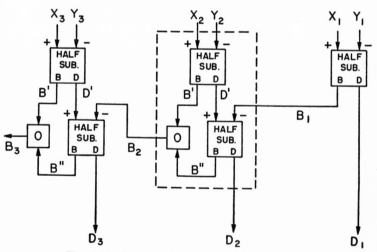

FIG. 4-26. Binary subtraction, second variation.

manner similar to carry propagation. When analyzing the speed of borrow propagation, it should be noted that two different types of situations must be taken into consideration; one is illustrated by the example of subtracting 0001 from 1000, and the other by an example such as the subtraction of 0111 from 1110. The speed is not necessarily the same in the two cases.

A third arrangement for binary subtraction is shown in Fig. 4-27. Here, the sum of the borrow and subtrahend digit is formed in a half adder. This sum is then subtracted from the minuend digit. The carry, C', from the half adder may be assumed to constitute a borrow because a carry signal occurs only when both inputs to the half adder receive

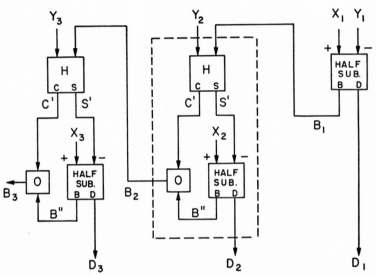

Fig. 4-27. Binary subtraction, third variation.

signals to be subtracted from the minuend, and the minuend digit will therefore necessarily be reduced below zero. The "or" circuit is used to combine C' with the borrow, B'', from the half subtracter to form the borrow, B, to be sent to the next higher order. That the arrangements shown in Figs. 4-25, 4-26, and 4-27 are equivalent from a mathematical standpoint may be established readily through the use of Boolean algebra.

The amount of equipment shown within the dotted lines in either Fig. 4-25, 4-26, or 4-27 is known as a full subtracter. A full subtracter is not necessarily made up of the components indicated in these figures, but is any device accepting three binary input signals and producing two binary output signals in accordance with the rules shown in Table 4-IV, where X is a digit of the minuend, Y is the digit of the corresponding order of the subtrahend, and B is the borrow from the next lower order.

Although a cursory inspection may reveal no important differences between the rules of binary addition and subtraction, the rules for sub-

118   Arithmetic Operations in Digital Computers

TABLE 4-IV.   BINARY SUBTRACTION RULES FOR FULL SUBTRACTER

X	0	1	0	0	1	1	0	1
Y	0	0	1	0	1	0	1	1
B	0	0	0	1	0	1	1	1
Difference	0	1	1	1	0	0	0	1
Borrow	0	0	1	1	0	0	1	1

traction are actually significantly more complicated. The reason is tied in with the fact that the X input of a subtracter is not interchangeable with the Y and B inputs; whereas with an adder, all three inputs are interchangeable.

Half Subtracter. From Table 4-III it may be seen that the Boolean algebra expressions for a half subtracter are

$$\text{Difference} = X\bar{Y} + \bar{X}Y$$

$$\text{Borrow} = \bar{X}Y$$

where X and Y are digits of a given order in the minuend and subtrahend, respectively. Circuits composed of "and" and "or" switches and inverters may be used in a straightforward manner to generate these functions. If the inverse of the input signals are not available and it is desired to generate the difference and borrow through the use of only one inverter, it may be done by developing the difference and borrow in the following manner.

$$\text{Difference} = (X + Y)\overline{(XY)}$$

$$\text{Borrow} = (X + Y)\overline{X}\,\overline{Y}\,Y$$

Full Subtracter. From Table 4-IV the following expressions for difference and borrow may be derived:

$$\text{Difference} = X\bar{Y}\bar{B} + \bar{X}Y\bar{B} + \bar{X}\bar{Y}B + XYB$$

$$\text{Borrow} = \bar{X}Y\bar{B} + \bar{X}\bar{Y}B + \bar{X}YB + XYB$$

As in the case of the adder, these expressions may be factored and rearranged in a wide variety of ways with each mode of expression representing a different physical circuit. One arrangement which will yield the difference and borrow through the use of only one inverter even when the inverted inputs are not available is:

Difference $= (X + Y + B)\overline{(XY + XB + YB)} + XYB$

Borrow $=$ (Difference $+ BY)(B + Y)$

Negative Balance. When the subtrahend is larger than the minuend, the difference will be negative; that is, a negative balance will result. Certain problems arise in the manner by which the negative balance should be treated, because the subtracter will present the negative balance in 2's complement form, which is analogous to the 10's complement which has been described previously for the decimal system. There are two reasons why the 2's complement presentation is objectionable. One reason is simply that it is not standard for pencil-and-paper work, and the other is that other arithmetic operations, notably multiplication and division, are rendered more complex by its use. The 2's complement representation should not be condemned categorically, however, because through its use addition and subtraction are very straightforward. For example, when adding a quantity to a negative balance and the balance becomes positive, a true representation will again be obtained without the necessity of providing for any corrective operations. Further, positive or negative quantities may be added or subtracted from positive or negative balances in any combination without need for corrective operations.

Two different procedures may be followed to remove the objections to the 2's complement presentation. One procedure is to convert the 2's complement number, whenever it appears, to true representation, and the other procedure involves the use of an "end-around borrow" to generate the 1's complement.

Mathematically, the most straightforward way of converting a 2's complement number to true form is to subtract from 2^n, since $2^n - (2^n - N) = N$. Frequently it is more convenient to invert each digit in the 2's complement number (a process which generates a 1's complement) and then add one. The generating of the 1's complement is the same as a subtraction from $2^n - 1$; therefore, $(2^n - 1) - (2^n - N) + 1 = N$. An alternative method of conversion is the use of the rule that the lowest order nonzero digit and all zeros in orders lower than this digit remain the same when converting, while all higher order digits are inverted. When an attempt is made to design equipment to perform the conversion, it is found that the various methods are not greatly different, although they aren't exactly the same, and the most adaptable method will depend upon the design of the other portions of the arithmetic unit in the computer.

The "end-around borrow" may be used to change the 2's complement representation to a 1's complement representation according to the following procedure. When the balance changes from positive to negative, a borrow signal will be obtained in the highest order of the subtracter unit. This borrow signal may first of all be used to indicate the change in sign of the balance, and it may also be entered as a borrow in the lowest order of the subtracter. To illustrate the process, consider the subtraction of 100101 (decimal 37) from 011101 (decimal 29).

Minuend		0 1 1 1 0 1
Subtrahend	(−)	1 0 0 1 0 1
		− 1 1 1 0 0 0
End-around borrow		(−) 1
Difference in 1's complement	−	1 1 0 1 1 1

The borrow signal which is obtained from the highest order is shown as being subtracted from the lowest order in a separate step, although actually this end-around borrow is handled at the same time as the borrow signals in any of the other orders. In the example given, the borrow signal when entered in the lowest order caused a borrow signal to be sent to the next higher order and so on. This does not mean, however, that when performing subtraction with end-around borrow that time has to be allowed for propagation of the borrow signal through the subtracter unit twice. If the end-around borrow is the result of a borrow signal propagated from some lower order than the highest order, it will not be propagated beyond the order in which it originated when entered into the lowest order, so time for propagation through the subtracter unit once is all that need be allowed. The subtraction of 110111 (decimal 45) from 110101 (decimal 43) will illustrate this point. That the use of the end-around borrow does, in fact, yield the 1's complement for negative balances may be checked either by the examples or by noting that the 2's complement of a number, N, is $2^n - N$ whereas the 1's complement is $2^n - 1 - N$, where n is the number of orders in use.

The advantage of the 1's complement lies in the ease with which the conversion to the true balance may be made, for in order to make the conversion it is necessary only to invert every digit. This simplicity of conversion is important in the execution of multiplication and division as well as in the mere presentation of the number.

When a positive balance is obtained as the result of adding a number to a negative balance, a carry signal will be obtained in the highest order of the adder unit. As in the case of a change in the sign of the balance when subtracting, this carry serves not only to indicate the change in sign from negative to positive but it should also be entered into the lowest order of the adder as an end-around carry to restore the true indication of the sum. As an example, 100101 (decimal 37) is added to −110111 (decimal −8).

Augend		−110111
Addend	(+)	100101
	+	011100
End-around carry		(+) 1
Sum		+011101

The time allotted for carry propagation through the adder need not be increased when this end-around carry is used.

Note that when a zero balance is obtained, the indication will sometimes be 000000 and sometimes −111111, depending upon whether the last previous balance was positive or negative, respectively. For some applications it is desirable to know from which direction a zero balance was approached, in which case this feature is desirable; in other applications it is preferred that a zero balance be always indicated as a positive quantity, and for these applications the feature is a nuisance. The two different indications for zero were not encountered when 2's complements were used.

Addition by Subtraction. Actually a subtracter unit by itself is probably of more academic than practical value. But it is noteworthy that both addition and subtraction can be executed on a subtracter. In order to add two numbers, E and F, to obtain the sum, $E + F$, the procedure to follow is to subtract E from zero to obtain $-E$, subtract F from $-E$ to obtain $-E - F = -(E + F)$, and then subtract $-(E + F)$ from zero to obtain the desired result.

Adder-Subtracter. From Tables 4-II and 4-IV it may be observed that the expression for the difference when subtracting is exactly the same as the expression for the sum when adding, except that B is substituted for C. Because of this similarity, an adder-subtracter unit may be constructed wherein one portion of the unit is used to develop a signal which may represent either the sum or the difference, and other portions of the unit are used to develop the carry and borrow. When adding, the carry is sent from each order to the next higher order; but when subtracting, the carry is suppressed and the borrow is sent from each order to the next higher order. It may be desirable to use two borrow generating devices, one for the case where X is the minuend and one for the case where Y is the minuend, because with these two different borrow generating devices it is possible to avoid entirely the use of complements. If, when subtracting, the subtrahend is larger than the minuend, a borrow signal will be obtained from the highest order of the adder-subtracter. As well as indicating the sign of the difference, this borrow signal may be used to indicate that the subtrahend is, in fact, larger than the minuend; in which case a switch to the other borrow generating device is initiated.

Specifically, the sum or difference may be expressed as

$$\text{Sum or difference} = (X + Y + Z)\overline{(XY + XZ + YZ)} + XYZ$$

where Z is the carry or borrow signal from the next lower order; the carry is

$$\text{Carry} = XY + XZ + YZ$$

the borrow, B_x, when X is the minuend is

$$\text{Borrow}_x = \overline{X}Y\overline{Z} + \overline{X}\overline{Y}Z + \overline{X}YZ + XYZ$$

$$= (Y + Z)\overline{(XY + XZ + YZ)} + YZ$$

and the borrow, B_y, when Y is the minuend is

$$\text{Borrow}_y = X\overline{Y}\overline{Z} + \overline{X}\overline{Y}Z + X\overline{Y}Z + XYZ$$

$$= (X + Z)\overline{(XY + XZ + YZ)} + XZ$$

The output of the carry-borrow portion of the adder-subtracter may then be expressed as

$$Z \text{ (for next higher order)} = AC + S_xB_x + S_yB_y$$

where A, S_x, and S_y are control signals, only one of which is active at any given time. A is active when addition is being performed, and S_x or S_y is active when subtracting, depending upon whether X or Y, respectively, is the minuend.

As an example of the use of the adder-subtracter, consider the following two numbers.

$$X \qquad 0\ 1\ 1\ 0\ 1\ 1\ 0\ 1$$
$$\overset{*}{}$$
$$Y \qquad 0\ 1\ 1\ 1\ 1\ 1\ 0\ 0$$

Assume that Y is being subtracted from X. Here, X and Y refer to entire numbers, not individual digits. A borrow will occur in the order marked with an asterisk; and this borrow will be propagated through all higher orders, that is, all orders to the left. When the borrow occurs in the highest order, it will be known that Y is larger than X and that, in effect,

X should be subtracted from Y. When X is subtracted from Y, a borrow will occur in this example in the lowest order, or the one on the right. This borrow will be propagated to higher orders but will stop at the order marked with an asterisk. The previous borrow need not "propagate back" but may be canceled from all orders simultaneously by applying control signal S_y a finite time after S_x is removed. This example

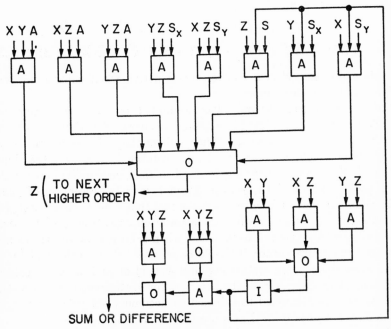

Fig. 4-28. Adder-subtracter.

illustrates that, except for the time required to switch from one borrow signal to the other, subtraction requires no more time than addition even when the wrong borrow signal is chosen first.

A simple rule for deciding which borrow signal, B_x or B_y, should be used first when subtracting is to assume that the positive number is the minuend and the negative number is the subtrahend. Note that, in subtraction, one number may always be considered positive and the other negative; for example, when subtracting X from Y and both X and Y are negative, X may be considered to be positive. In cases where the subtrahend turns out to be larger than the minuend, the borrow from the highest order will be an indication of a negative difference as well as an indication that the other borrow signal should be used in forming a true representation of the difference.

Physical circuits for an adder-subtracter may be worked out in a fashion similar to that used for the full adder. One arrangement requiring only one inverter and requiring that the carry-borrow pass through only one "and" and one "or" switch per order is shown in Fig. 4-28. The carry-borrow (Z signal) is generated according to the following expression.

Z (for next higher order)

$$= AXY + AXZ + AYZ + SZ\overline{(XY + XZ + YZ)}$$
$$+ S_x Y\overline{(XY + XZ + YZ)} + S_x YZ + S_y X\overline{(XY + XZ + YZ)} + S_y XZ$$

In this expression, S is a control signal active when subtracting with either number as the minuend.

Subtraction Accumulators. The accumulators which were described for addition may be modified in a simple manner so that they will execute the function of subtraction. When subtracting, the counters in the accumulator should count in reverse, but counting in reverse in the binary system is the same as counting forward in that each individual counter alternates back and forth between 0 and 1 upon the reception of pulses to be counted. The difference lies in the fact that a pulse (borrow signal) is sent from a given order when the counter changes from 0 to 1 instead of when it changes from 1 to 0. Also, when a borrow pulse arrives at a counter from a lower order, it should be propagated on to the next higher order when the counter is standing on 0 instead of on 1 as in the case on addition. Therefore, any of the accumulator arrangements in Figs. 4-13 to 4-23 may be converted to subtraction accumulators by interchanging 1 and 0 output lines from the counters in the addend register.

Remarks concerning negative balance, 1's and 2's complements, and end-around carry or borrow made in connection with subtracters apply equally well to subtraction accumulators.

Subtraction by Addition of Complements. In some, perhaps most, computers it has been found more convenient to execute subtraction through the addition of the complement representation of numbers instead of through the use of a subtracter. Either the 1's complement or the 2's complement may be used; the 1's complement has the outstanding advantage of simplicity of conversion back and forth between the true and complement forms, but there are many other factors entering into the determination of the most desirable number representation.

When subtracting two numbers one from the other, say N_1 from N_2, through the use of 1's complements, $2^n - 1 - N_1$, which is the 1's complement of N_1, would be added to N_2. As before, n is the number of orders in use, and note that the powers of two represented by the n orders range from 2^0 to 2^{n-1}. The sum, $(2^n - 1 - N_1) + N_2$, must be treated differently, according to whether $N_1 < N_2$ or $N_1 \geq N_2$. If $N_1 < N_2$, then $N_2 - N_1 \geq 1$ and the sum would be equal to or greater than 2^n; that is, a carry signal would occur in the highest order (2^{n-1} order) of the adder. Instead of entering this carry into the 2^n order, which is nonexistent, it is entered into the units order in end-around fashion. The result is, therefore,

$$-1 - N_1 + N_2 + 1 = N_2 - N_1, \quad (N_1 < N_2)$$

which is the desired difference. If $N_1 \geq N_2$, no carry will occur in the highest order and the result will then be

$$2^n - 1 - (N_1 - N_2), \quad (N_1 \geq N_2)$$

which is the 1's complement of the desired difference. In this latter case, the difference is either zero or negative, while in the previous case, it was positive; therefore, the end-around carry can be used to indicate the sign of the difference.

In the previous paragraph, N_1 and N_2 were both assumed to be positive quantities, whereas either one or both could have been negative. If N_1, the subtrahend, were negative, it presumably would have been presented in complement form. Then, upon complementing for subtraction, its true form would be obtained at the input lines to the adder, and the net result would be an addition as is desired when subtracting a negative quantity. If N_2 were negative, it similarly would be presented in complement form and the addition of $2^n - 1 - N_1$ to $2^n - 1 - N_2$ would always produce a carry in the highest order. This carry, when added into the units order, would produce the result,

$$-1 - N_1 + 2^n - 1 - N_2 + 1 = 2^n - 1 - (N_1 + N_2)$$

which is the 1's complement of the "difference." If both N_1 and N_2 are negative quantities and N_1 is subtracted from N_2, the mathematical principles involved in forming the difference will be the same as when both are positive, except that the roles of N_1 and N_2 will be interchanged.

With the above arrangement the fact that the capacity of the adder has been exceeded may be detected by the occurrence of an end-around carry when, in effect, a quantity is added to a positive balance, or by the absence of a carry when, in effect, a quantity is subtracted from a negative balance.

A further property of the above arrangement is that a zero balance will be indicated as a negative quantity always, because the result, $+0000$, will never occur, and zero will always be indicated as -1111. For example, -1100 (decimal -3) plus $+0011$ (decimal $+3$) is -1111;

also $+0011$ minus $+0011$ is -1111 because the subtrahend is inverted and added. This result is always obtained, even though it is possible to add or subtract "positive zero" to either a positive negative quantity and obtain the correct result. An example of the latter situation is the subtraction of $+0000$ from -1111, which yields -1111 because the subtrahend is inverted and added with end-around carry. A trivial exception to the rule is the addition of $+0000$ to $+0000$. If it is desired that zero be identified as a positive quantity, one procedure that may be followed is to represent positive numbers in 1's complement form and negative quantities in true form. Then, when subtracting N_1 from N_2 when $N_1 = N_2$, the result will be $2^n - 1 - N_1 + N_1$, as before, which is zero in 1's complement form; but, since all positive balance will appear in complement form, zero will be represented as a positive quantity. Another means for getting zero to be indicated as a positive quantity is to use a subtracter, in which case subtraction is executed in a straightforward manner, and addition is accomplished through the subtraction of complements.

Adaptation of Complement Subtraction to Circuits. Although obtaining the 1's complement of a binary number is one of the simplest functions

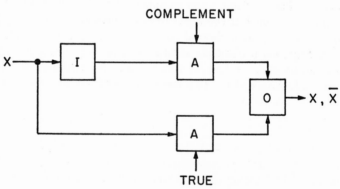

FIG. 4-29.   True-complement arrangement.

one can imagine, it is easy to forget the amount of equipment required to accomplish it. Figure 4-29 shows a functional arrangement for obtaining either the true or complement representation of a binary digit. The input lines marked "True" and "Comp." are control lines used for selecting the representation to be produced on the output line. For a parallel system this amount of equipment must be duplicated for each order, and perhaps, in the case of an adder, for both the augend and the addend.

When using an accumulator, a different technique is available for converting back and forth between true and 1's complement representation. By providing a third input to each "or" circuit feeding a counter in the accumulator register, a pulse may be applied to each counter simultaneously to produce the complement of the number previously standing in the register. A second pulse will restore the original number. With this method of complementing available, true numbers may be entered into the accumulator, and also a true representation of the balance may be obtained regardless of the sign (positive or negative) of the numbers involved. For example, when subtracting N_1 from N_2 and both are positive quantities, N_2 would appear in the accumulator and would be converted to complement form. A positive difference would be indicated as positive by the absence of an end-around carry and would appear in complement form, but could be readily converted to true form. If N_2 were a negative number standing in the accumulator register and a positive number N_1 were added to it, N_2 would again be the number to be converted to complement form, but in this case a positive difference would appear in true form and would be indicated by the occurrence of an end-around carry. The situation of subtracting a positive number (or adding a negative number) to a negative balance would be substantially the same as adding two positive numbers.

The Difference Between the Two Subtraction Methods. It may be suspected that there is no real difference between direct subtraction and subtraction by the addition of complements, because there are so many points of similarity in the two methods. However, when comparing an adder with appropriate complementing devices for a single order with a subtracter for a single order, it is found that there is a real physical difference between them. This difference can be established by an examination of the carry signal or borrow signal, as the case may be, which is sent from a given order to the next higher order. If X is a digit of the minuend and Y is the corresponding digit of the subtrahend, it can be shown that when using a subtracter the borrow signal is

$$\overline{X}Y + \overline{X}B + YB$$

where B is the borrow signal from the next lower order. When using an adder with complementing devices, Y, and not X, would be complemented so that the carry signal would be equivalent to

$$X\overline{Y} + XC + \overline{Y}C$$

where C is the carry from the next lower order. Because of the difference in the signal propagated through the orders, it follows that there is, in fact, a physical difference in the two types of units.

The Use of an Extra Order to Indicate Sign.   An examination of the rules for determining the sign of the balance after an addition or subtraction operation will reveal that they are exactly the same as the rules for binary addition.   Therefore, an adder which is identical to the adders used for adding the digits may be used for generating the sign of the balance.   This point may be visualized more readily simply by observing the system of binary counting, which in the vicinity of zero is with 1's complement notation as follows:

+2	00010
+1	00001
0	00000 or 11111
−1	11110
−2	11101

Note that the highest-order digit changes from 0 to 1 as the sign of the number changes from plus to minus.   The highest-order digit may therefore be assigned as a sign indication.   The adder for the sign order uses as its carry input the carry output from the highest digit order and carry output of the signs adder is used as the end-around carry to the units order in the 1's complement system.   That this procedure works may readily be established by working out a few examples.

Binary Point.   In the previous discussion, the location of the binary point was not specified.   Beyond the specification that it be in the same relative location for the two numbers involved in an addition or subtraction process, its location is of no consequence.   In other words, the physical construction of the addition-subtraction equipment is independent of the binary point, and the only requirement is that corresponding orders of the two numbers involved be sent to the same order of the addition-subtraction equipment.

Serial Operation.   Binary addition and subtraction in serial fashion differs from the parallel method in that a single-order addition-subtraction unit is used.   The binary digits of the two numbers to be added together or subtracted one from the other are applied serially in time to two input lines of the unit, and the sum or difference emerges also serially in time from the output line.   It is usually necessary that the two input numbers be applied "in phase," that is, with corresponding digits of the two numbers appearng on the respective input lines simultaneously.   In some respects serial operation is fundamentally no different from parallel operation, but in other respects the differences in the two systems are so great that the design procedures followed in the two cases bear little resemblance to each other.

The basic rules for the addition and subtraction of binary digits, as given in Table 4-I to 4-IV, are the same for serial as for parallel operation. For this reason, half and full adders and half and full subtracters as described for parallel operation may be adapted for use in a serial system. However, there are some differences in the method by which the carry or borrow is handled which should be considered. For example, Fig. 4-30 shows the arrangement which would be used for handling the carry when a full adder is used in a serial system. The carry, which must be added to the digits of the next higher order, is applied through a delay unit to the third input of the full adder. The amount of the delay must be such that, when added to the delay of carry generation in the

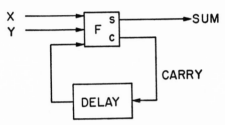

Fig. 4-30. Serial operation of a full adder.

adder, the carry will be applied at the adder input at the same time that the digits of the next higher order are applied. An important consequence of this requirement is that it is the next higher and not the next lower order which must be applied to the adder subsequent to a given order, and therefore serial operation is almost always conducted with the digits appearing in ascending order of significance. It would be possible to assemble a system which would handle the numbers with the digits in descending order of significance, but not in any simple or straightforward way.

In a serial computer the speed of addition is usually set by factors which have little relationship to the adder. It is most often the case that the speed or pulse repetition rate which is used for number transmission is a function of the physical characteristics of the particular number storage device which is used in the computer; and once this speed has been decided upon, the adder is designed so that it will accept numbers at this speed and consequently yield a sum at the same speed. Once the speed of number transmission is set, nothing can be done in the carry portion of the adder to increase the speed of addition. It follows that the high-speed generation of the carry does not have the importance in serial operation that it does in parallel operation; in fact, because of the delay which must be inserted in the carry circuit for serial operation, the design objectives with regard to carry speed are not the same in the two cases.

Half adders may be used to form a serial addition unit by using either of the two arrangements shown in Fig. 4-31, which are the serial counterparts of the circuits shown in Figs. 4-1 and 4-2.

From an engineering standpoint, further variations in the adder circuits which may be used can be developed from the variety in the

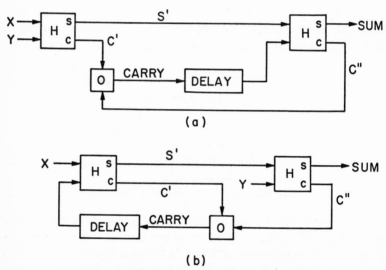

Fig. 4-31. Half adder adapted to serial operation.

nature of signals which may be used to represent the numbers. In Fig. 4-32(a) the d-c method of representation is shown. To represent a 1, the signal (usually an electrical potential) is held positive all during the time allotted for the representation of the digit; and to represent a zero, it is held negative. Here, "positive" and "negative" are relative to each other; any two d-c levels may be chosen. When two or more 0's or two or more 1's occur in sequence, there is no change in signal level between the digits.

The pulse method of representaton is illustrated in Fig. 4-32(b). A 1 is represented by a pulse, and a zero by the absence of a pulse. With the pulse method of representation the "inverter" function is more difficult to realize that when using the d-c representation; specifically, the presence of a pulse can be converted readily to the absence of a pulse, but the conversion of the absence of a pulse to the presence of a pulse is usually not so straightforward.

As examples of the use of pulses for digit representation, the functional arrangements for a binary adder as shown in Fig. 4-6 are repeated in Fig. 4-33 but adapted to serial operation and pulse-type signals. A new function called the "unless" function is introduced, and the block labeled "unless" in Fig. 4-33 will pass a pulse arriving at the input on the top side of the block unless a pulse appears at the input shown on the side of the block. This second input signal is sometimes called an inhibiting

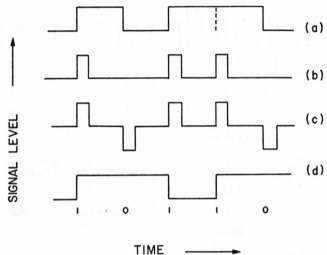

FIG. 4-32. Methods of serial representation.

pulse because its presence inhibits a pulse from appearing on the output line. A semicircle is shown around the arrow of the inhibiting pulse input to distinguish it from the regular input lines. The arrangement of Fig. 4-33(a) would be thought of as functioning according to the rule, "the sum will be 1 if any one of the three input signals is 1 unless two of three input signals are 1, or if all three of the input signals are 1." In order to translate the arrangement of Fig. 4-6(b) to that of Fig. 4-33(b), the trick of inverting the presence or absence of a pulse must be used. The "unless" block in Fig. 4-33(b) has as its input a continuous series of pulses timed in synchronism with the digit pulses of the numbers to be added, with the result that pulse will be passed each time that no pulse appears on the inhibiting input and will not be passed when an inhibiting pulse occurs. This adder, then, functions according to the rule, "the sum will be 1 unless at least two input signals are 1 or all three are 1, and at least one input signal is 1."

Many additional variations in adder circuits can be worked out when using a digit representation such as shown in Fig. 4-32(c), where 0 is indicated by a negative pulse. Still further variations are possible when two lines are used to carry a binary number in serial fashion. With two lines, a signal (either a d-c signal or a pulse) on one line would indicate a 1, and a signal on the other line would indicate a zero. Both of these schemes of representation offer the possibility of error detection. When pulses of opposite polarity are used, the absence of a pulse would

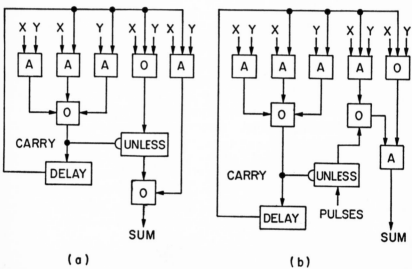

(a)   **(b)**

Fig. 4-33. Functional arrangements of full adder adapted to pulse-serial operation.

indicate an error. With the two-line system, a signal on neither line or signals on both lines simultaneously would indicate an error. The subject of error detection is an extensive one, and since error detection is described in some detail in a later chapter, no attempt will be made to cover it here. However, it will be remarked that the use of these types of binary digit representation are not particularly attractive for most applications because of the increased complexity and amount of equipment required for their use.

Another type of binary digit representation is shown in Fig. 4-32(d). In this case the signal is not unique for a 1 or a 0; instead, a 1 is represented by a change and 0 by no change. It is sometimes called the "non-return to zero" system when used in connection with recording on magnetic tapes or drums. The two states represent opposite directions of magnetization. Since the system is extremely awkward to use in the arithmetic portion of a computer, it is usually advantageous to transform the representation to one of the forms shown in (a) or (b) when arithmetic operations are to be performed.

"Accumulator" is a term which is frequently used in connection with serial addition. From a mathematical function standpoint, a serial accumulator serves a purpose similar to that of a parallel accumulator in that it stores the sum, but otherwise it is quite different. A serial accumulator is only a storage device and plays no part in the actual addition as do the counters in a parallel accumulator. It is possible, however, to execute binary addition serially through the use of a counter; but it would be necessary to apply sequentially the carry pulse from the next lower order and the pulses representing the digits of the given orders of the augend and addend. For most practical purposes, a parallel accumulator with counters has no close counterpart in serial operation.

Subtraction with Serial Operation. All the points concerning subtraction which were described in connection with parallel operation could be applied to serial operation. However, the execution of end-around carry or borrow with the serial mode of operation is much more cumbersome than with parallel operation, with the result that the relative advantages of the 1's and 2's complement systems of notation are different in the two cases. To add the end-around carry in a serial system, it is necessary, after the addition, to pass the sum through the adder a second time. By using the 2's complement, the end-around carry may be avoided.

If N_1 is subtracted from N_2 by the addition of the 2's complement of N_1 to N_2, the result is $(2^n - N_1) + N_2$, where, again, n is the number of orders involved, and the digits of N_1 and N_2 correspond to powers of two from 2^0 to 2^{n-1}. If $N_1 \leqq N_2$, the result will be equal to or greater than 2^n, and a carry will occur in the addition of the highest-order digits. This carry, in effect, replaces the borrow from the 2^nth order, which was used in the original formation of the 2's complement of N_1, and is an indication that the result is positive, is of value $N_2 - N_1$, and is in true and not complement form. If $N_1 > N_2$, there will be no carry from the highest order, and the result will be $2^n - (N_1 - N_2)$, which is 2's complement representation of the magnitude of the difference between N_1 and N_2, and the absence of the carry may be used to indicate a negative balance.

The original conversion of N_1 from true to 2's complement form may be readily accomplished by inverting to form a 1's complement and then adding 1, since $2^n - 1 - N_1 + 1 = 2^n - N_1$. The addition of the 1 may be accomplished by entering a 1 in the carry circuit of the adder at the time the lowest-order digits are being added. This procedure can be followed because no carry will be appearing from other sources at this time. The conversion of the negative balance, which appeared in 2's complement form, to true form may be performed if desired, although it is necessary to send the result through the adder a second time. This conversion may be avoided by storing the negative balance in 2's complement form. Then, if it is subsequently added to another number, it will be sent directly to the adder in the desired 2's complement form, or if it is subsequently subtracted (which is, in effect, adding a positive quantity), it will be automatically converted to true form through the same process of inversion and adding 1 to the lowest order.

The practice of using the highest-order digit to indicate the sign of a number may be used in serial as well as in parallel operation.

If the use of complement representation is objectionable in the storage devices of the computer, it turns out that the complements may be avoided with only moderate difficulty and lost time by actually executing the conversion to true form each time a complement is obtained. This process necessitates the transmission of the numbers with the sign indication before instead of after the digits because, for example, the addition of a positive number is handled differently from the addition of a negative number, and therefore the sign of the number must be known before the addition process commences. When numbers are sent to the adder in true form only, there are the following three cases which must be considered: addition of two positive numbers (this case includes subtraction of a negative number from a positive number), addition of one positive and one negative number, and addition of two negative numbers. The first and third cases are substantially the same; in neither case are any complements involved, and the sign of the balance is the same as the sign of the original numbers. In the second case, one or the other of the two numbers is complemented before entry into the adder. If it is always the negative one which is complemented, the result will be in complement form if a negative balance occurs and it must be converted to true form by passing it through the adder again. The amount of time which will be lost depends upon the nature of the problem being solved by the computer. In some problems the conversion may be required frequently, but in many problems the first and third cases will predominate. When performing the inital conversion on a number being entered into an accumulator, regardless of whether this number or the previous balance is negative, it turns out that the conversion of the result is required only when the sign of the balance changes in a series of additions and subtractions. With this scheme, again depending upon the nature of the problem, even less extra conversions may be required.

The Storage of Positive and Negative Numbers. With either serial or parallel operation, a problem which always arises in the design of a computer is determining the manner in which the complements that arise in subtraction should be handled with regard to the storage of positive and negative numbers. With the possibility of using true, 1's complement or 2's complement form, there are nine different variations in the ways in which positive and negative numbers may be represented. Of the nine variations, four are of interest.

	Positive	*Negative*
1.	True	True
2.	True	2's Comp.
3.	True	1's Comp.
4.	1's Comp.	True

The principal advantages of the first scheme, whereby both positive and negative numbers are stored in true form, arise from the facts that the numbers conform better to familiar usage and that multiplication and division (to be described in more detail in the next chapter) of negative factors are more straightforward. With the second scheme, addition and subtraction can be accomplished in a more straightforward manner. With the third and fourth schemes, all four arithmetic operations can be accomplished in a reasonably straightforward manner; the outstanding difference between the two schemes is that zero appears as a negative number in the former and as a positive number in the latter.

The choice of the convention to be used with regard to the storage of negative numbers is frequently a difficult one to make because numerous other considerations often arise. Among the factors which affect the choice are the facilities for complementing in the computer, the form of the numbers sent to and taken from the computer through the input and output mechanisms, the relative frequencies of the various arithmetic operations in the problems to be solved, and the contemplated need for examining numbers in storage when servicing the computer.

Chapter 5

BINARY MULTIPLICATION AND DIVISION

Binary Multiplication. Multiplication by the paper-and-pencil method using the familiar decimal system is accomplished with the aid of a multiplication table, which is usually memorized. Multiplication in the binary system may be accomplished in the same way, although the binary multiplication table is so simple that it is almost trivial. It is shown in Table 5-I.

TABLE 5-I. BINARY MULTIPLICATION TABLE

Multiplicand
Digit

	0	1
0	0	0
1	0	1

Multiplier
Digit

In the decimal system, when multiplying 45 by 7, for example, the 5 is first multiplied by 7 to obtain 35, which yields 5 in the units order and 3 to be carried into the tens order. The 3 is added to the product of 4 and 7, to yield the number 31, the digits of which comprise the hundreds and tens orders of the product. The simplicity of binary multiplication arises principally from the fact that there are no "carries"; in fact, when 0 and 1 are the only alternatives for the multiplier digit, either zero or the multiplicand itself is used in the formation of the product. The binary multiplication table may as well be forgotten, but this statement should not be construed as meaning that the problem

136

stops here, because there is yet the task of summing partial products in
the formation of the product of two binary numbers.

Multiplicand (x)		1111
Multiplier (y)		1101

Partial Products	A	1111
	B	0000
	C	1111
	D	1111

Product	11000011

In the foregoing example of a binary multiplication, 1111 (decimal 15)
is multiplied by 1101 (decimal 13) to obtain the product 11000011 (decimal 195). The partial products are clearly zero or equal to the multiplicand, according to whether the corresponding multiplier digit is 0 or 1.
That the partial products are recorded in the proper columns (orders)
can readily be proved, but this fact should be apparent to anyone who
is at all familiar with multiplication procedure. The customary way to
sum the partial products is to add the digits in the partial products,
one column at a time, starting with the lowest order. Strangely, except
to a person exceedingly skilled in the handling of binary numbers, this
operation is more difficult in the binary system than in the decimal
system, in spite of otherwise simple nature of the binary multiplication
process. The reason is, again, in the "carries." When summing the
partial products in a decimal system multiplication, the carry from one
column to the next seldom exceeds ten except when both the multiplicand
and multiplier are very large numbers. Even when the decimal carry
does exceed ten, it is not difficult to handle. In binary multiplication,
carries of 10 (decimal 2) and much greater are commonly encountered,
even though the multiplicand and multiplier are of moderate size. The
handling of multiple-order carries, although elementary in principle, is an
awkward process to execute mentally and is difficult to perform without
error. The problem is encountered in the example which was given, and
four-digit binary numbers are certainly not very large since they correspond to scarcely more than one decimal digit. The difficulty may be
easily overcome by adding only one partial product at a time in the formation of the product, although the recording of more intermediate sums
would be required. In the mechanization of multiplication it is almost
universal practice to handle the partial products one at a time, although
probably the reasons for doing so are slightly different.

"Simultaneous" Multiplier. The term "simultaneous multiplier" is intended to mean the type of multiplication device to which steady-state signals representing the multiplicand and multiplier are simultaneously applied to the input lines; and, after the transients in the device have disappeared, signals representing the product appear on the output lines. The product representation will remain as long as the input signals are maintained.

A straightforward way to go about designing a simultaneous multiplier is to use half adders and full adders in parallel arrangements of the types described previously. For example, partial products A and B in the previous example of a binary multiplication may be added together in one parallel binary adder; partial products C and D may be added in a second parallel adder; and these two sums may then be combined in a third parallel adder to form the product. The input signals to the first two adders must represent either zero or the multiplicand and must be under the control of the multiplier digits. This control function may be obtained through the use of a series of "and" switches, each with two input lines. If a signal representing a multiplier digit is applied to one input line on each of a set of these "and" switches, and if signals representing the multiplicand are applied to the other input lines, the multiplicand will or will not pass according to whether the multiplier digit is 1 or 0, respectively. The resulting multiplier arrangement is shown in Fig. 5-1.

The reasons for the various half adders and full adders (or no adder at all for the formation of P_1) in Fig. 5-1 are not exactly obvious, but it is not difficult to determine their functions from an examination of the positioning of the partial products in a multiplication. The "or" switch which is used in the formation of P_8 deserves special mention. It might be expected that a half adder should be in this position with the carry output representing a ninth digit in the product. A multiplication of 1111 by 1111 proves that the largest possible product of two four-binary digit numbers contains only eight digits; further, it may be shown that, in general, the maximum number of digits in a product is equal to the sum of the numbers of digits in the factors regardless of the radix of the system in use. Therefore, it must be impossible that signals would appear simultaneously on both input lines of a half adder in the position which would yield P_8 and P_9 in this case. Since the carry from this position will always be nonexistent, a simple "or" switch may be used.

To determine the speed of multiplication it is necessary to know the number of half adders, full adders, and switching circuits through which the input signals must pass in reaching the output lines. From Fig. 5-1

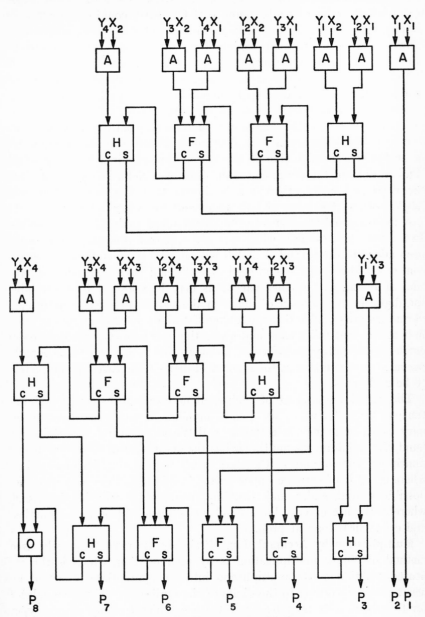

Fig. 5-1. Simultaneous multiplier.

it can be seen that, if Y_1, X_2, Y_2, and X_1 are all 1's, a carry will occur in the lowest-order half adder, and that this carry could conceivably be propagated through any one of four different paths to the P_8 output line. However, when all possible combinations of numbers for the multiplicand and multiplier are considered, it is found in every case where P_8 is 1 that the signal arrived there through a less distant path. No simple way is known for determining the maximum length path for the general case of a multiplier designed to handle factors with an arbitrary number of digits; but, if the "maximum conceivable" path is used in determining multiplication time, the determination is certain to be equal to, or on the conservative side of, the actual time required for all possible combinations of factors in the multiplication. Note, in particular, that the maximum conceivable path is shorter than the sum of the path lengths of any two rows of half adder and full adder units.

A multitude of variations in the simultaneous multiplier are possible. In the four-digit example which was given, partial product C could have been added to the sum of A and B with partial product D added to the sum of the three, or the sum of A and D could have been added to the sum of B and C. Further variations may be obtained by scrambling the digits in any column of digits in the partial products. Additional variations are possible through adding the digits column by column with half adders and full adders and generating the necessary multiple-order carries with appropriate circuits, although this design procedure rapidly becomes more complex as the number of digits is increased in the factors to be multiplied.

The very large amount of equipment necessary to assemble a simultaneous multiplier which will handle numbers of useful size (say, 16 binary digits or larger) is certainly a detracting feature. On the other hand, the simultaneous multiplier has the distinction of being the fastest multiplier known and is therefore worth considering in applications where speed is of extreme importance. In addition, there is always the possibility that adder and switching components will be developed, whereby the use of very large numbers of them will be more practical and economical than at present.

Multiplication by Accumulation. Probably the most frequently used method of binary multiplication is by accumulation, which is the repeated addition of the multiplicand into the appropriate orders of an accumulator according to the digits of the multiplier. The accumulator for this application may be a parallel accumulator of one of the types described previously, or it may be either a parallel or serial adding unit with a storage register to store the accumulated sum of the partial products. When accumulating the partial products, a complication is encountered which was not encountered in the accumulation of a series of numbers in an ordinary addition problem. The complication arises from the fact that the number representing each partial product is the same (the multiplicand) but that it must be shifted relative to the accumulated sum for each addition. The shifting may be applied to either the partial product or the accumulated sum. Although the mathematical principles are substantially the same whether a parallel or a serial accumulator is employed, the means for performing the shifting function are quite different in the two cases, and therefore the two modes of operation will be discussed separately.

Parallel Operation. If with parallel operation it is desired to shift the multiplicand for entry into the proper orders of the accumulator, a functional arrangement as shown in Fig. 5-2 is necessary. In Fig. 5-2(a), lines A, B, C, and D are control lines to which signals are applied according to whether partial product A, B, C, or D in the previous example is being entered into the accumulator. The seven output lines from the parallel shifting arrangement are applied to the lowest seven orders of accumulator. If the digit in the eighth order of the product is to be a 1, as it may when two four-digit binary numbers are multiplied, the 1 will arrive in the eighth order as a carry from the seventh order in every case.

From the nature of the shifting arrangement as shown in Fig. 5-2(a), it can be seen that the amount of switching circuitry which is required is dependent upon the number of digits in both the multiplicand and the multiplier. More specifically, the number of "and" switches is equal to the product of the numbers of digits in the multiplicand and multiplier, and the number of input lines to the "or" switches is approximately equal to this same product.

An alternative shifting network is given in Fig. 5-2(b). Here, control lines A_0 and B_0 are operative when no shift is desired. For a shift of one order to the left, a control signal is applied to A_1 instead of A_0, and for a shift of two orders a control signal is applied to B_2 instead of B_0. Of course, a shift of three orders may be obtained by combining the one-order and two-order shifts. When this scheme of shifting is expanded to handle larger numbers and shifts of four orders, eight orders, and so on, it turns out that somewhat less equipment is required than for the arrangement given in Fig. 5-2(a), although the fact that the input signals have to pass through a succession of "and" and "or" switches may be a disadvantage.

If the shifting is done in the accumulator instead of the input lines to the accumulator, two advantages may be gained. One advantage is in the amount of equipment required for adding, and the other is in the amount of equipment required for shifting.   To understand how these advantages may be realized it is necessary to examine the multiplication

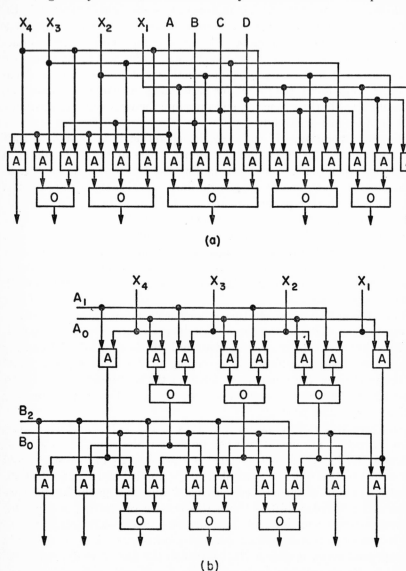

FIG. 5-2.   Functional arrangement for parallel shifting.

process which utilizes the shifting of the accumulated sum.   In Fig. 5-3 a nine-order accumulator is represented; and the multiplicand, $X_4X_3X_2X_1$, is shown as being entered into the fifth to eighth orders, inclusive. The counter or storage device in each order of the accumulator is constructed with the ability to transfer (shift) the digit which it is storing to the counter or storage device in the next lower order and at the same time accept the digit which was being stored in the next higher order. With this arrangement, the first step in the multiplication process is to enter the multiplicand or not, according to whether the lowest-order digit of the multiplier is 1 or 0. The digit in each order of the accumulator is then shifted to the next lower order. The multiplicand is again entered or not, but under the control of the second multiplier digit, and a second shift to lower orders in the accumulator is made. This process is repeated for each digit of the multiplier, and, with an

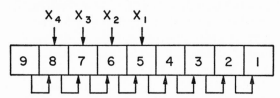

FIG. 5-3. Multiplication through the use of a shifting accumulator.

accumulator of the size shown in Fig. 5-3, the multiplier may have a maximum of four digits. An important feature of this arrangement is that the orders numbered one to four in the accumulator need not perform an accumulation function at all. After entry of the first partial product, the lowest-order digit of the final product is determined and will not be altered by subsequent additions. After entry of the second partial product, the second digit in the final product is determined; and this situation continues for as many digits as there are digits in the multiplier. The lowest four orders in the accumulator therefore need not be capable of performing any arithmetic operation other than shifting, and the number of actual accumulating orders is equal to the number of the digits in the multiplicand plus one additional order (the ninth in the figure) to accept and hold temporarily the carries from the eighth order. This number of accumulating orders is less than the number required when shifting the multiplicand, where the required number of accumulating orders was equal to the sum of the number of digits in the multiplier and multiplicand.

A comparison of the amount of equipment required for shifting the multiplicand by the method shown in Fig. 5-2 with the amount required for shifting the accumulated sum is difficult to make because the means for shifting are not the same in the two cases. One factor to be considered in making the comparison is that the number of digits to be shifted when shifting the accumulated sum is equal to the sum of the numbers of digits in the multiplicand and multiplier, and the amount of equipment needed to perform the shifting is proportional to the number of digits to be shifted. It follows that, for large multiplicands and multipliers, less equipment for shifting is required when shifting the accumulated sum than when shifting the multiplicand by the method shown in Fig. 5-2 because with that method the amount of equipment was approximately proportional to the product of the numbers of digits in the multiplicand and multiplier.

An important feature of the shifting accumulator, as shown in Fig. 5-3, is the possibility of storing the multiplier in the nonaccumulating orders on the right-hand end of the accumulator. Note that the number of the nonaccumulating orders had, for other reasons, determined the maximum permissible number of digits in the multiplier. The multiplier, when stored in these orders, is then shifted to the right each time the accumulated sum of the partial products is shifted. With this scheme the multiplicand is entered into the accumulator, or not entered, according to the multiplier digit which appears in the lowest (first) order of the accumulator. After each shift, the multiplier digit which was in the lowest order is lost, but no harm is done because it no longer has a bearing on the final product. The details of the multiplication process can be understood more clearly through an examination of the following example, which shows the contents of the accumulator after each step in the multiplication of 1111 by 1101. The digits of the multiplier are distinguished by underlining:

Initial Setting	0 0000 <u>1101</u>
Add 1111	0 1111 <u>1101</u>
Shift	0 0111 <u>1110</u>
Add Zero	0 0111 <u>1110</u>
Shift	0 0011 <u>1111</u>
Add 1111	1 0010 <u>1111</u>
Shift	0 1001 <u>0111</u>
Add 1111	1 1000 <u>0111</u>
Shift (Final Product)	0 1100 <u>0011</u>

Shifting Registers. The shifting accumulator which was used in the above method of multiplication deserves somewhat more attention. Instead of describing shifting accumulators in detail, some fundamentals will be given for the design of a shifting register for any purpose, and an adaptation of the fundamentals to an accumulator will be fairly straightforward except for one or two difficulties, which will be explained.

Probably the simplest functional arrangement for a shifting register is shown in Fig. 5-4. Each binary storage device has two input and two output lines. A signal arriving on the top input line causes the device to change to the state representing 0 if it was not already in that state, and when the device is in the 0 state a steady signal will appear on the top output line. The bottom input and output lines function similarly for the state representing 1. When it is desired to shift the digits in each storage device to the next storage device on the right, a pulse-type signal is applied to one input of each "and" switch with the result that, for each storage device, a signal representing its state

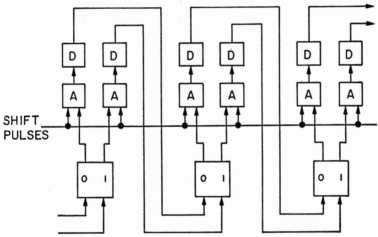

Fɪɢ. 5-4. Shifting register.

will be sent to the next storage device on the right and will cause it to store the indicated digit.

A difficulty which may be encountered with the arrangement shown in Fig. 5-4 is that one storage device may respond to the signal coming from the left before a satisfactory signal is sent to the right. The difficulty may be overcome by inserting devices to delay the signals in either the input lines or output lines of the storage devices. In the figure they are shown in the input lines. With this arrangement the signals to be sent from one storage device to the next may be generated, and the initiating pulse may be terminated before the signals to any given storage device arrive from the device on the left.

An arrangement which can more readily be made reliable in its action, but which requires more components, is shown in Fig. 5-5. In this figure only the top row of storage devices are in the main shifting register; the storage units in the bottom row serve merely for temporary intermediate storage. The shifting register operates through the application of pulses successively on control lines 1, 2, 3, and 4. The pulse on control line 1 sets all the intermediate storage devices in the 0 state ("clears" them). The pulse on line 2 causes any 1's stored in the main shifting register to be stored in the corresponding intermediate storage units also. The pulse on line 3 then clears the main shifting register. Finally, a pulse on line 4 causes the 1's in the intermediate storage devices to be returned to the main shifting register with each digit one position to the right of its original position. With this method of shifting, no delay devices are needed to secure reliable operation.

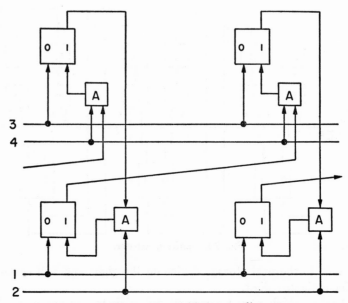

Fig. 5-5.   Shifting register with intermediate storage.

An important variation in the shifting register shown in Fig. 5-5 may be obtained through the use of "and" circuits in both input lines of each storage device and appropriate connections from the 0 output lines. The 1 and 3 control lines, which are used for clearing, may be eliminated, and, in effect, the 0's as well as the 1's are transferred and shifted.

A quite different approach to the problem of designing a shifting register may be made through the use of what might be called "dynamic" storage devices in place of the "static" storage devices used in all previously described schemes. A functional diagram of one arrangement for a dynamic storage device is shown in Fig. 5-6. Binary storage is effected by the existence or nonexistence of a pulse circulating in the loop through the delay device. A continuous series of pulses with a uniform frequency is applied to one of the input lines of the "and" circuit, as shown. If a pulse is not already circulating in the dynamic storage device, no pulses will be returned through the delay device to a second input line to the "and" switch, with the result that no pulses will pass the "and" circuit into the dynamic storage device. To initiate a circulating pulse, a single pulse in proper phase relative to the continuous series of pulses may be applied to the "or" switch at the point marked "1 input." After a pulse is once entered, it will be returned to the "and" switch with the amount of delay necessary to make it coincide with the next pulse in the continuous series of pulses. Since a steady signal is normally applied to the third input of the "and" switch

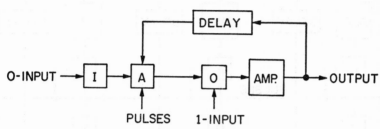

Fig. 5-6. "Dynamic" storage device.

from the inverter, the pulse will be returned to the loop and will continue to circulate. The amplifier, indicated by a block labeled "AMP.," is necessary to maintain the amplitude of the circulating pulse, although with some types of components this function may be incorporated into one of the other functions in the loop. If a pulse is applied to the line marked "0 input," the signal from the inverter to the "and" switch will be removed temporarily and will cause the circulation of the pulse to cease. The dynamic storage device may be considered to be storing a 1 or a 0 according to whether or not a pulse is circulating, and it may be transferred from one state to the other by a pulse on the appropriate input line.

A shifting register employing dynamic storage devices is shown in Fig. 5-7. The input and output lines are omitted for simplicity in illustrating the shifting function. In the figure, two control lines marked "store" and "shift" are indicated. While a number is being stored in the register without shifting, a steady signal is maintained on the "store" line and no signal is applied to the "shift" line. A pulse in any given storage device will then be allowed to return to the device through the switching circuits, and it will continue to be circulated, that is, stored. To shift the digits, the signal on the "store" line is removed temporarily and a signal is applied to the "shift" line, which is connected to one input of an "and" switch in each storage device. The pulse, if any, circulating in a storage device is applied to the other input line of the "and" circuit corresponding to the storage device to which the digit is to be shifted. Therefore, if the "shift" signal is held operative for a length of time equivalent to the time of one pulse and is properly phased relative to the primary source of input pulses, the digit in each delay device will be sent to the next device, which is the one to the right in Fig. 5-7, in the shifting register. After the shift is executed, the "store" signal is reapplied.

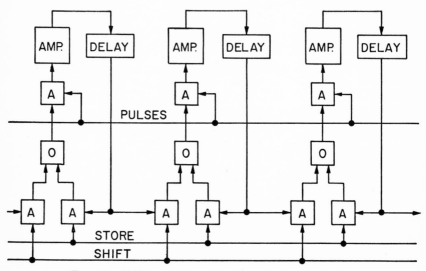

Fɪɢ. 5-7. Shifting register with dynamic storage devices.

High-speed Asynchronous Multiplier. The principle of the synchronous adder described in the previous chapter can be applied to a multiplication unit directly; but, if certain modifications are incorporated, the speed of multiplication can be increased substantially. The principal modification is to generate each individual sum digit as a 0 or a 1 and send it directly to the accumulator position to the right, rather than perform this shifting in a separate operation. The functional block diagram is given in Fig. 5-8.

The set of "and" switches and the "or" switch located in the diagram between the accumulator and addend registers are for the purpose of forming the sum of the digits held in the registers. A steady-state signal appears on one of the three lines marked 2, 1, and 0 in accordance with the value of the digits to be added. When adding the contents of the addend register to the accumulator, as is desired when a multiplier digit is 1, a pulse-type signal is applied to the no-carry (N) input of the lowest order.

This pulse then progresses through all orders and follows paths determined by the values of the various digits involved. In particular,

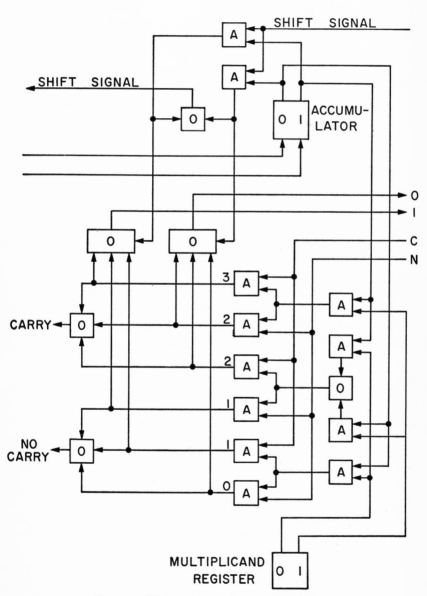

Fig. 5-8.   High-speed asynchronous multiplier.

if a carry is to be sent from a given order to the next higher order, the pulse will appear on the carry output line; otherwise, it will appear on the no-carry output line. The C or N input is combined with the sum in a set of six "and" switches so that the sum including the carry, if any, from the next lower order appears as a pulse on one of six lines indicated in the figure by the numbers, 3, 2, 2, 1, 1, and 0. Clearly, if the sum including carry is 3 or 2, a carry should be sent to the next higher order, but if it is 1 or 0, a no-carry signal should be transmitted. This function is accomplished through the "or" switches on the left-hand part of the figure.

The digit to be stored in the accumulator register is 1 if the sum including carry is 3 or 1, but is 0 if the sum is 2 or 0. "Or" switches are used to combine the signals from the six lines and transmit a 0-signal or 1-signal to the next lower order of the accumulator register. The addition operation therefore "ripples" through the system. Actually, small amounts of delay are needed on either the input or output lines of the triggers in the accumulator register, but the delay in the action of the triggers themselves may be sufficient.

When the multiplier digit is 0, it is necessary to shift the number in the accumulator without adding the number in the addend register. With the arrangement in Fig. 5-8, the shifting is accomplished by applying a pulse on the input line marked "shift signal" of the lowest order. The outputs of the "and" switches are used not only for the signal to be sent to the next lower order trigger, but also they are combined in an "or" switch to form the shift signal for the next higher order. The effect is a sort of "ripple shift."

The completion of an operation, which may be either an addition with shift or a shift only, can be sensed by combining the output signals of the highest order in an "or" switch. This signal may then be used to sense the next multiplier digit and initiate the next operation. In some applications it is not necessary to wait for the completion of one operation before starting the next one. It is possible to have two or more signals rippling along the accumulator at the same time, one behind another. In this case, the limiting factor is the resolution time of the triggers; a second operation may be started as soon as the transients from the first operation have died out in the lowest order.

Serial Operation. The shifting function required for multiplication is, in principle, much more simple when serial operation is employed. To shift the digits to higher orders, it is necessary merely to delay the presentation of the digits by a number of pulse periods equal to the number of orders desired in the shift. A shift to lower orders is accomplished by presenting the digits at an earlier time than when not shifting. While a pulse delaying device may be readily realized physically, a pulse "advancing" device is an impossibility, and it is necessary to consider the nature of number storage with serial operation to understand thoroughly the shifting operation.

With serial operation, the digits of a number may be stored statically and sensed one at a time when the number is to be sent from one place in the computer to another. In this case the number cannot be truly shifted forward in time, although it is possible to sense, for example, the second digit in the number first, in which case the second and all succeeding digits will appear in the transmission line one digit period earlier than otherwise. A second method of storage is through the use of a delay device in which all the digits of a number, or perhaps even all the digits of several numbers, are continuously circulated. With a delay device, the digits of a number are presented one after the other (serially) over and over again, and time may be defined, crudely at least, as starting at zero each time the first digit of a number is presented. Time then increases continuously until the first digit has been recirculated in the delay line and is presented again, when time may be assumed to return to zero. With delay storage of this type, the series of digits comprising a number may be delayed or advanced in time by increasing or decreasing, respectively, the amount of delay in the circulation path.

Before proceeding to a description of multiplication, it will be pointed out that the delay-type storage devices mentioned in the preceding paragraph can be any one of at least three different forms. Static storage may be used as a delay device by continuously sensing the digits one after another and automatically returning to the first in the series after the last has been sensed. Storage devices employing cathode-ray tubes, in which the digits are recorded and sensed on the tube face by means of an electron beam, are well adapted to this type of operation. Most static storage devices require elaborate switching systems to provide access to the individual elements, but the electron beam in a cathode-ray tube is easily deflected from one position to another. A second type of delay storage involves pulses traveling along a "delay line." Practical electrical delay lines with sufficient delay to store a reasonable number of digits are not yet available, although mechanical vibrations generated and detected by means of piezoelectric crystals and transmitted through various substances, particularly mercury, have been employed in successful and useful storage systems of the delay line type. In a third variation in delay storage, the digits are recorded by some means or other and then physically transported to another location, where the recording is sensed, and the time of transportation produces the delay. In this category are "magnetic drums," which are continuously rotating cylindrical elements with a surface coating of magnetic material on which digits may be recorded by the state of magnetization of small areas in the surface. The state of magnetization can be established by applying an electrical pulse to the coil of a "magnetic head" held near the surface of the drum, and the sensing is accomplished through pulses induced in the coil of the same or a different head as the magnetized area passes in close proximity to it.

With all three of the delay-type storage devices, the digit signals obtained from the sensing mechanism are seldom of the proper wave form and timing to be returned to the delay device directly. To avoid degeneration of the stored signals, it is necessary to send properly shaped and timed signals to the delay-type storage device each time the number is circulated. Therefore, instead of returning the signals directly, the signals detected by the sensing mechanism are used to control the entry of suitable pulses from a separate pulse generating device.

When all the details required for serial multiplication are included, the resulting arrangement can turn out to be relatively complex in spite of the functional simplicity of the components. The number of variations in functional arrangements which may be used to form a multiplier is, as might be expected, very great. No attempt will be made to describe all of them, but one multiplication circuit will be explained in an effort to illustrate the nature of the problems involved and to indicate possible means for solution.

A functional arrangement for a multiplier operating on numbers transmitted in serial form is shown in Fig. 5-9. Four delay-type storage devices are provided, each with n time units of delay, where a time unit is the amount of time between successive digits in the serial representation. Each delay unit is therefore capable of storing a number composed of n digits. Initially, one of the storage devices is assumed to be storing the multiplier and another is storing the multiplicand. The one-digit delay shown in the circulation loop of the multiplicand storage is not necessary for storage, but it will be used for multiplication. The other two storage devices are initially cleared of digits; at the end of the multiplication, one will hold the n highest digits of the product and the other will hold the n lowest digits of the product. It is, of course, not absolutely necessary that the multiplier and multiplicand each be composed of the same number, n, of digits, but it is the usual practice, with only a few exceptions, to use in a computer only numbers with a given number of digits. The operation of the multiplier will be explained with reference to the timing chart at the bottom of Fig. 5-9, which shows the sequence of appearance of the digits in the various delay units with the assumption that $n = 4$.

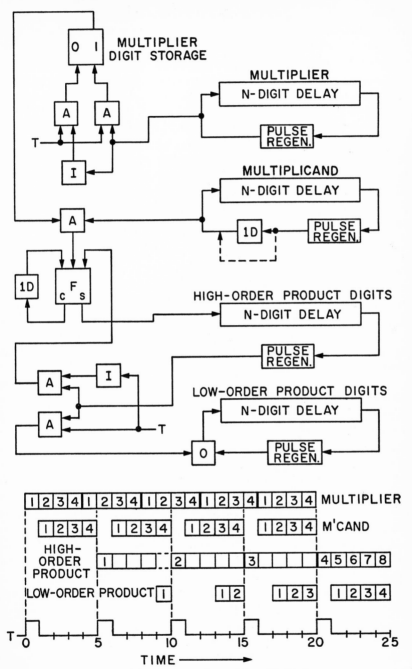

FIG. 5-9. Arrangement for serial multiplication.

At the beginning of the multiplication operation, which is at time T_0, the multiplicand and multiplier are assumed to be circulating in phase (digits of corresponding orders appearing at the same time) in their respective delay units. To start the multiplication, the one-digit delay is inserted in the multiplicand delay loop and the input line to the adder is closed at the point marked with an X in order to allow entry of the multiplicand under control of the multiplier digits. Timed control signals, T, are applied to the "and" switches connected to the input lines of the multiplier digit-storage device. From the timing chart and the connections of the switches it can be seen that the multiplier digit-storage device will be set to 0 or 1, depending upon whether the first (lowest-order) digit of the multiplier is a 0 or 1, respectively. If the first multiplier digit is a 1, a signal will be applied to one input of an "and" switch which then allows the multiplicand to pass to the adder. Because of the one-digit delay which has been inserted in the multiplicand storage loop, the first digit of the multiplicand appears at time T_1. The first partial product then enters the storage device which will eventually store the high-order digits of the final product.

At time T_5, the first partial product begins to emerge from the delay device into which it was sent, and at time T_5 the timed control signal, T, performs two functions. For one thing, the first digit of the partial product is the first digit of the final product and it therefore need not be returned to the adder. Pulse T is applied to an "and" switch which channels this first digit into the delay unit intended for storage of the low-order digits of the product. Also, at T_5, the second digit of the multiplier appears, and T is used to set the multiplier digit-storage device to correspond to it. The second entry of the multiplicand is then under control of the second digit of the multiplier. At time T_6, the first digit of the multiplicand appears at the adder to be added to the second digit of the first partial product as it should be. At time T_9, the first digit of the final product emerges from the delay unit storing the lower-order digits, and this digit is immediately entered again into this delay unit for storage. The second digit, which has been determined, of the final product emerges from the high-order digit-storage device and is switched to the low-order digit-storage device at T_{10}. Note that at time, T_8, the last digit of the first partial product is being added to the third digit of the multiplicand. This addition may produce a carry which will be added to the fourth digit of the multiplicand at T_9, and this addition may produce another carry, which will be returned through the adder at T_{10}. However, this last carry causes no difficulties because no multiplicand digits appear at this time and because the partial product digit which appears at this time is not being sent to the adder.

The process continues in similar fashion until T_{20}, at which time all desired entries of the multiplicand have been made and the circuit from the multiplicand storage device to the adder is opened. After the T pulse at T_{20} has been used to transfer the fourth product digit from the high-order storage device to the low-order storage device, the multiplication is complete.

Many of the details have been omitted from the multiplication arrangement, especially the details concerned with the starting and stopping of the multiplication and the details concerned with entry of the factors to the multiplier and the withdrawal of the product from the multiplier. A useful multiplier must, of course, include provisions for these details, but a discussion of them would add little to an understanding of the multiplication process.

A Serial-parallel Multiplication Arrangement. A practical and very fast arrangement for multiplication where one factor is presented

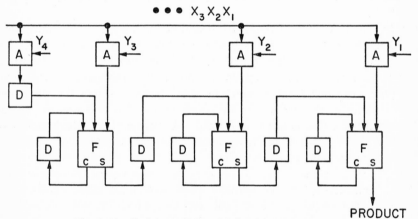

FIG. 5-10. Serial-parallel multiplication arrangement.

serially and the other in parallel is shown in Fig. 5-10. One factor, $Y_4Y_3Y_2Y_1$, is applied in parallel with one signal connected to one input of each of the "and" switches which, in turn, are connected to the full adders in the multiplier. The other factor, $\cdots X_3X_2X_1$, is applied serially to the other input of each "and" switch. Either factor may be visualized with some justification as being the multiplier, but for purposes of explanation it will be assumed that the X factor is the multiplier and that the Y factor is the multiplicand. The "and" switches act as "gates" which allow the digits of Y to pass when a digit of X is 1. If the first digit of X is 1, the multiplicand is sent in parallel to the adders and will constitute the first partial product. The digits pass through the adders and the lowest-order digit appears on the output line as the first digit of the product. The other digits encounter delay units, each of which delays the signal an amount of time equal to the time between the digits in the multiplier. When the second digit of the multiplier appears, each digit of the multiplicand will have passed through one delay unit and will be appearing at one of the input lines of the next adder to the right. Then, if the second multiplier digit is a 1, the multiplicand will be entered and added to the proper orders of the first partial product. The second digit of the product will now appear on the output line. The third entry of the multiplicand is the same as the second except that the carries from the second addition will be entered into the adders along with the third entry of the multiplicand. This process is repeated for each digit of the multiplier, and note that the multiplier may have as many digits as desired. The amount of equipment in the multiplication unit is determined by the number of digits in the multiplicand and is independent of the number of digits in the multiplier.

After the last entry of the multiplicand under control of the multiplier, there may still be some digits in the multiplication unit which must be "run out" to complete the formation of the product. The time required to execute a multiplication by this method is therefore equal to the time required to transmit the product in serial fashion, where the time between digits in the product is the same as the time between digits in the serial transmission of the multiplier. As before, the product contains, in general, a number of digits equal to the sum of the numbers of digits in the multiplicand and multiplier.

During the "run out" part of the process as well as during the addition of the multiplicand, if the addition of a carry digit generates another carry digit, this second carry digit will be returned through the delay device to the same adder to be added to the next succeeding digits appearing at the adder. The next succeeding digits will correspond to the next higher order, as is desired for the proper propagation of carries through successively higher orders.

It is instructive to work out an explanation of the serial-parallel multiplication arrangement with the assumption that X is the multiplicand and Y is the multiplier.

The amount of equipment required for the serial-parallel multiplier may be reduced by using the configuration shown in Fig. 5-11. One factor, which will be assumed here to be the multiplicand, M, is applied serially on the line indicated. The multiplicand is doubled by passing it through a one-digit delay device, and the tripled multiplicand is obtained by adding the multiplicand to its doubled value. The lines on which the doubled and tripled values appear are indicated by $2M$ and

$3M$, respectively. The digits of the multiplier, R, are used in groups of two with R_1 and R_2 used to select the desired multiple to be added to the first adder; R_4 and R_8 provide for the selection of the multiple to be applied to the second full adder, and so on. Since the quantities applied to the various adders are separated by two binary orders of the multiplier, a two-digit delay is inserted between successive adders.

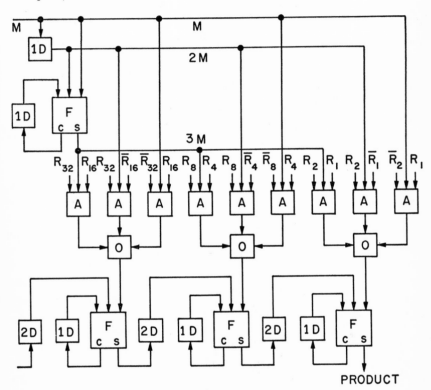

Fig. 5-11. Serial-parallel multiplication arrangement requiring less equipment.

The speed of multiplication with the arrangement shown in Fig. 5-11 is exactly the same as for the one shown in Fig. 5-10. The amount of saving in equipment is dependent upon the number of digits in the multiplier. For only four binary digits in the multiplier, there is practically no saving at all in equipment; but for multipliers of many digits, the saving is approximately equivalent to trading each alternate full adder for a nine-diode switching circuit. Note that the full adder used for generating $3M$ is the only one required in this part of the circuit, regardless of the number of digits involved; and the number of adders for accumulating the partial products is less than half the number of multiplier digits.

The above idea can be extended to the handling of the multiplier digits in groups of three (or more) and the generating of multiples up to the 7th of the multiplicand. However, the saving in equipment is questionable even when a very large number of digits is involved, be-

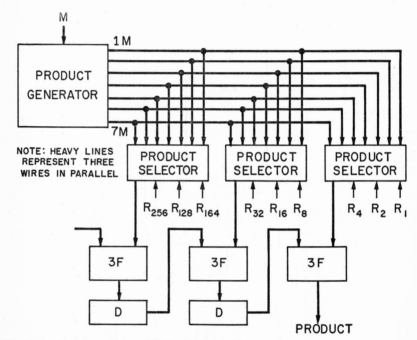

Fig. 5-12. Serial-parallel multiplication with digits of both factors grouped by 3's.

cause the switching circuits necessary to select the desired multiples become substantially more complex.

By handling the binary digits of both the multiplier and multiplicand in groups of 2, 3, 4, or more, the serial-parallel multiplication method can be made even faster, although the amount of equipment required becomes considerable. The over-all functional block diagram for the case of grouping by 3's is given in Fig. 5-12, where the blocks labeled "product generator" and "3F" are shown in more detail in Fig. 5-13(a) and (b), respectively.

The multiplicand, M, is entered into the product generator three binary digits at a time on three parallel wires. The doubled multiplicand, $2M$, is generated by shifting each digit to the next higher order with the highest-order digit of the three returned through a one-digit delay device to become the lowest-order digit of the next group of three. The tripled multiplicand is formed by adding M and $2M$ in a set of three parallel binary adders with the carry from the highest order returned

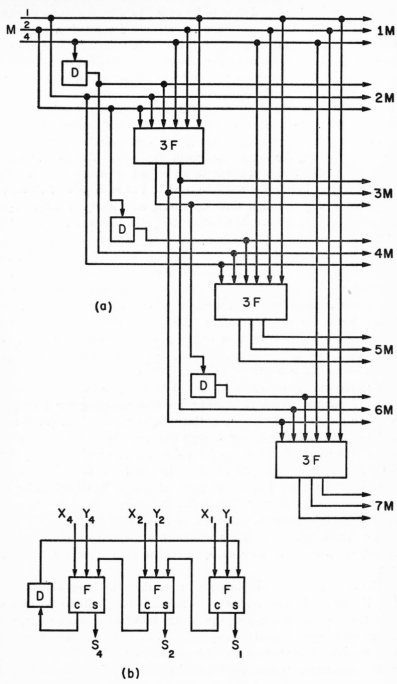

(a)

(b)

Fig. 5-13. Product generator and 3F block (see Fig. 5-12).

through a one-digit delay device to be added to the next group of three digits. Higher multiples up to the seventh are generated in an analogous manner, as indicated in Fig. 5-13(a). Note that, if there are any delays in forming the sums in the adders, compensating delays should be installed in the appropriate lines to cause all multiples to appear on the output wires at the same time.

The "product selectors" in Fig. 5-12 are essentially 3-pole, 8-throw switches and may be assembled with "and" and "or" switches in a reasonably straightforward fashion along the lines indicated for the components performing the same function in Fig. 5-11. The assembling of the partial products also proceeds in an analogous manner except that three full adders in parallel must be used to add each pair of numbers. Since there is only one digit time separating each group of three digits, one-digit delay devices are inserted in the paths between the groups of adders. Although multiplication speeds may be increased by a factor equal to the number of digits in each group (3 in this case), the substantial amount of equipment required for the product generator and the product selectors causes this method of multiplication to be of interest only in those applications where speed is of extreme importance.

Other Methods of Multiplication. All four of the binary multiplication methods which have been described employed, essentially, the addition of one factor called the multiplicand under the control of the digits of the other factor called the multiplier. It turns out to be very difficult to devise any multiplication methods substantially different from these. One other method worth mentioning involves grouping the multiplier digits into groups of, for example, three digits each. Each group may then be considered to represent a single octonary digit. Then, in multiplication the multiplicand would be added a number of times equal to the number represented by the octonary digit and a shift of three binary orders would be made before the entry of the multiplicand under the control of the next octonary digit in the multiplier. Since, on the average, more additions are required for multiplication by this method, it does not appear attractive unless components are used whereby shifts of three orders are much more easily executed than three shifts of one order.

If the factors to be multiplied are larger than the largest factors for which the multiplication unit was intended, it may still be possible to obtain the product by breaking the factors into two or more parts, performing several individual multiplications, and then adding the individual products with due regard to corresponding orders. However, this process, sometimes known as "expanded accuracy" multiplication, is more a matter of "programming" a problem than a matter of multiplication.

Multiplication Involving Negative Factors. If one or both of the factors entering into a multiplication are negative, the multiplication may be carried out in the same manner as described previously, provided the representations of the numbers are in true and not complement form. It is only necessary to compare the signs of the two factors with the sign of the product being positive or negative according to whether the signs are alike or different, respectively. A functional arrangement which is the same as is used for generating the sum in a half adder may be used for sign comparison. When the negative factors appear in 1's complement form, the simplicity of conversion to true form causes the same multiplication procedure to be attractive, although it must be remembered that the signs of the factors must be known prior to the start of the multiplication process, which may be of concern in serial computers.

When negative numbers are represented by means of the 2's complement notation, the complexities in converting to true representation may be great enough to warrant consideration of multiplication procedures which deal directly with the complement forms. Consider the multiplication of two factors, X and Y, where Y is negative and is presented as $2^n - Y$, with n being the number of orders in Y. The fact that a quantity is negative will be indicated by a 1 in the sign position of the number. The product of the two factors will be negative and should be represented as $2^{2n} - XY$ if both factors are composed of n orders, as will be assumed. But the product of X and $2^n - Y$ is $X2^n - XY$; therefore a correction of $(2^n - X)2^n$, which is the 2's complement of X multiplied by 2^n, should be added to the product obtained by the usual multiplication method to obtain the correct result. As an example, the multiplication of (0) 1111 (decimal $+15$) by (1) 0011 (decimal -13) is shown.

$$
\begin{array}{ll}
\text{(0) } 1111 & X \\
\text{(1) } 0011 & 2^n - Y \\
\hline
1111 & \\
1111 & \\
0000 & \\
0000 & \\
\hline
00101101 & \\
0001 & \text{Add } (2^n - X)2^n \\
\hline
\text{(1) } 00111101 & 2^{2n} - XY \text{ (decimal } -195)
\end{array}
$$

When X is negative and Y is positive, the result of the multiplication, if followed in the usual manner, will be $Y2^n - XY$; and the proper correction term would be $(2^n - Y)2^n$. But in some multiplication arrangements, as was explained in previous paragraphs, the multiplier digits are discarded one at a time as they are used in the multiplication process. A trick which may be used that effectually adds in the 1's complement of Y when X is negative is the adding of the sign digit of X each time the multiplier digit is 0. In addition to generating the 1's complement, this process causes it to be multiplied by 2^n, as is desired, when added to the product. Since the 2's complement may be obtained by adding 1 to the 1's complement, it is then necessary simply to add a corrective 1 in the proper order of the product. To illustrate the process, the multiplication of (1) 0001 (decimal -15) by (0) 1101 (decimal $+13$) is shown.

$$
\begin{array}{ll}
\text{(1) 0001} & 2^n - X \\
\text{(0) 1101} & Y \\
\hline
0001 & \\
10000 & \text{``sign'' of } X \\
0001 & \\
0001 & \\
\hline
00101101 & \\
\qquad\quad 1 & \text{Corrective 1} \\
\hline
\text{(1) 00111101} & 2^{2n} - XY \text{ (decimal } -195) \\
\end{array}
$$

When both factors are negative, the multiplication will yield

$$(2^n - X)(2^n - Y) = 2^{2n} - X2^n - Y2^n + XY$$

Because Y is negative, the correction term involving X should be

$$[2^n - (2^n - X)]2^n = X2^n$$

and because X is negative, the quantity $[2^n - (2^n - Y)]2^n = Y2^n$ should be added. When both corrective terms are added, the result is $2^{2n} + XY$, but the 1 in the 2^{2n} order may be ignored, and the product is, in effect, $+XY$, as desired. The following is a sample multiplication with both factors negative.

$$(1)\ 0001 \quad 2^n - X$$
$$(1)\ 0011 \quad 2^n - Y$$

0001	
0001	
10000	"sign" of X
10000	"sign" of X

11000011	
1111	Add $X2^n$

10110011	
1	Corrective 1

$$(0)\ 11000011 \quad XY\ \text{(decimal } +195)$$

The multiplication of (1) 1011 (decimal -5) by (1) 1010 (decimal -6) is shown as another example.

$$(1)\ 1011 \quad 2^n - X$$
$$(1)\ 1010 \quad 2^n - Y$$

10000	"sign" of X
1011	
10000	"sign" of X
1011	

10111110	
0101	Add $X2^n$

00001110	
1	Corrective 1

$$(0)\ 00011110 \quad XY\ \text{(decimal } +30)$$

In each of the above examples the sign of the product was determined from the fact that the product is negative when one, but not both, of the factors is negative. It is possible, by including the signs of the factors in the corrective terms, to develop the sign of the product in a 2^nth order of the accumulator, in which the product is being assembled, although no important advantage in this step is apparent.

The above procedure for multiplication of negative factors works independently of the location of the binary point. Note, in particular, that if pure fractions instead of integers had been assumed, n would have been zero and the corrective terms could have been assumed to be added directly without a multiplication by 2^n because $2^0 = 1$. There would be no physical difference in the equipment required in the two cases.

Another multiplication process which may be used when negative numbers are represented in 2's complement form involves the examination of the multiplier digit to the right (one lower order) of a given multiplier digit in the determination of the step to be taken with regard to the multiplicand. The process may be reduced to three simple rules.

1. If a given multiplier digit is 1 and the next lower-order multiplier digit is 0, subtract the multiplicand.

2. If a given multiplier digit is 0 and the next lower-order multiplier digit is 1, add the multiplicand.

3. If a given multiplier digit is the same as the next lower-order multiplier digit, add or subtract nothing.

In the process the sign digits of the numbers are operated upon exactly the same as though they were the highest-order digits of the numbers. As examples (0) 1111 (decimal +15) will be multiplied by (0) 1101 (decimal +13) and (1) 0011 (decimal −13).

$$\text{(0)} \ 1111$$
$$\text{(0)} \ 1101$$

	000000000
Subtract	01111

	111110001
Add	01111

	000001111
Subtract	01111

	111010011
	0000

	111010011
Add	01111

$$\text{(0)}11000011 \quad \text{(decimal } +195)$$

$$(0) \quad 1111$$
$$(1) \quad 0011$$

Subtract	000000000
	01111

111110001
0000

Add	111110001
	01111

000101101
0000

Subtract	000101101
	01111

$$(1)00111101 \quad \text{(decimal } -195)$$

The process yields the correct product with negative as well as positive multiplicands. Also, the location of binary point is of no consequence.

Although both of the procedures which have been described for the multiplication of negative numbers in 2's complement form are reasonably simple and straightforward, the extra-circuit functions which must be included to incorporate the procedures into a computing machine may be considerable in number and complexity. The attractiveness of the procedures is therefore not very great for most applications.

Binary Division. In either division or multiplication, three numbers are involved, one of which is the product of the other two. In multiplication, the two factors to be multiplied are given, and the problem is to find the product. In division, the product (now called the dividend) and one of the factors (called the divisor) are given, and the problem is to find the other factor (called the quotient). Because of this connection between the two operations, it seems natural to attempt to analyze division through a comparison with multiplication, and one of the first questions to be answered is whether the divisor should be compared with the multiplier or the multiplicand. Even though either factor may be used as the multiplier in multiplication, the divisor in division rather definitely corresponds to the multiplicand and not the multiplier. To perform division by a process which may be considered to be the reverse of multiplication, one factor should be repeatedly subtracted, with appropriate shifts, from the dividend. Since the quotient is not yet known, it cannot be subtracted, and therefore the role corresponding to the multiplicand must be assigned to the divisor. In spite of the many features that division has in common with multiplication, there are some important problems which arise in division which were not encountered in multiplication.

The problems encountered when incorporating the process of division into a computer are of such magnitude that it is sometimes found desirable to omit the division function from the arithmetic portion of a computer, even though the computer in question may be a large general-purpose one. However, the omission of division from the arithmetic portion of a computer does not mean that the computer is incapable of performing division. There are certain iterative formulas involving only addition, subtraction, and multiplication which may be used to obtain the reciprocal of a number, and the reciprocal of the divisor may be multiplied by the dividend to effect division. Two such formulas are, in binary notation,

$$b_{K+1} = b_K(10 - xb_K)$$

and

$$b_{K+1} = b_K[11(1 - xb_K) + (xb_K)^{10}]$$

where x is the number for which the reciprocal is desired, and the b_K are successive approximations of the reciprocal, $1/x$. The first of the two equations is second order and the other is third order, which means that, once a reasonable approximation to the reciprocal is obtained, the number of significant digits in the approximation is roughly doubled and tripled, respectively, after each application of the iterative formula. The initial approximation, b_0, must lie between 0 and $10/x$; otherwise, the series of the b_K will not converge. The details of the use of an iterative formula to perform division belong more properly in a discussion of the programming of problems to be solved on a computer, but the formulas are mentioned to illustrate the practicality of eliminating a dividing unit in a general-purpose computer. Other factors to be considered in judging the desirability of a dividing unit in a computer are the relative frequency of the division operation in the problems to be solved by the computer, required speed, and ease of programming division on the computer.

The Basic Principle of Binary Division.   The obtaining of the quotient in binary division is accomplished through successive subtractions of the divisor from appropriate orders of the dividend. Each time the subtraction leaves a positive remainder, a 1 is added to the corresponding order of the quotient. Each time a negative remainder would result, steps must be taken which will, in effect, nullify the subtraction and leave the quotient unchanged. At least three important problems are encountered when working out the details of the division process which have no counterpart in multiplication. One of the problems is the determination of the correct orders from which the divisor should be subtracted the first time. The second problem is related to the first but it is usually treated in a much different manner, and it involves the means for handling the situation when the subtraction of the divisor produces a negative remainder. The third problem is the determination of the disposition of the remainder after the quotient has been obtained to the desired accuracy. The description of the division process will proceed through a description of these three problems.

The Problem of Starting the Division Process. Probably the most elementary way to perform division is to "line up" the binary points of the dividend and divisor. The quotient may then be obtained by counting the number of times that the divisor may be subtracted before a negative remainder is obtained. Although it is simple, the process is time consuming, and it is useful for obtaining only the integral and not the fractional part of the quotient. It is generally more satisfactory to multiply the divisor by a power of two by appropriate shifts and obtain the highest order nonzero digit of the quotient on the first subtraction regardless of the order of this first digit. At least this is what is done when dividing by the pencil-and-paper method. But a computing machine does not usually have the ability to ascertain relative magnitudes of numbers by "inspection," as does a person; consequently, different rules are usually used in a computer for determining the orders from which the first subtraction should be made.

If an eight-digit dividend and a four-digit divisor are taken as an example, it might be expected after a study of multiplication that the proper orders from which the divisor should be subtracted to obtain the first quotient digit would be the fourth to the seventh orders, inclusively, from the lowest order. In those cases where the dividend and divisor are numbers which could occur in a corresponding multiplication process involving two four-digit factors, the fourth to the seventh orders would be the proper ones. However, the numbers involved in the division need not correspond to any four-by-four multiplication, and because of this fact certain difficulties will be encountered for some combinations of dividend and divisor when the fourth to seventh orders are chosen. For example, when the dividend is any eight-digit number equal to or greater than 11111000 (decimal 248), it will be possible to subtract the divisor twice before reducing the remainder to a negative value even when the divisor is the largest possible four-digit number, namely, 1111 (decimal 15). Therefore, the first subtraction of the divisor from the fourth to seventh order of the dividend will not necessarily yield the highest-order digit of the quotient. The difficulty in the situation can be more acute when the divisor is less than its maximum value, and particularly when the higher orders of the divisor are 0's, such as when the divisor is, for example, 0011 (decimal 3). Because of this difficulty it is usually found necessary to impose restrictions on the relative magnitudes of the divisor and dividend.

The restriction placed on the relative magnitudes of the dividend and divisor may be stated in a number of ways. In continuance of the above discussion, it is sufficient to say that the divisor must be large enough relative to the dividend to cause a negative remainder when a second subtraction from the fourth to seventh orders is made. When programming a problem for solution on a computer, it is often difficult to predict that the dividends and divisors in the various division operations will fall within the desired limits. For this reason it is desirable to make a test at the beginning of each division operation. A simple way to determine that the divisor is sufficiently large relative to the dividend is to subtract it from the fifth to eighth orders, inclusively, of the dividend, which is equivalent to subtracting it twice from fourth to seventh orders. Then if the first subtraction produces a negative remainder, it will be known that the divisor is sufficiently large (or the dividend sufficiently small), and the division process may then proceed.

The locations of the binary points in the factors entering into the division process are of no real consequence, although it is, of course, necessary to keep track of where the points are when programming a problem for a computer. If the binary points are visualized as being to the left of all significant digits as in a fractional computer, the requirement on the relative magnitude of the dividend and divisor may be reduced to a simple statement. It is then only necessary to state that the divisor must be larger than the dividend, because if the divisor were equal to or less than the dividend, the quotient would be equal to or greater than unity, which is beyond the capacity of the machine.

Other arrangements for handling the initial steps of a division process may be used for special situations, particularly when floating-point type of computations are employed, but a detailed discussion of them would be beyond present purposes.

The Problem of Correcting a Negative Remainder. It has already been mentioned that, if the subtraction of the divisor produces a negative remainder, the quotient which is being built up should be unaltered and steps should be taken which will nullify the subtraction. One straightforward way to nullify the subtraction is to add the divisor back into the remainder each time a negative remainder occurs. To illustrate the process more clearly, the steps involved in dividing 10001100 (decimal 140) by 1100 (decimal 14) are shown in the following example.

	10001100	
Subtract	1110	
	————	Check to prove that dividend
	(−)10101100	and divisor have proper rela-
Add	1110	tive magnitude
	————	
	10001100	
Subtract	1110	
	————	
	0011100	1---
Subtract	1110	
	————	
	(−)100100	10--
Add	1110	
	————	
	011100	Quotient
Subtract	1110	
	————	
	00000	101-
Subtract	1110	
	————	
	(−)0010	1010
Add	1110	
	————	
	0000	Final remainder

Note that when a subtraction leaves a positive remainder it is not necessary to make a second subtraction from the same orders, because it is known that no digit in the quotient can be greater than 1. Also, there can be no "carries" in the quotient because each determination of a quotient digit is final when the quotient digits are determined in this way.

Although it is straightforward, the above procedure for division can be improved upon from the standpoint of the number of additions and subtractions required to complete a division operation. Instead of correcting a negative remainder by adding the divisor into the same orders from which it was last subtracted, it may be shifted to the right one position (which effectually divides it by two) and then added. Since in the previous method of division the divisor was in each case shifted to the right and subtracted, it can be seen that the two procedures produce the same result. In the previous method, the operation could be expressed as $+D - \frac{1}{2}D$, where D is the divisor and in the present case the operation is simply $+\frac{1}{2}D$. If, after adding $\frac{1}{2}D$, the remainder is still negative, it is known that the next quotient digit is zero, and the divisor is shifted another position to the right and added. The arithmetic steps in a sample division by this process are shown below.

$$
\left.
\begin{array}{rr}
 & 10001100 \\
\text{Subtract} & 1110 \\
\hline
 & (-)10101100
\end{array}
\right\}
\begin{array}{l}
\text{Check to prove that dividend} \\
\text{and divisor have proper rela-} \\
\text{tive magnitude}
\end{array}
$$

$$
\begin{array}{rrl}
\text{Add} & 1110 & \\[4pt]
 & (+)00011100 & \ \ 1{-}{-}{-} \\
\text{Subtract} & 1110 & \\
\hline
 & (-)100100 & \ \ 10{-}{-} \\
\text{Add} & 1110 & \\
\hline
 & (+)000000 & \ \ 101{-} \\
\text{Subtract} & 1110 & \\
\hline
 & (-)0010 & \ \ 1010 \\
\end{array}
\left.
\begin{array}{l}
\\ \\ \\ \\ \\ \text{Quotient} \\ \\ \\ \\
\end{array}
\right.
$$

A great number of details and fine points could be included in a discussion of this method of division, but most of them can be obtained through a study of the example. However, one detail which bears pointing out involves the final remainder, which was not obtained in the above example. To obtain the final remainder (0000 in this example), it is necessary to add the divisor into the orders from which it was last subtracted. Although such a step fits well into the previously described method of division, it would be a special operation in this method of division because the normal procedure is to shift right once before adding. A further complication will be exposed if additional division examples are worked out; namely, the final remainder must in some cases be obtained by a subtraction instead of an addition. In many applications the final remainder is of no consequence and is discarded, and for these applications this division method is attractive because only one addition or subtraction per quotient digit is required. But in applications where the final remainder is required, the corrective steps which must be taken at the conclusion of the division process cause substantial complications in the design of a dividing unit.

A third method of handling the negative remainder problem follows the pencil-and-paper division process quite closely. There are several variations to the method, and the adaptability of the various variations depends upon the type of computer components in use. With some types of components, none of the variations appears useful. The method involves a comparison of the divisor with the appropriate orders of the dividend (or the remainder after one or more subtractions have been performed) and executing the subtraction only when the comparison indicates that the remainder will be positive. The comparison may be made digit by digit in either ascending or descending order of significance. When making the comparison with the digits appearing in ascending order of significance, a "high-low" storage device is set to indicate "high" or "low," as the case may be, when corresponding digits of the two numbers being compared are not the same. When corresponding digits of the two numbers are the same, the setting of the storage device is not changed. The last setting will indicate whether or not the divisor, if subtracted, will produce a negative remainder. If the digits of the two numbers to be compared appear in descending order of significance, the first pair of digits which indicate a difference will denote which of the numbers is the larger, and the "high-low" storage device should be set accordingly. Since in a serial computer the digits are normally presented in ascending order of significance, the former method of comparison would probably receive the more serious consideration in most cases. It is possible to work out circuit arrangements whereby the comparison for the succeeding subtraction is performed during the time that a given subtraction is being executed. The major steps involved in division by this method are shown in the example below.

Compare only	10001100 1110	Check to prove that dividend and divisor have proper relative magnitude
	10001100	
Compare and subtract	1110	1---
	0011100	
Compare only	1110	10--
	011100	
Compare and subtract	1110	101-
	00000	
Compare only	1110	1010
	0000	

Quotient

When parallel operation is being employed, the comparison of the divisor with the dividend may be made by means of an adder with true-complement switching on the input lines or by means of a subtracter. Only that portion of the unit which generates the carry or borrow is needed to make the comparison. If a borrow signal is obtained from the highest order (in the case when a subtracter is used) it will be known that a negative remainder will result and that the subtraction should not be carried out. In arrangements where a subtracter is being used in connection with a storage register to produce an accumulating function, the portion of the subtracter unit which generates the difference can be used to generate the difference for each step in the division process, but the difference should be entered into the storage unit only for those steps in which it is positive. Additional forms of dividing units employing this method of division can be worked out whereby the borrow position of a subtracter unit is used in combination with an accumulator employing binary counters.

The Problem of the Final Remainder. Although the problem of the final remainder has already been encountered in the discussion of correcting a negative remainder, there are further points concerning the final remainder which deserve consideration. In the examples of division which were shown, the final remainder was zero in each case, which indicates that the dividend was an exact multiple of the divisor. That the dividend be an exact multiple of the divisor is not generally a requirement applied to the factors entering into a division operation. Each of the division procedures that have been described will produce a quotient that corresponds to the largest multiple of the divisor which is equal to or less than the dividend. The difference between this largest multiple and the dividend is the final remainder, and when the final remainder is not zero the quotient that has been obtained is not an exact representation of the desired result. To increase the accuracy of the quotient, the division process may be continued until as many quotient digits as desired are produced; but, as was pointed out, some ratios of integers cannot be represented exactly by a single number, and eventually the remainder must be either discarded or stored separately.

Although the remainder is usually of no interest and is therefore discarded, there are occasional examples when the remainder is of importance. One such example is the determination of the angular position of a wheel or other rotating object after a specified number of degrees of rotation. If the rotation in degrees is divided by the number of degrees in a circle, the remainder will indicate the angular position. Because problems of this type are relatively rare, it is often preferable to discard the remainder in all cases and reconstruct it when necessary by subtracting from the dividend the product of the unrounded quotient and the divisor.

The Physical Realization of a Divider Unit. Four quite different physical arrangements for performing multiplication were described, and the various physical arrangements which may be used for division will be explained through comparisons with the multiplier units. Although the details which must be considered in making a complete divider unit are considerable in number, they are for the most part merely details, and no attempt will be made to present a thorough discussion of them.

A simultaneous divider to correspond to the simultaneous multiplier shown in Fig. 5-1 is a possibility, although it does not appear to be a very practical possibility. Any of the division procedures described previously could be used in the design of a divider unit whereby steady signals representing the dividend and divisor could be applied to the input lines; and, after all switching transients had died out, signals representing the quotient, and possibly the remainder also, would appear on the output lines. However, the number of adders, subtracters, and miscellaneous switches necessary to complete a simultaneous divider by any known arrangement is so great that this type of divider seems worthy of consideration only in the rarest of cases.

For parallel operation, an accumulator capable of subtraction as well as addition provides a straightforward and practical means for assembling a divider unit. Either the divisor may be shifted according to the arrangement shown in Fig. 5-2, or a shifting accumulator analogous to that shown in Fig. 5-3 may be used. The shifting accumulator should, of course, shift to the left for division instead of to the right as is required for multiplication. One word of caution is in order when subtraction is accomplished through the addition of 1's complements. The end-around carry should be entered into the order corresponding to the lowest order of the divisor in each case unless, when adding the complement of the divisor, 1's are entered into all orders of the accumulator lower than that corresponding to the lowest order of the divisor. In the latter case, the end-around carry may be entered into the lowest order of the accumulator. With the shifting accumulator, no particular difficulties are caused by the requirement, but when shifting the divisor it should be remembered that it may be necessary to shift the end-around carry also.

When a serial computer is under consideration, division arrangements analogous to the multiplication arrangements shown in Fig. 5.9 become of interest. Since division is a somewhat more complicated process than multiplication, the factors do not circulate quite as "smoothly" through the delay-type storage devices, and additional complexities in the switching and control functions must be included.   However, no important new ideas are involved.

No arrangement for division which corresponds closely to the serial-parallel multiplier shown in Fig. 5-10 has ever been worked out so far as is known.   It is suspected that such a divider is an impossibility, although a proof of the impossibility is not known either.

Division Involving Negative Factors.   Since division involves both addition and subtraction of the divisor, it turns out to be possible to use substantially the same division process for negative factors expressed in 2's complements that is used for the case when both the dividend and divisor are positive.   However, certain complications arise in the correct determination of the very last quotient digit.   A possible round-off procedure (to be described in the next section) involves the placing of a 1 in the lowest order of the quotient regardless of the factors in the division.   When this round-off procedure is used, the division process is satisfactory; but when a more accurate round-off procedure is required, it becomes more desirable to use true instead of 2's complement representation for negative numbers entering into the division.

No useful division process for negative factors is known which corresponds closely to the multiplication process involving corrective terms or to the multiplication process involving the examination of the multiplier digits in pairs.

Round-off Procedures.   Either the multiplication or division process may produce more digits in the result than are desired.   In multiplication the number of digits in the product will be equal to the sum of the numbers of digits in the two factors, but the number of significant digits in the product will be no more than the lesser number of significant digits in either of two factors.   In divison, the quotient may in some cases be comprised of an infinite series of digits regardless of the size or the number of significant digits in the factors involved.   It is the usual practice to retain only the required number of digits in the product or quotient, and the problem is then to obtain the number which is closest to the desired number.   If, for example, the eight-digit number 1011XXXX is being rounded to a four-digit number, it is usually desired to record the number as 1011 when the right-hand four digits are less than 1000, and to record the number as 1100 when the right-hand four digits are greater than 1000.   When the right-hand four digits are exactly 1000, either choice for the number would be satisfactory except that it is customary to choose the larger of the two, or 1100 in the present case.

The most straightforward way to obtain the desired rounded number is to add a 1 in the highest order which is to be dropped. If a carry is propagated to the next higher order, it is known that the quantity being dropped is equal to or greater than 1000 in the example. Note that when the 2's complement notation for negative numbers is being used, the round-off may occur in an undesired direction. For example (1)0010.1 (decimal −13.5) will be rounded to (1)0011 (decimal −13) instead of (1)0010 (decimal −14). To avoid the difficulty, the number may be converted to its true representation before rounding. When negative numbers are represented in 1's complement form, correct rounding may be achieved by subtracting 1 from the highest order which is discarded. Then, since the 1's complement representation is (1)0010.0 (decimal −13.5), the number will be rounded to (1)0001 (decimal −14) as desired.

The amount of equipment required to produce a rounded product or quotient by the above method may be deemed excessive for some applications. The amount of required equipment may be particularly excessive in the case of division because the quotient may otherwise be built up in a register which has no adding or carry propagating properties. In applications where the rounding operation has as its primary purpose the function of producing a result which has an equal probability of lying above or below the exact result, a different and somewhat simpler rounding procedure may be used. The procedure is to make the lowest-order digit to be retained a 1 regardless of the other digits in the number. With this method of rounding, 10111111 and 101000, as examples, would both be rounded to 1011. In the first case, 00001111 is dropped and in the second case 00010000 is "added." Since the error with this method of rounding may be twice as great as with the previously described method, it is not as desirable, but it is relatively easily incorporated into a computer, and the average error over a large number of round-offs is usually sufficiently small.

The above procedure has the minor disadvantage that zero is never obtained as a result after a rounding operation regardless of the factors entering into the computations. A variation in the procedure is to add 1 to the lowest-order retained digit when that digit is a 1 and to do nothing when it is a 0. A register with carry propagating properties is required; but it is not necessary to store, even temporarily, any digits which will be subsequently dropped.

A fourth round-off procedure is to add a 0 or a 1 chosen in a random fashion into the lowest order to be retained. Although this method does require that the number to be rounded be placed in an accumulator or other device capable of propagating carries, it does not require that any more digits be saved than are desired in the final number. The amount of error which occurs with this method of rounding may vary, as in the previous example, from 00001111 too low to 00010000 too high. However, besides requiring a random number generator, the method has the disadvantage of making the computations difficult, if not impossible, to repeat exactly in the computer.

Chapter 6

DECIMAL CODES

The considerations involved in choosing a representation for a decimal digit in a computer are considerably more complex than was the case with binary digits. With the binary system the only significant choices were a signal or no signal, a signal on one of two different lines, or a "positive" or a "negative" signal to represent a 0 or 1, respectively. In the decimal system a single digit may have any one of ten different values, and one of the more obvious ways of representing a decimal digit is through the use of signals having the possibility of ten different amplitudes. A considerable amount of thought has been given to decimal digit representations of this type, but very little progress has been made in the adaptation of multiple-amplitude signals to digital computers. Consequently it has been necessary to look for other means of digit representations.

Since most computer components are inherently binary in nature or else work most satisfactorily when employed in binary fashion, it has been almost universal practice to use binary-type signals to represent the decimal digits. One method of representing a decimal digit by means of binary signals is to use ten separate lines and to place signals on a number of the lines corresponding to the digit value. For example, signals on six of the lines would indicate the digit, 6. It is more common practice to specify that only one signal at a time will be placed on any of the ten lines, and then each of the ten lines is identified with one of the ten digits. This representation is frequently used in transmitting decimal digits from a manual keyboard to a computer. Also, binary components may be used to transmit a decimal digit on a single line if time is employed as a variable. For example, the duration of a signal may be varied in ten equal steps to represent the ten decimal digits, or the signal may be repeated a number of times equal to the value of the digit. Another method is to use the timing of a single pulse-type signal.

177

Although the various "one-out-of-ten" schemes for digit representation that have been mentioned are relatively simple and straightforward, other forms of representation frequently are found to be more desirable in the design of computers where factors such as speed, savings in components, and reliability are important. It has already been mentioned that it is possible to represent a decimal digit with a minimum of four binary signals by using ten and ignoring six of the possible sixteen different combinations of the four signals. But of the more than 29 billion $(16!/6!)$ different ways by which ten of the sixteen combinations can be assigned to the ten decimal digits, only a few of the ways are useful, and the problem of selecting the best way for a given application is frequently a formidable one. The problem is further complicated by the fact that the use of more than the minimum of four binary signals may provide means for gaining important advantages in some applications. A particular way of assigning groups of four, five, or more binary signals to the ten decimal digits is called a decimal code, and it is the object of this chapter to point out the distinguishing features and some of the advantages and disadvantages of several of the codes which may be used.

The Weighted 4-bit Codes. Of the many possible 4-bit (where a "bit" refers to a binary digit) codes, only relatively few have the property that values, or weights, can be assigned to each of the four bits with the decimal digit being represented equal to the sum of the weights. All known weighted 4-bit codes are listed in Table 6-I, although the listing is more for the record than for any practical value. Since the codes were found by a cut-and-try search process, it cannot be guaranteed that all such codes have been found.

TABLE 6-I. WEIGHTED 4-BIT CODES

*5211	8421	631-2	842-3	74-2-1
*4311	531-1	*731-2	621-4	84-2-1
5311	*631-1	441-2	721-4	72-3-1
6311	522-1	541-2	821-4	72-4-1
*4221	*622-1	*641-2	*751-4	84-3-2
5221	432-1	841-2	861-4	*87-4-2
6221	*532-1	*632-2	632-4	
*3321	632-1	*443-2	*832-4	
4321	732-1	543-2	*652-4	
5321	*442-1	643-2	653-4	
6321	542-1	843-2	643-5	
7321	642-1	621-3	*753-6	
4421	742-1	721-3	63-1-1	
5421	842-1	751-3	63-2-1	
6421	621-2	542-3	54-2-1	
7421	531-2	*642-3	64-2-1	

To illustrate the meaning of the listings in Table 6-I, three of the more useful codes and one code involving a negative weight are displayed in detail in Table 6-II.

TABLE 6-II. DETAILED LISTING OF SOME OF THE 4-BIT WEIGHTED CODES

	8421	2421	5421	753-6
0	0000	0000	0000	0000
1	0001	0001	0001	1001
2	0010	0010	0010	0111
3	0011	0011	0011	0010
4	0100	0100	0100	1011
5	0101	1011	1000	0100
6	0110	1100	1001	1101
7	0111	1101	1010	1000
8	1000	1110	1011	0110
9	1001	1111	1100	1111

The 8,4,2,1 code is one of the most straightforward 4-bit codes because, with it, each decimal digit is represented in a conventional binary system. Therefore, the code has the advantage that the relatively simple binary techniques may be used, to some degree at least, in the arithmetic manipulations involving decimal digits. A disadvantage of the code is that the binary representations for ten to fifteen, inclusive, have no meaning, and steps must be taken to eliminate or correct these binary combinations each time they occur in an arithmetic operation. Another disadvantage of the code is that it is not "self-complementing," a self-complementing decimal code being one in which the 9's complement of each decimal digit may be obtained by changing the 1's to 0's and the 0's to 1's in the coded representation of the digit. Since a simple inversion yields the 15's complement, it is necessary in obtaining the 9's complement to add 10 to the result obtained by inversion or to add 6 to the digit before inversion. In the first of the two methods, a carry from the "8's" order will be obtained, but this carry is ignored, which effectually subtracts 16 from the result. That the two processes yield the 9's complement may be illustrated mathematically by the equation

$$(15 - D) + 10 - 16 = 15 - (D + 6) = 9 - D$$

where D is the decimal digit.

When the bits of the 8,4,2,1 code are presented in parallel, a somewhat simpler scheme than adding and inverting may be used to generate the 9's complement. By an examination of the code in Table 6-II, it may be observed that the 1-bit should always be inverted in generating the 9's complement, the 2-bit is always the same in the 9's complement as in the original digit; the 4-bit in the 9's complement is a 1 when the 2-bit or the 4-bit, but not both, in the original digit is 1; and the 8-bit in the complement is 0 when the 2-bit, 4-bit, or 8-bit in the original digit is 1. In Boolean algebra notation these relationships are

$$C_1 = \overline{T}_1$$

$$C_2 = T_2$$

$$C_4 = T_2\overline{T}_4 + \overline{T}_2T_4$$

$$C_8 = \overline{T_2 + T_4 + T_8}$$

where, here, the letters, T and C, refer to true and complement, respectively. The functional arrangement is shown in Fig. 6-1.

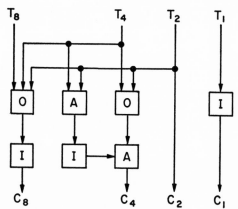

Fig. 6-1. Functional arrangement for generating the 9's complement with the 8,4,2,1 code.

Those codes in Table 6-I which are marked with an asterisk do have the property of being self-complementing, that is, the changing of the 0's to 1's and the 1's to 0's in each representation of a decimal digit will yield the 9's complement of that digit. Note that the sum of the weights in each self-complementing code is nine. That a sum of nine is a requirement may be easily understood by observing that 0000 must be a representation of the decimal digit, zero, in any of the weighted codes, and therefore 1111 must be a representation for the decimal digit, nine.

The 4,2,2,1 code, which is self-complementing, is shown in Table 6-II although the first two columns have been interchanged to indicate a 2,4,2,1 arrangement to correspond to common practice with this particular code. With the 2,4,2,1 code, the representations for the decimal digits two to seven, inclusive, are not necessarily unique. For example, either

0011 or 1001 may be used to indicate three, but the self-complementing feature is not effected because 1100 and 0110 are both proper representations of six. The self-complementing codes with only positive weights are useful also when changing from a 4-bit code to a single-line decimal code with the true or complement representation of the decimal digit being indicated by the number of pulse-type signals appearing on the

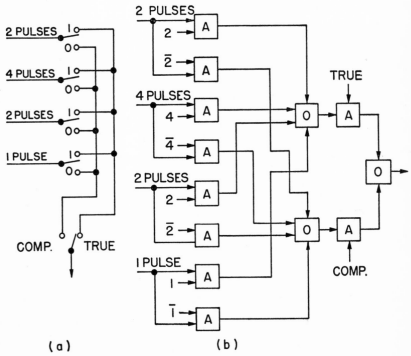

(a)   (b)

FIG. 6-2. Conversion from parallel 4-bit code to a series of pulses on a line.

line. Fig. 6-2(a) shows an electrical circuit utilizing relay contacts, which may be used to perform the conversion; and Fig. 6-2(b) shows the functional arrangement. Although the self-complementing weighted codes, particularly the 2,4,2,1 code, have been used in a few computers, they create difficulties when attempting simple arithmetic operations such as addition, and therefore their use has not been widespread.

The 5,4,2,1 code is included in Table 6-II mainly for the purpose of comparison with the 2,4,2,1 code, although it is not without practical application. Note that the first bit in each code is 1 for the decimal digits five through nine, but in the 5,4,2,1 code the other three bits are the same for the five through nine as for zero through four, which is not

182   Arithmetic Operations in Digital Computers

the case in the 2,4,2,1 code. The usefulness of the 5,4,2,1 code may be
found in certain multiplication and division systems which employ
only halving and doubling. The 2 and 4 factors may be obtained by
doubling, and the 5 factor may be obtained by multiplying by 10 (shifting) and halving.

The study of codes with negative weights can be a source of great
fascination; however, no advantages of them deemed worth recording
have as yet been found.

Nonweighted 4-bit Codes. For some applications, rather unusual considerations may assume a role of magnified importance, with the effect
that one of the nonweighted codes may be the best choice. For example,
it may be desired to minimize the amount of power required to store
or transmit the digits; and, with an objective such as this, a code with as
few 1's as possible may be desirable. The 8,4,2,1 code has a total of
fifteen 1's, and by using, say, 1010 instead of 0111 for the digit 7, the
number of 1's may be reduced to fourteen, which is the minimum possible
with a 4-bit code. It so happens that the 7,4,2,1 weighted code also has
only fourteen 1's. For another example, it may be desired that all decimal digits including zero be represented by at least one 1 so that the
absence of a signal can be detected positively. Again, it is possible to use
a weighted code such as the 5,3,1,−1 code for the purpose where zero is
0011; but, if the weighted properties are not useful, one of the nonweighted codes may be better.

Still another example is in the use of a 4-bit code for storage when
the code used for computations is a 5-bit code. With 5 bits there are ten
different combinations with two 1's, and when the ten decimal digits are
represented in this manner, it is possible to distinguish any digit without
the use of inverters, which is an advantage. However, only 4 of the 5
bits are really necessary for unambiguous representation so, by dropping
one of the five digits a nonweighted 4-bit code for storage is obtained.
The fifth bit may be generated when needed. One variation of the scheme
is shown in Table 6-III. This variation is sometimes called the 7,4,2,1,0
code because, except for zero, the bits have these weights.

Although all of the ideas presented in this section have been seriously
proposed at one time or another and may have actually been used in a
few instances, it should be understood that the difficulties encountered
when attempting to use the codes in a computing device usually offset
the advantages which have been mentioned.

One nonweighted code of more importance is called the excess-3 code
because it may be generated by adding a binary 3 to each digit representation in the conventional 8,4,2,1 code. Table 6-IV shows the excess-3
code in detail.

TABLE 6-III. A 5-BIT CODE REDUCED TO A 4-BIT CODE FOR STORAGE

	2 out of 5 Code 74210	Code as Stored
0	11000	1100
1	00011	0001
2	00101	0010
3	00110	0011
4	01001	0100
5	01010	0101
6	01100	0110
7	10001	1000
8	10010	1001
9	10100	1010

TABLE 6-IV. EXCESS-3 CODE

0	0011
1	0100
2	0101
3	0110
4	0111
5	1000
6	1001
7	1010
8	1011
9	1100

The excess-3 code has several useful properties. First of all, except for certain corrections which must be applied, straight binary techniques may be used in the performance of many of the arithmetic operations involving the digits. When adding two digits, the decimal carry is readily generated by using the carry from the highest-order binary digits. That the carry may be obtained in this manner may be understood by observing that, when two excess-3 digits are added, the sum is excess-6, which automatically eliminates the six unwanted binary configurations. Further advantages of the code are that it is self-complementing and that all decimal digits have at least one 1 in their representation so that zero and the condition of no digit at all may be distinguished. On the other hand, the fact that the excess-3 code is not weighted frequently introduces considerable disadvantages. For example, it is more difficult to learn and remember than the 8,4,2,1 and other weighted codes. Certain forms of arithmetic operations are more difficult with the excess-3 codes than with other codes including the frequently required operation of conversion between a 4-bit code and one of the various one-out-of-ten systems of representation. Also, in some computers a redundancy bit is used for checking purposes, and when this is done the advantage of the excess-3 code with regard to the representation for zero is largely nullified.

Codes Involving 5 or More Bits. One reason it might be desirable to use 5 or more bits in the representation of a decimal digit in spite of the availability of 4-bit codes is that it may be possible to effect simplifications in the arithmetic circuits in some cases. The use of a 5-bit code with each decimal digit represented by two 1's in the 5 bits has already been mentioned as providing an improved means for sensing the individual digits. When addition is being performed by switching circuits, the 8,6,4,2,1 or the 5,4,3,2,1,0 weighted codes offer certain advantages. All three of these codes have been employed in computers built at Harvard University; however, the use of codes with more than 4 bits for the purpose of circuit simplification has not become widespread.

A second advantage that can be gained by using 5 or more bits in the representation of decimal digits is the ability to detect errors. In the code involving two 1's out of 5 bits, for example, the existence of three 1's or only one 1 in the representation of a digit would be recognized as an error. Another code, known as the biquinary code, has 7 bits with the weights of 5,0,4,3,2,1,0. With this code, arithmetic operations may be performed in a moderately straightforward manner, although whether or not there is a net simplification when compared with the 4-bit codes is a debatable point. The main reason for the use of 7 bits is the ability to detect errors. From the detailed listing of the code in Table 6-V it may be observed that one of the first two bits and one of the last five bits is 1 in the representation of each decimal digit.

Another 7-bit code is the quibinary code, where the bits have the weights of 8,6,4,2,0,1,0. This code has properties which are similar for many applications to the properties of the biquinary code except that the

TABLE 6-V. BIQUINARY CODE (a) AND QUIBINARY CODE (b)

	5043210	8642010
0	0100001	0000101
1	0100010	0000110
2	0100100	0001001
3	0101000	0001010
4	0110000	0010001
5	1000001	0010010
6	1000010	0100001
7	1000100	0100010
8	1001000	1000001
9	1010000	1000010
	(a)	(b)

group of 2 bits and the group of 5 bits are interchanged. The quibinary code is listed in Table 6-V for comparison.

Error-detecting and Error-correcting Codes in General. In any code composed of binary bits, if a single error in a bit combination can produce another bit combination which is also in the code scheme, the error cannot, in general, be detected. For example, in the 8,4,2,1 code, 0110 (decimal digit 6) may appear as the proper representation for six, but if there were an error and it should be 0111 (decimal digit 7) or 0010 (decimal digit 2), there would be no way of detecting from the coded representation itself that the bits were an erroneous representation of some other digit. In order to detect the presence of a single error in the bits of a code it is necessary that the code be such that at least two changes must be made in the bits of the code when changing from the representation of one digit to the representation of any other digit. The 2-out-of-5 code shown in Table 6-III is an example of a code satisfying this requirement. To change from the representation of decimal 3 to decimal 8, for example, it is necessary to change both the first and the third bits of the code. The changing of any one of the bits in any of the code combinations will result in a combination which can be recognized as an error, and the code is therefore known as "error-detecting." However, the detection of an error does not mean that it can be corrected. For example, the bit combination, 11010, would be recognized as an error because there are three instead of only two 1's, but there would be no way of knowing from the code itself which of the three 1's should be a 0. The code is therefore not "error-correcting." For similar reasons the biquinary code in Table 6-V is error-detecting but not "error-correcting." If two or more errors occur simultaneously with either of the error-detecting codes which have been mentioned, the errors may pass undetected because the result of the errors may be the production of a bit combination which is a proper representation of one of the digits.

To be error-correcting, a code must be such that at least three changes in the bit combination must be made when changing from the representation of one digit to the representation of any other digit. With a code meeting this requirement, an error will produce a bit combination that can be recognized to contain an error, as before, but further, the individual bit in error can be determined. The finding and correcting of the incorrect bit can be accomplished through changing the bits one at a time and observing when a bit combination is obtained that is a correct representation of one of the digits. When two errors occur simultaneously the resulting bit combination will be recognized as not corresponding to any digit, but the changing of one bit may produce a bit

186   Arithmetic Operations in Digital Computers

combination which corresponds to one of the digits, but not the desired digit. Therefore, the error-correcting code will fail with the occurrence of two errors in the representation of a given digit.

By using a code requiring four changes in the bits when changing from the representation of one digit to the representation of any other digit, "double-error-detecting" properties may be obtained. With a code such as this, two simultaneous errors will produce a bit combination which not only may be recognized as not corresponding to any digit, but also may not be changed to any digit-representing combination by the change of any one bit. Therefore, the code is capable of producing an indication that two errors have occurred in a given digit representation, and the ability to correct a single error is not lost. However, it is still not possible to correct two simultaneous errors, because the alteration of 2 bits can yield a bit combination corresponding to one of the digits but not necessarily the desired one. Also, the occurrence of three or more simultaneous errors may cause a failure in the error-detecting and error-correcting scheme.

"Double-error-correcting," "triple-error-detecting," and more powerful schemes may be devised through the use of codes requiring still more changes in the changing of the representations of the various digits, although the number of bits required for the code soon reaches an impracticable value. For the error-detecting, error-correcting, and double-error-detecting codes, a minimum of 5, 7, and 8 bits, respectively, is necessary.

An interesting property of error-detecting and error-correcting codes is that correcting power can be traded for increased detecting power. For example, an error-correcting code can be used as a double-error-detecting code; although, if it is used in this manner, the ability to correct single errors is lost. Similarly, a code requiring four changes in proceeding from one digit representation to another may be used as a triple-error-detecting code, but then the ability to correct single errors is lost. The properties of the codes as a function of the number of changes are summarized below, where a notation such as "1E Det" stands for single-error detection.

Changes	Property
1	No error-detecting or error-correcting properties
2	1E Det
3	1E Cor or 2E Det
4	2E Det with 1E Cor or 3E Det
5	2E Cor or 3E Det with 1E Cor or 4E Det

Although the concepts presented in this section are of interest in the understanding of the nature of error-detecting and error-correcting codes, these concepts have not been found to be of much value in the devising of useful codes. The concept of redundancy, which is discussed in the next section, appears to be a more useful tool for the development of practical codes for the detection and correction of errors.

Redundancy Checks. Among the more obvious ways of checking for errors in digit transmission is the transmission of each digit twice. If there is a discrepancy in the two transmissions, it may be concluded that an error has occurred. By transmitting the digit three times, it is possible not only to detect the error but also to correct it, because two of the three transmissions should be the same unless two or more errors have occurred, in which case the method fails. More powerful checks may be secured through additional transmissions and comparisons for each digit, but the increased complexity which would be required in the equipment causes the scheme to be unattractive.

The above method of checking involves the use of redundant information. Since the purpose of the redundant information is only to check and correct errors in the original informaton, it is possible to use less redundant information than is necessary for the complete duplication of the transmissions. For example, a coded decimal digit is represented by a set of signals indicating a certain configuration of 0's and 1's, and the configuration has elementary properties which will be changed in the presence of an error. Therefore, in order to check for an error it is sufficient to use one of these elementary properties for the redundant information. The number of 1's is one such property that may be used, but a simpler property and one that is well adapted to the binary nature of the signals which are usually employed is the fact that the number of 1's is either odd or even. Then, if an extra bit is transmitted along with the coded representation of the digit, the extra bit may be used to indicate whether the number of 1's is odd or even, and a discrepancy in the indication will signify that an error has occurred. This extra bit is redundant information because it may be derived directly from the coded digit.

In order to use redundancy bits for the correction as well as detection of errors, it is necessary to devise a system whereby discrepancies in one or more of the odd-even checks can be identified with individual bits in the code. One arrangement that may be used incorporates the checking of several digits into a single operation. Each digit is provided with a redundancy bit and also each "column" of bits in the several digits is provided with a redundancy bit. If any bit in the digit representing part of the code is in error, two of the checks will fail and the error may be located in Cartesian coordinate fashion. The decimal number, 69,073 in the 8,4,2,1 code in shown with its redundancy bits in Table 6-VI. Note

TABLE 6-VI. REDUNDANCY BITS FOR ERROR CORRECTION

$$
\begin{array}{c c c c c c}
 & 8 & 4 & 2 & 1 & R \\
\phantom{\text{Decimal Number}} \begin{array}{c} 6 \\ 9 \\ 0 \\ 7 \\ 3 \end{array} &
\begin{array}{c} 0 \\ 1 \\ 0 \\ 0 \\ 0 \end{array} &
\begin{array}{c} 1 \\ 0 \\ 0 \\ 1 \\ 0 \end{array} &
\begin{array}{c} 1 \\ 0 \\ 0 \\ 1 \\ 1 \end{array} &
\begin{array}{c} 0 \\ 1 \\ 0 \\ 1 \\ 1 \end{array} &
\begin{array}{c} 1 \\ 1 \\ 1 \\ 0 \\ 1 \end{array}
\end{array}
$$

Decimal Number { 6 9 0 7 3 }

R   0 1 0 0 0

that the redundancy bit is 1 whenever the number of 1's in the bits being checked is even. The opposite convention could have been used, although the digit, zero, would have no 1's in its representation which, as has already been mentioned, is sometimes undesirable. If only one check fails, it may be assumed that the check bit itself is in error unless more than one error has occurred. By including a check on the redundancy bits (the bit in the lower right-hand corner of Table 6-VI), the checking system becomes double-error detecting as well as single-error correcting. If it is assumed that the lower-right redundancy bit checks the bottom row (and not the right-hand column): (a) an error in one of the information bits will cause a failure in one row check bit and one column check bit; (b) an error in one of the row redundancy bits will cause the check in only that row to fail; (c) an error in one of the column redundancy bits will cause that column check and the bottom row check to fail; and (d) an error in the lower-right redundancy bit will cause a check failure only in the bottom row. If any other combination of checks fail, two errors are present. Note that the presence of three or more simultaneous errors will in some cases cause the system to break down.

By using three redundancy bits for each digit represented with a code of 4 bits, it is possible to develop a digit-by-digit error-correcting code. One variation of the method when applied to the 8,4,2,1 code is to use one redundancy bit (A) to check the 1's in the 4, 2, and 1-bits; a second redundancy bit (B) for the 8, 2, and 1-bits; and a third redundancy bit (C) for the 8, 4, and 1-bits. The pattern and the 8,4,2,1 code with its redundancy bits are shown in detail in Table 6-VII.

From Table 6-VII it may be observed that the location of any error may be determined by the combination of checks which fail. If, for example, checks B and C fail, the error must be in the 8-bit. If all three checks fail, the error is in the 1-bit, or, if only one check fails, the error is in the redundancy bit itself. The occurrence of two errors in the representation of a single digit will cause a failure in the system, although

TABLE 6-VII. THE 8,4,2,1 CODE WITH ERROR-CORRECTING REDUNDANCY BITS

8	4	2	1	A	B	C
A	A	A	A			
B		B	B		B	
C	C		C			C

	8	4	2	1	A	B	C
0	0	0	0	0	1	1	1
1	0	0	0	1	0	0	0
2	0	0	1	0	0	0	1
3	0	0	1	1	1	1	0
4	0	1	0	0	0	1	0
5	0	1	0	1	1	0	1
6	0	1	1	0	1	0	0
7	0	1	1	1	0	1	1
8	1	0	0	0	1	0	0
9	1	0	0	1	0	1	1

a fourth check bit (D) for indicating the 1's in all four of the original digit positions could be used to make the code double-error detecting. Note that the coded representation for each decimal digit differs from the representation of each of the other digits by at least 3 bits, which is in line with the discussion in the preceding section.

Four redundancy bits, A, B, C, and D may be used to generate an error-correcting code involving eleven information-carrying bits by following the pattern shown in Table 6-VIII.

TABLE 6-VIII. PATTERN FOR AN ERROR-CORRECTING CODE INVOLVING ELEVEN INFORMATION-CARRYING BITS

1024	512	256	128	64	32	16	8	4	2	1	A	B	C	D
	A	A	A	A			A	A	A	A				
B		B	B			B	B		B	B	B			
C	C		C			C	C	C		C			C	
D	D	D	D	D	D	D								D

Again, the bit in error can be ascertained by the combination of checks which fail. For example, if checks A, B, and D fail, the 256-bit is in error. In general, n redundancy bits may be used to form an error-correcting code involving $2^n - n - 1$ information-carrying bits.

In most instances, redundancy bits are useful only in the checking of the transmission of digits. Computations involving the digits usually must be checked by some other means, although there are a few schemes for calculating the new redundancy bits which are necessary after arithmetic operations have been performed on the digits. For digits which are the results of computations, the simple generation of the new redundancy bits according to the pattern in use affords no checks at all in the computations.

Many of the ideas which have been presented on the subject of error-detecting and error-correcting codes may be found in the text, *The Design of Switching Circuits*, by Keister, Ritchie and Washburn (D. Van Nostrand Co., Inc., New York, 1951).

Check Sums. Although it may be deemed impractical to incorporate a system that will detect multiple errors which occur in a random fashion, it is sometimes feasible and highly desirable to install circuits for detecting certain special types of multiple errors. Such a situation occurs in the transmission of digits in parallel where one of the transmission lines may fail in such a manner that signals are always or never present on this line. A common example of this type of error is in the sensing of punched cards, where a failure of a sensing brush will cause a consistent failure of signals to be transmitted.

A straightforward way of detecting consistent errors in one of several parallel transmission lines is through the use of a check sum. A check sum is generated by adding a series of numbers both before and after the transmission, and observing whether or not the sums are the same. With each of the numbers transmitted in parallel, a consistent error will cause the check sum to be too large when the defective line is picking up erroneous digits; but if the line is dropping desired digits, the check sum will be too small.

It should be observed that, for a complete check, it is necessary to transmit the check sum over a different path from the one used for the transmission of the numbers being checked; otherwise, some types of errors will not be detected. For example, in checking the transmission of the two binary numbers, 1001 and 1101, the check sum would be 10110. If the 1's in the 4-bit column were consistently dropped, the error would not be detected because the checking circuits would add 1001 and 1001 to obtain 10010 which would match the incorrectly transmitted check sum. It may be shown that a shift of the check sum one or more positions to the left (but not to the right) is sufficient to satisfy the requirements of a different path for the check sum. In other words, by shifting the check sum in the example to 101100, it is possible to detect all consistent errors in any one column.

An undesirable feature of the check sum error-detecting system is the fact that the check sum will, in general, have more digits than the numbers being transmitted because of the carries which may occur in the highest order when forming the sum. One way to avoid this difficulty is to add the carries in end-around fashion into the lowest order. It is then necessary to limit the length of the list of numbers which enter into the formation of a given check sum. In the case of 4-digit binary numbers, if a check sum is formed for more than 15 numbers being checked, there is a possibility of some errors escaping undetected when the end-around carry is used. When a shift to the left of one position is combined with end-around carry, the maximum is reduced to 7. In general, with these conditions the check sum may be formed on a maximum of $R^{n-1} - 1$ numbers, where R is the radix and n is the number of digits in the numbers being checked. For large n or R this limitation is not, of course, so severe.

Distinguishing Between Errors and the Absence of Information. When using an error-detecting code, a peculiar but severe problem sometimes arises in those cases where a set of information bits contains only one 1. For example, in the 8,4,2,1 code with a redundancy bit, the representation for 4 would be 01000 if the first 4 bits are the information bits and the last bit is the redundancy bit (to make the number of 1's odd). Now if this digit is transmitted from one point to another and an error occurs in the 4 bit with the result that all 5 of the bits are 0, the receiving instrument would not be capable of distinguishing whether a digit with an error was transmitted or whether no information at all was transmitted.

An outstanding instance where this problem is encountered is in the sensing of information recorded on magnetic tape. The location along the length of the tape where the information is recorded is not, in general, known exactly. If it is assumed that the 5 bits are recorded on five parallel tracks, the tape will pass under the sensing heads with the heads indicating that no information is recorded until at least one of the heads senses a 1. Then it is known that some information is being detected; but in the cases where there was only one 1 originally and it is lost through an error, the receiving instrument will not detect the error even though an error-detecting code is employed; instead, it will indicate that no information is being sensed.

There are two principal ways to get around this problem. One way is to send a separate signal from the transmitter to the receiver to signify when information is being transmitted. In most parts of a computer, these "alerting" signals are usually present, although, perhaps inconspicuously, in the form of various timing and control signals. When magnetic tape is the transmitter, the alerting signal may be recorded on a sixth track. The other way to insure that all digits with one error are sensed is to avoid those combinations which have only one 1. In those applications where all bit combinations are needed, this scheme cannot be used, but in the case where 4 bits are used for a decimal digit, there are sufficient combinations to spare. With the 8,4,2,1 code, the desired result may be accomplished without losing the useful binary properties of the code by inverting all 1's and 0's. Then 4, for example, would be 10111 where the redundancy bit creates an even number of 1's.

Chapter 7

COUNTING, BINARY AND DECIMAL

In a digital computer, counting is that process which records the number of pulse-type signals that occur in succession on a single line. In general, the pulses may be randomly distributed in time except that the physical properties of any counting device always set a minimum time separation between the pulses to which the device will respond properly. The counting device is said to be "fast" or "high speed" when this minimum time is relatively small. With some systems the pulses must appear at uniformly spaced intervals, but at any such given time a pulse may or may not be present with its presence determined in a random manner.

In almost all practical examples, the pulse-type signals are in themselves of a binary nature, although the system for counting them may employ any radix. When the binary number system is used, the counting device consists of a set of bistable storage elements, each of which transfers back and forth between its two stable states upon the reception of pulses. The pulses to be counted are applied to one of the bistable elements. Each time that this element changes from the state representing 1 to the state representing 0, a pulse is caused to be sent to the second element in the set. When the second element transfers to 0, a pulse is sent to the third element; and this process continues in a similar manner for all of the bistable elements in the set. With the decimal number system, elements having ten stable states are used; and each time a given element changes from the state representing 9 to the state representing 0, a pulse is sent to the next element. As was mentioned in connection with binary accumulators, the term, "counter," may be used to refer to any one of the multistable elements, or it may be used to refer to the counting device as a whole. In this chapter the term will be used only with the second meaning, and "digit counter" will be used to describe the individual multistable counting elements when confusion would otherwise result. These definitions apply to both the binary and decimal systems.

Some "computers" perform no function at all other than counting. Many practical examples of simple counting are to be found, and they vary from counters such as those which are used on a printing press to count the number of papers printed to the high-speed electronic counters used for counting nuclear particles. Also, counters may be found as components of more elaborate computers; in particular, counters are used to count and keep track of the "program steps" in a computation.

Binary Counting. An elementary arrangement for counting in the binary system is shown in Fig. 7-1. The input pulses to be counted

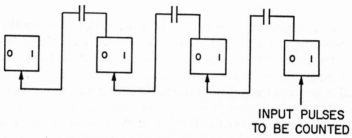

INPUT PULSES
TO BE COUNTED

FIG. 7-1. Binary counter, first variation.

are applied to the binary digit counter corresponding to the lowest order. Each time that this digit counter changes from a 1 to a 0 indication, a pulse-type signal is sent to the digit counter in the next higher order. The condenser in the signal line between the two digit counters signifies that the otherwise steady-state output signal is differentiated to yield the desired pulse-type signal when the digit counter changes to 0.

Although the counting speed for the counter arrangement shown in Fig. 7-1 is limited only by the speed of the lowest-order digit counter, the time required for the "carry" to progress through several orders may be objectionably long. For example, when the counter indicates 0111 (decimal 7) and one additional pulse to be counted is received, the digit counters change successively, one at a time, to the indication, 1000 (decimal 8). The time lag required for the counter to present an indication of the new total may be substantially eliminated through the use of the counting arrangement shown in Fig. 7-2. With this arrangement the input pulses are applied simultaneously to all digit counters through "and" switches. If, for any given digit counter, the digit counters of all lower orders are standing on 1's, steady-state signals will be applied to the remaining input lines of the "and" switch and allow the input pulse to pass. The delay devices are needed to prevent the application of a signal to an "and" switch when a digit counter changes from 0 to 1 before the input pulse has terminated. However, the delay devices do not necessarily cause a reduction in the maximum speed of the counter; and, in cases where the action of the digit counters is slow relative to the duration of the input pulses, the delay devices may not be required.

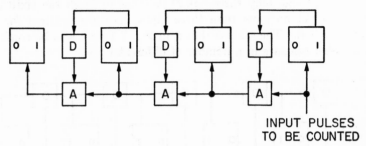

INPUT PULSES
TO BE COUNTED

Fig. 7-2. Binary counter, second variation.

The amount of switching required for the carry method in Fig. 7-2 becomes very great when a large number of orders are employed in the counter. A reduction in the amount of switching equipment may be achieved at a moderate cost in carry speed by the method shown in Fig. 7-3. In Fig. 7-3, the input pulse is sent on to the next higher order each time the corresponding counter is standing at 1. The input pulse,

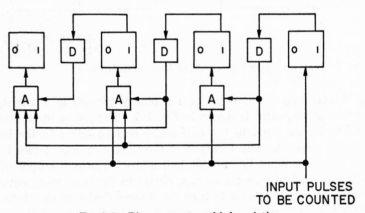

INPUT PULSES
TO BE COUNTED

Fig. 7-3. Binary counter, third variation.

therefore, has to pass through a series of "and" switches to reach any of the counters except the first one; but this process may, depending upon the nature of the various components in the counter, be much more rapid than the successive operations of the digit counters as in Fig. 7-1. The delay devices in Fig. 7-3 serve the same purpose as in Fig. 7-2.

Compromises between the schemes shown in Figs. 7-2 and 7-3 may be achieved, and one such compromise is shown in Fig. 7-4. The first three digit counters and the fourth to sixth, inclusive, digit counters handle the carries as in Fig. 7-2, but the carry is passed between the two groups of three as in Fig. 7-3. The result is that the input pulse has to pass through only three "and" switches to reach the sixth digit counter, and yet no more than three input lines are required for any one "and" switch. The scheme shown in Fig. 7-1 may also be combined with the other schemes in a number of different ways.

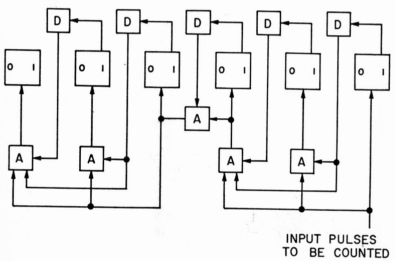

INPUT PULSES
TO BE COUNTED

FIG. 7-4. Binary counter compromising features shown in Figs. 7-2 and 7-3.

Half adders may be used to form a binary counter in a variety of ways. One arrangement is shown in Fig. 7-5. The pulses to be counted are applied to one input of the half adder corresponding to the lowest order in the counter. The 1-output of the binary storage device is applied to the other input line of this half adder. The sum output of the half adder is used to turn the storage device to the state representing 1, and the carry output is used to turn the storage device to the state representing 0 as well as to send a carry pulse to the next higher order. From the functional operation of a half adder, it can be seen that the storage device will alternate back and forth between its two stable states upon the reception of input pulses, and a carry pulse will be sent to the next higher order each time it changes to the state representing 0. The digit counters in the next higher order and succeeding orders operate in exactly the same way. The advantage of this arrangement lies in the fact that the individual binary storage devices have two separate input lines, which may allow more positive transfer action between the two stable states than when bistable devices with a single input line are used. Since the carry portion of each half adder is a simple "and" switch, carry propagation can be made reasonably rapid.

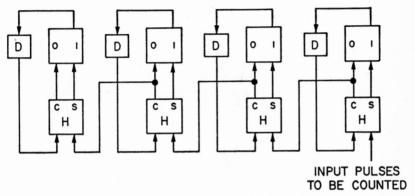

INPUT PULSES
TO BE COUNTED

FIG. 7-5. Binary counter employing half adders.

Another counter arrangement employing half adders is shown in Fig. 7-6. Each half adder in combination with a delay element is used as a dynamic binary storage device. The first pulse to be counted will cause a pulse to appear on the sum output of the lowest-order half adder, and this pulse will be returned through the delay element to the other input line of the half adder. The pulse will continue to circulate; that is,

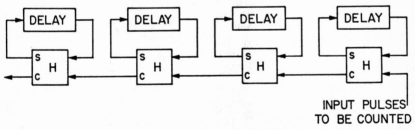

INPUT PULSES
TO BE COUNTED

FIG. 7-6. Binary counter with half adders and dynamic storage.

it will be stored. The second pulse to be counted must come at a time when the first stored pulse is entering the half adder, and when two pulses are applied simultaneously to the input lines of the half adder a pulse will appear on the carry output to be sent to the next higher order to start a pulse circulating there. No pulse will appear on the sum output, which will stop the circulation of a pulse in the lowest-order digit counter. The third pulse to be counted starts a circulating pulse in the lowest order again, and the counting process continues in a like manner for all succeeding pulses. Certain important details have been omitted from Fig. 7-6. In particular, means must be provided for amplifying, reshaping, and retiming the circulating pulses. A more difficult problem may arise from the slight delay which will occur to the input pulses as they pass through the half adders in succession because this delay will necessitate a phase difference in the circulation of the pulses in the various storage devices.

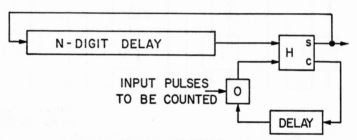

FIG. 7-7.   Binary counter with n-digit delay line for storage.

A third method of employing a half adder to form a counter is shown in Fig. 7-7. The first pulse to be counted may come at any time. The pulse will then circulate through the half adder and the n-digit delay line, where n is the number or orders in the counter. The second pulse must come at a time the first is emerging from the delay line; in fact, all succeeding pulses must come at times corresponding to the arrival of the lowest-order digit at the half adder. The carry which occurs when the second pulse is added to the first one is returned to the half adder after a 1-digit delay, and it then circulates through the loop as the digit corresponding to the next higher order. When, in counting, the addition of the carry creates a new carry, the new carry is returned with another 1-digit delay which, in effect, causes it to be entered in the next higher order in succession, as is desired in the counting procedure. The sum of the counted pulses appears on the output line in serial form each time the number in the loop completes its circulation.

Decimal Digit Counters Formed with Binary Elements. In Fig. 7-1, for example, four orders of a binary counter are shown, and the counter is capable of registering numbers of pulses from zero to fifteen. If more than sixteen pulses are applied, the counter will return to zero and repeat its operation, and an output signal may be obtained from the highest order upon application of the sixteenth pulse. The four-order binary counter could therefore be used as a digit counter of radix sixteen. To make a decimal digit counter with the four binary elements it is necessary to include means for nullifying six of the sixteen stable states, and there are several ways by which this may be accomplished. They will be discussed under the headings of feedback connections, pulse blocking, pulse advancing, and parallel connections.

Feedback Connections. One way to nullify effectually some of the stable states in a counter is to enter output pulses from the digit counter of one order to the input of a digit counter in a lower order. Means will have to be included to insure that only one pulse at a time will reach any given counter and that the time separation between the pulses will be sufficient to allow them to be counted, but this problem may be solved simply, in principle at least, by delay devices inserted in the feedback lines. Consider, for example, the counter arrangement shown in Fig. 7-8(a). A counter of $n = n_1 + n_2 + n_3$ orders is shown with a feedback connection around the n_2 orders. The delay device in the feedback line and the "or" function in the input line of the lowest order binary digit counter in the n_2 group have been omitted for simplicity. Also, it is assumed that each digit counter passes a signal to the next higher order when it changes from 1 to 0. The problem of determining how many input pulses are required to generate an output pulse may be solved by considering separately the three groups of digit counters. An output pulse from the n_1 group will be applied to the n_2 group for every 2^{n_1} input pulses. An output pulse from the n_2 group will be obtained after each 2^{n_2} input pulses to this group except that one additional pulse will be added to the group through the feedback connection each time an output pulse from the group is obtained. The feedback reduces the required number of input pulses to $2^{n_2} - 1$. The n_3 group functions in the same manner as the n_1 group; and, since the number, N, of input pulses per output pulse for the three groups together is the product of numbers for the individual groups,

$$N = 2^{n_3}(2^{n_2} - 1)2^{n_1} = 2^{n_1+n_2+n_3} - 2^{n_1+n_3}$$

Two feedback connections are shown in Fig. 7-8(b) and, for similar reasons,

$$N = 2^{n_3}(2^{n_2} - 1)(2^{n_1} - 1) = 2^{n_1+n_2+n_3} - 2^{n_1+n_3} - 2^{n_2+n_3} + 2^{n_3}$$

The feedback connection around the n_2 group is intended to be applied to the input of the n_2 group only, and not to the input of the n_1 group also, as might be implied from the simple diagram.

In Fig. 7-8(c), the feedback connection around the n_2 group reduces the count of that group to $2^{n_2} - 1$, and the feedback connection around all three groups reduces N by 1, so that

$$N = 2^{n_1}(2^{n_2} - 1)2^{n_3} - 1 = 2^{n_1+n_2+n_3} - 2^{n_1+n_3} - 1$$

$$N = 2^{n_1}(2^{n_2}-1)2^{n_3} = 2^{n_1+n_2+n_3} - 2^{n_1+n_3}$$

(a)

$$N = (2^{n_1}-1)(2^{n_2}-1)2^{n_3} = 2^{n_1+n_2+n_3} - 2^{n_1+n_3} - 2^{n_2+n_3} + 2^{n_3}$$

(b)

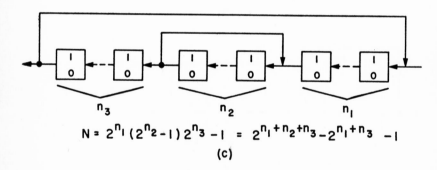

$$N = 2^{n_1}(2^{n_2}-1)2^{n_3} - 1 = 2^{n_1+n_2+n_3} - 2^{n_1+n_3} - 1$$

(c)

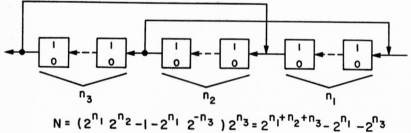

$$N = (2^{n_1}2^{n_2}-1-2^{n_1}2^{-n_3})2^{n_3} = 2^{n_1+n_2+n_3} - 2^{n_1} - 2^{n_3}$$

(d)

Fig. 7-8. Feedback arrangements.

Two interlocked feedback connections are shown in Fig. 7-8(d). The feedback connection around the n_1 and n_2 groups causes the count of that group to be $2^{n_1+n_2} - 1$; but, every 2^{n_3} times an output pulse is produced by these two groups, the feedback connection around the n_2 and n_3 groups effectually adds 2^{n_1} pulses to the first two groups.   Therefore,

$$N = \left(2^{n_1+n_2} - 1 - \frac{2^{n_1}}{2^{n_3}}\right) 2^{n_3} = 2^{n_1+n_2+n_3} - 2^{n_1} - 2^{n_3}$$

Note that setting $n_2 = 0$ in Fig. 7-8(d) does not produce the same counter arrangement as setting $n_3 = 0$ in Fig. 7-8(b).

The analysis of three or more feedback connections is more complex, but it may be accomplished through extensions of the procedures which were used for two.

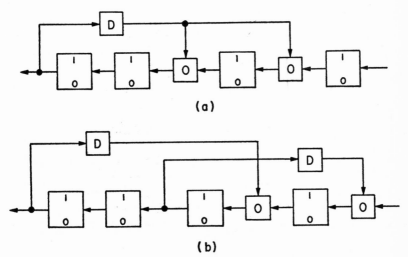

(a)

(b)

FIG. 7-9. Decimal counters employing feedback connections.

Fig. 7-9 shows in more detail two of the several ways by which feedback connections may be used to form a decimal digit counter.

Note that, for a given design for individual binary counters, the speed of the decimal counter arrangement in Fig. 7-9(a) is greater than for the arrangement shown in Fig. 7-9(b). The reason is that, in (a), the lowest-order binary counter receives only the incoming pulses to be counted and therefore its full speed capabilities may be utilized; whereas in (b), the lowest-order binary counter must accept two pulses in some steps of its operation. Since the other binary counters in either arrangement receive pulses less frequently, they are capable of recording two pulses at some steps in the operation of the decimal counter without

202 Arithmetic Operations in Digital Computers

being a limiting factor on speed. This same principle applies as well to the counters to be described in the next three sections.

Pulse Advancing. Instead of feeding back pulses from the high-order binary digit counters to the lower-order counters, the input pulses may be sent to counters other than the lowest-order counter in order to nullify some of the stable states. In general, the advancing of the input pulses around the lower-order counters must be done under control of higher-order counters by means of switching circuits. Three decimal counter arrangements employing this scheme are shown in Fig. 7-10.

In Fig. 7-10(a), each time the highest and lowest orders indicate a binary 1, steady-state signals are applied to two of the three input lines of the "and" switch. The next input pulse is then applied to the second and third orders as well as to the first order, which has the same effect as counting six additional pulses. The next stable state of the counter is with all four orders indicating binary 0's, and the counter then continues on in normal fashion with each decimal digit indicated in the 8,4,2,1 code.

The circuits may be made in a somewhat more straightforward manner if the arrangement shown in Fig. 7-10(b) is used. Here, the input pulse is advanced to higher orders on the next count after the equivalent of decimal 8 has been reached. No delay devices are needed because none of the binary digit counters will be receiving more than one pulse at this time; the first three counters will be changing from 0 to 1, and no carries will be propagated. However, with this arrangement, the stable state representing 9 does not conform to the 8,4,2,1 code. In Fig. 7-10(c), a scheme is shown for adding 3 twice during the counting of ten pulses, and the counter happens to operate with a 5,4,2,1 code.

In Fig. 7-10(d), the input pulse is applied to the second and third individual binary counters when the counter as a whole stands on 0100 (decimal 4). The effect of this arrangement is to cause the counter to operate in the 2,4,2,1 code, which is self-complementing. In order that carries may be propagated from one individual binary counter to the next, a signal must be maintained on the line marked "count." To complement the contents of the counter, the signal is temporarily removed from the "count" line, and a pulse is applied to the line marked "complement." This operation causes each individual binary counter to change to its opposite state without interruption from the carries. The obtaining of the 9's complement in this manner is sometimes useful in executing subtraction because input pulses are, in effect, subtracted as they are applied when the counter is storing the complement representation of the total.

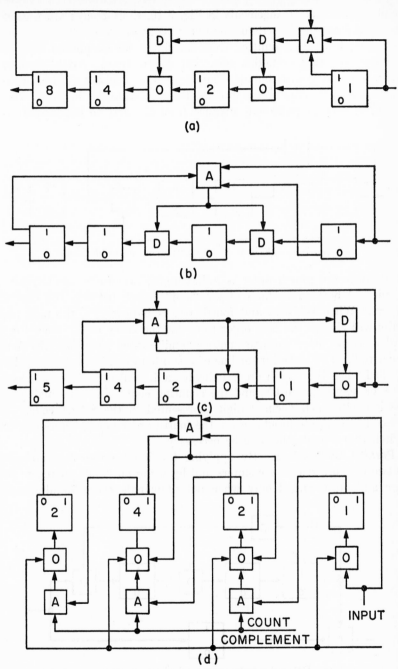

Fig. 7-10. Decimal counters employing pulse advancing.

In each of the arrangements in Fig. 7-10, short delays are needed in the lines from the outputs of the binary counters to the "and" switches, but these have been omitted from the figure for simplicity.

Pulse Blocking. Another idea that is sometimes used in forming a decimal counter with binary elements is the blocking of the entry of the pulses into some orders under certain conditions. In Fig. 7-11, for example, a carry pulse can advance from the first to the second order

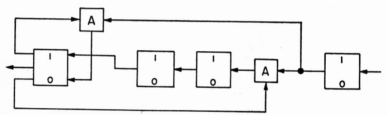

Fig. 7-11. Decimal counter employing pulse blocking.

only when the fourth order is indicating 0, because a signal must be applied to both input lines of the "and" switch between the first two orders. When the first and fourth orders indicate 1's, the next input pulse will change the first order to 0, but the carry to the second order will be transmitted through another "and" switch to change the fourth order to 0. The second input line of this other "and" switch has a signal applied when the fourth order indicates a 1. All orders in the decimal counter now indicate 0's, and the counting continues in normal binary fashion with each decimal digit represented in the 8,4,2,1 code. The use of two separate input lines in the fourth order merely saves one "or" switch that would otherwise be necessary.

Parallel Connections. By applying the input pulses to be counted to two or more separate counters and by using an "and" switch to provide an output signal only when output signals occur simultaneously

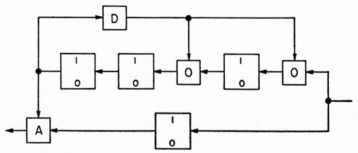

Fig. 7-12. Decimal counter composed of two counters in parallel.

from all counters, it is possible to devise a variety of new counter arrangements. The number of input pulses required to produce an output pulse will be equal to the least common multiple of the same numbers for the individual counters. In particular, a 5-counter and a 2-counter can be used to form a decimal counter, since 10 is the least common multiple of 5 and 2. Fig. 7-12 shows a decimal counter arrangement of this type. Feedback connections are used in the 5-counter, and this is operated in parallel with a single binary digit counter. The same number of binary counters, namely four, are required as in all previously described decimal counters.

Ring Counters. Digit counters of any radix may be formed by assembling a series of bistable devices in "ring" fashion. In the ring only one (usually) of the bistable devices is "on," or in the state representing 1, and the rest are "off," or in the state representing 0. The "on" state proceeds from one of these devices to the next in succession as the pulses to be counted are applied to the ring circuit as a whole. The ring may or may not be "closed"; that is, the "on" state may proceed automatically from the last device in the ring to the first, or it may be that separate means are provided for turning on the first bistable device in the ring. A ring circuit may be used to perform a function similar to that of an electromechanical commutator, and for this reason the term "commutator circuit" is sometimes used instead of "ring." In fact, it is probably true that commutator-type applications of ring circuits prevail because a ring is wasteful of bistable devices in simple counting applications. However, a decimal ring counter does offer the advantage that a static decimal indication of the digit stored may be obtained in a more straightforward manner than with counters employing less than ten bistable devices.

One form of ring counter is shown in Fig. 7-13(a), where the pulses are applied to the input line of each bistable device which causes the device to be turned off. Since only one was on (as indicated by an X under the 1), only one device changes state. A signal from the device which changed state from on to off is sent to the next one in the series and causes it to be turned on. A delay unit is shown in series with each line between two bistable devices. The delay allows the input pulse to die out, but, as in previously described applications of this nature, the operation of the bistable devices may be slow enough for the delay unit to be omitted.

By using "and" switches as shown in Fig. 7-13(b), the input pulses may be directed to the desired bistable devices. The 1-output from the device which is on is applied to the corresponding "and" switch, and the

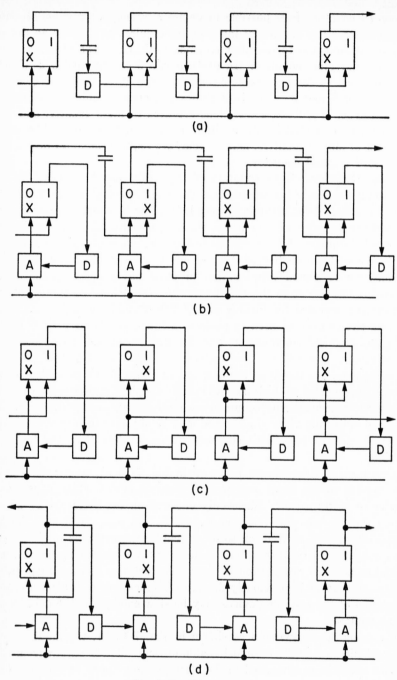

FIG. 7-13. Ring counters.

input pulse is thereby allowed to pass through this switch while its passage is blocked through all of the other "and" switches. The location of the delay units in this circuit allows a more rapid counting action than in Fig. 5-13(a), because no delay need be employed in the transmission of the pulses from one bistable device to the next.

A counting action which is even faster may be obtained by using the arrangement in Fig. 7-13(c). The input pulses not only turn off the bistable device which is on, but they are also used to turn on the next

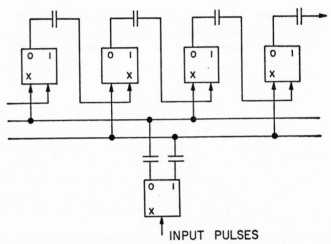

INPUT PULSES

Fig. 7-14. Ring counter with alternate input lines connected together.

device in the series. Therefore, the two devices operate simultaneously rather than one after the other.

In the arrangement shown in Fig. 7-13(d), the input pulses are used to turn the appropriate bistable devices on. At the time a given device is to go on, a signal from the 1-output of the preceding device in the ring is applied to the corresponding "and" switch to allow the input pulse to be applied. When a device is turned on it causes a signal to be transmitted to the preceding device to turn it off.

A type of ring circuit which employs a binary digit counter, but requires no delay units, even in principle, is shown in Fig. 7-14. The input pulses are applied to the binary digit counter, which generates pulses on its 0 and 1-output lines alternately. Each output pulse is applied to alternate stages in the ring. With the ring in the condition as indicated by the X's in the figure, the next input pulse will change the binary counter from 0 to 1, and the pulse on the 1-output line will turn "off" the bistable device which is second from the left. The pulse obtained from the 0-output of this bistable device is used to turn "on" the next one, and since no other pulse was applied to this next one, no delays need to be used.

A binary digit counter may be used in a similar fashion for any of the other ring circuits shown in Fig. 5-13, and in each case the delay units may be eliminated. As before, in (b) and (c), advantages in counting speed may be gained; and in (d) one device comes "on" before the preceding one goes "off." One disadvantage in the use of the binary counter is that closed rings must be composed of an even number of stages.

Decimal Counters. Any of the carry schemes shown in Figs. 7-1 to 7-4, inclusive, may be applied to the decimal system. In Fig. 7-1, decimal digit counters may be substituted directly for the binary digit counters, which are shown. It is necessary, of course, that the decimal digit counter yield a signal when it reaches 0. For the arrangements in Figs. 7-2 to 7-4 the counter must provide a static output signal when it is registering the digit, 9. The means that may be used for accomplishing this depend upon the nature of the digit counter which has been selected. With an 8,4,2,1 counter as in Fig. 7-10(a) or in 7-11, for example, the 1-output signals from the 8 and 1 binary digit counters may be combined in an "and" switch to indicate 9. It is sometimes possible to make the arrangement in Fig. 7-1 a bit faster in its operation by using a "leaving 9" signal instead of an "arriving or 0" signal to transmit the carry.

Counter Components Having More than Two Stable States. Although the analysis of counting action which has been presented fits many types of components very well, there are at the same time many other types of counting components that are not covered by the analysis, except by rather farfetched extensions. Among the latter are digit counters which collect charge in a condenser and reset to an initial value when a certain potential across the condenser plates is reached; gaseous counter tubes that support glow discharges which move from electrode to electrode upon reception of pulses; and many forms of the ordinary mechanical counter wheel. In general, the analysis covers only those schemes involving essentially binary components. No functional analysis has been worked out for components having more than two stable states; each such component requires its own description.

Chapter 8

DECIMAL ADDITION AND SUBTRACTION

As in the case of addition and subtraction with the binary system of numbers, decimal addition and subtraction may be accomplished in computing machinery through the use of either of two different types of devices. One type involves adders (subtracters for subtraction), where signals representing the digits to be added are applied to appropriate input lines in steady-state fashion, and, after transients have died out, signals representing the sum appear on the output lines. The other type employs counters, which are devices that change from one stable state to the next upon the reception of pulse-type signals. Either type may be used in either parallel or serial systems. Because there are so many ways by which individual decimal digits may be represented, the number of different ways by which addition and subtraction may be performed is tremendous, and no attempt will be made to describe them all. On the other hand, there are relatively few new ideas or principles which can be applied to the decimal system and which were not also applicable to the binary system.

Decimal Adders. A decimal adder requires a minimum of nine input lines and five output lines, since a minimum of 4 bits, and therefore four lines, are required in the representation of a decimal digit when signals of a binary nature are employed. Fig. 8-1 shows the assignment of the input and output lines of a decimal adder. The two digits to be added are X and Y, and each is applied through the use of four separate lines as indicated by the subscripts a, b, c, and d. The ninth input line, C, is the carry from the next lower order in the addition process. The sum digit, S, appears on the four output lines indicated by S with subscripts, and the carry, if any, to the next higher order appears on the output line marked carry. Note that in addition the carry is never greater than 1, regardless of the radix being used, and therefore a single line is sufficient for its transmission. If the code used for the decimal digits contains more than 4 bits, the number of input and ouput lines on the adder must be increased accordingly. Further, there is no inherent reason why the same code must be used throughout; that is, one code may be used for X, another for Y, and the code for S may be different from either of the first two. Even with a given set of codes for X, Y, and S, there is a great variety in the functional arrangements which may be used to form an adder.

Adder for the 8,4,2,1 Code. Among the more straightforward codes from the standpoint of adder design is the 8,4,2,1 code, because, with this code, the simple binary addition methods may be used to a large degree.

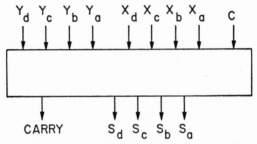

FIG. 8-1. Decimal adder.

However, two problems do arise which were not encountered in the pure binary system. One problem is in the generation of the decimal carry. A carry signal should be sent to the next higher order when the sum is equal to or greater than ten, but an indication of ten or greater cannot be obtained solely by a carry from the 8-order. A decimal carry is also desired when 1's are present simultaneously in the 8 and 2-orders or in the 8 and 4-orders of the sum. The other problem is that a carry has the effect of carrying sixteen instead of just ten when a carry from the 8-order is obtained and the sum must be corrected by adding six. For example, the sum of eight and nine (seven with a carry) is obtained in the following manner.

$$
\begin{array}{lll}
 & 1000 & \text{Eight} \\
 & 1001 & \text{Nine} \\
\hline
\text{Carry} \quad (1) & 0001 & \\
 & 11 & \\
\hline
 & 0111 & \text{Seven} \\
\end{array}
$$

If the sum is from 10 to 15, inclusive, the carry is detected by the other means, and it is necessary to subtract 10 from the indicated sum.

The subtraction of 10 may be performed by the addition of 6 and the subtraction of 16, with the subtraction of 16 accomplished by ignoring the carry which now occurs in the 8-order. An example is in the addition of 5 and 7 to produce a sum of 2 with a carry.

$$
\begin{array}{ll}
0101 & \text{Five} \\
0111 & \text{Seven}
\end{array}
$$

Carry, detected by presence of 1's in 8 and 4-orders $\Big\} \to (1)$

$$
\begin{array}{l}
1100 \\
\underline{11}
\end{array}
$$

Ignore $\to (1)$ 0010 Two

A functional arrangement for an adder operating in this way with the 8,4,2,1 code is shown in Fig. 8-2. The half and full adders may be

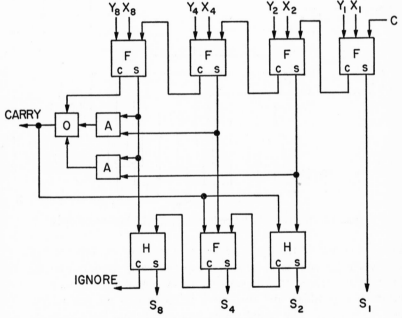

Fig. 8-2. Adder for 8,4,2,1 code.

exactly the same as described in the chapter on binary addition and subtraction. The signal representing the decimal carry, when it occurs, is added into the 2 and 4-orders (as shown in the bottom row of half and full adders) to effect the addition of 6.

If several decimal adders of the type shown in Fig. 8-2 are used to add decimal numbers in parallel fashion, the speed of carry propagation

212   Arithmetic Operations in Digital Computers

becomes of interest as it did in the case of parallel binary addition. When the sum of two decimal digits is 9 and a carry is received from the next lower order, the sum should be changed to 0 and a carry should be sent on to the next higher order. In Fig. 8-2 when the sum is 9, signals appear on the sum output lines of the full adder which adds X_8 and Y_8 and the full adder which adds X_1 and Y_1. No signal will appear on

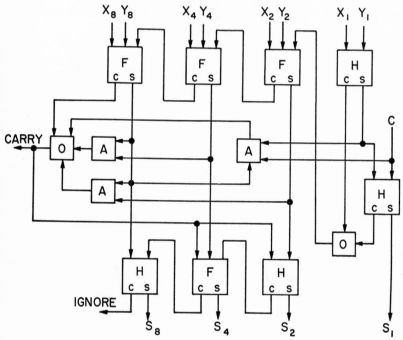

FIG. 8-3. Adder for 8,4,2,1 code, equipped with high-speed carry.

the carry output of the latter adder because X_1 or Y_1, but not both, will be 1 when the sum is 9. Then, when the carry signal from the next lower order arrives, it will cause a carry signal to be present on the output of this adder, and this carry is applied to the full adder which adds X_2 and Y_2. The signal which now appears on the sum output line from this adder is sent to an "and" switch, the other input of which is the sum output from the 8-order. The signal will now pass through the "or" switch and become the decimal carry to be sent to the next higher decimal order.

The two full adders through which the decimal carry must be sent when the sum is 9 may be by-passed by using a functional arrangement for a decimal adder as shown in Fig. 8-3. The full adder for adding

X_1 and Y_1 is broken up into two half adders and an "or" switch, following the procedure described in Chapter 4 on binary addition and subtraction. A third "and" switch is provided, and when the sum of the two decimal digits is 9, two of the three input lines to this "and" switch will receive signals from the half adder which adds X_1 and Y_1 and from the sum output line of the 8-order. When a carry signal from the next lower order arrives, it supplies the third input signal to the "and" switch and the decimal carry is thereby propagated through the decimal order by passage through only one "and" switch and one "or" switch.

The several half adders, full adders, "and" switches, and "or" switches could be combined into a single decimal adder unit wherein the individual components lose their identity in the same way that the two half adders and an "or" switch can lose their identity when combined into a full adder. The variety of ways by which a decimal adder may be assembled with "and" switches, "or" switches, and inverters is tremendous. Most of the ways offer no particular advantages; the functional arrangements shown in Fig. 8-2 and 8-3 are, at least, straightforward and relatively easy to understand. However, it is possible to reduce the required number of components somewhat.

Reducing the Number of Components in the Decimal Adder. As a general rule, when a circuit is designed to accept all possible combinations of input signals where in actuality certain combinations will never occur, it is likely that more components than necessary have been used. The discovery that this situation exists in a given circuit does not necessarily give any indication of how to go about eliminating the unnecessary components or to find a rearrangement requiring less components. These steps still depend upon the designers ingenuity. In the adder of Fig. 8-2, clues that the number of components may be reduced appear in at least two places. For one thing, when the correction is added, it is always either 0 or 6 even though the bottom row of half and full adders is capable of accepting any one of the values 0, 2, 4, or 6. Also, the X and Y inputs are never greater than 9, whereas the top row of full adders would function properly with X and Y values up to the full limit of 15. After discovering these clues, the problem is to find, if possible, an improved circuit configuration.

One way to go about the task of actually achieving a component reduction is to abandon the concept of correction by the addition of 0 or 6 and instead to examine the desired output in relation to the uncorrected output. The uncorrected output, U, may have any value from 0 through 15; in some cases it will remain unchanged and in other cases it will be altered as illustrated below:

$$U_8 \quad U_4 \quad U_2 \quad U_1$$

0	0	0	0	→ 0 1 1 0	
0	0	0	1	→ 0 1 1 1	If $C_a = 1$
0	0	1	0	→ 1 0 0 0	(If $C_8 = 1$)
0	0	1	1	→ 1 0 0 1	
0	1	0	0		
0	1	0	1		
0	1	1	0		
0	1	1	1		No correction required
1	0	0	0		
1	0	0	1		
1	0	1	0	→ 0 0 0 0	
1	0	1	1	→ 0 0 0 1	
1	1	0	0	→ 0 0 1 0	Always
1	1	0	1	→ 0 0 1 1	$(C_a = 1)$
1	1	1	0	→ 0 1 0 0	
1	1	1	1	→ 0 1 0 1	

If the uncorrected output is 0000, a correction may or may not be desired, depending upon the input signals which caused this particular output. When 0000 is the result of adding two decimal zeros, the uncorrected sum should remain unchanged; but when it is the result of adding 7 and 9, for example, the true sum is 6 with a decimal carry (C_a) and a correction is required. Similar remarks hold for uncorrected sums of 1, 2, or 3. In other words, the correction should be made if $C_a = 1$. Note also that when $C_a = 1$ in these cases, $C_8 = 1$, where C_8 is the carry from the binary adder which adds the 8 bits.

When the uncorrected sum is 4 through 9, no correction will be required regardless of the combination of input digits which produced this sum. If the uncorrected sum is 10 through 15, a correction will always be required, as indicated.

From an examination of the desired output signals in terms of the uncorrected output, U, it may be observed that the desired sum, S, may be expressed by the following Boolean algebra equations:

$$S_1 = U_1$$

$$S_2 = U_2\overline{C}_a + \overline{U}_2C_a$$

$$S_4 = U_4\overline{C}_a + U_2U_4 + \overline{U}_2C_8$$

$$S_8 = U_8\overline{C}_a + U_2C_8$$

The derivations of the expressions for S_1 and S_2 are reasonably obvious, but the expressions for S_4 and S_8 deserve a bit of explanation. For S_4, the term $U_4\bar{C}_a$ equals 1 (Boolean) in those cases where the decimal sum is 4 through 7 without a carry.   The term U_2U_4 equals 1 where the un-

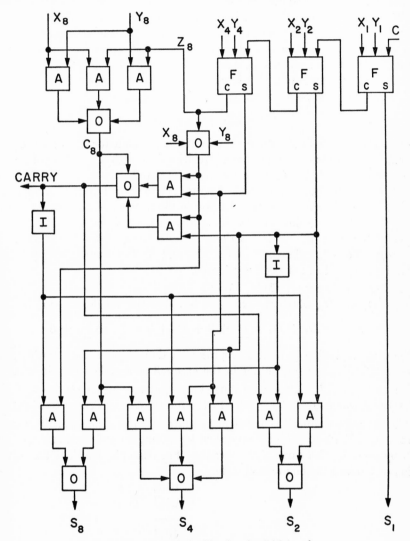

Fig. 8-4.   Simplified adder for the 8,4,2,1 code.

corrected sum is 14 or 15 and the desired sum is 4 or 5, respectively, and $\bar{U}_2C_8$ equals 1 when the desired sum is 6 or 7 as a result of an uncorrected sum of 0 or 1, respectively, when a decimal carry occurred.   These latter two terms have no particular arithmetic significance; they just happen to yield the correct result. Similarly, for S_8, the term, $U_8\overline{C}_a$ equals 1 when the uncorrected sum is 8 or 9 without a carry, and $U_2C_8 = 1$ when a carry occurs and the desired sum is 8 or 9.

Because of the fact that the input signals never represent digits greater than 9, it follows that there will never be three simultaneous input signals to the 8-bit binary adder; that is, $X_8Y_8Z_8 = 0$ in every case, and provision for this term need not be made in designing the decimal adder.

At least one more reduction in components can be achieved. Normally, U_8 would be generated according to the expression,

$$U_8 = (X_8 + Y_8 + Z_8)\overline{C}_8$$

where C_8 is as defined above; but in the expression for S_8, where U_8 is used, it is combined in an "and" relationship with $\overline{C}_a$. Since $C_a = 1$ whenever $C_8 = 1$, the $\overline{C}_8$ term may be eliminated.

The resulting functional block diagram is shown in Fig. 8-4. It is conceivable that an even further reduction in the number of components may be achieved by viewing the decimal adder as a whole instead of a collection of binary half and full adders, because some of the clues are still present. For example, the fact that X_8 and X_2 inputs are never present simultaneously has not been considered.

Adder for Excess-3 Code. When using binary adders to add two digits, D_1 and D_2, which are expressed in the excess-3 code, the sum is

$$\text{Sum} = D_1 + D_2 = \underline{D}_1 + 3 + \underline{D}_2 + 3 = \underline{D}_1 + \underline{D}_2 + 6$$

where an underline is used to represent a digit expressed in the 8,4,2,1 code. Clearly, the sum is not in the excess-3 code unless certain corrections are applied. Two cases must be considered: when $\underline{D}_1 + \underline{D}_2 < 10$ (ten) and when $\underline{D}_1 + \underline{D}_2 \geq 10$. In the former case, no carry to a higher order is required, and it is sufficient to subtract 3 from the sum. The subtraction of the 3 may be accomplished by adding 13 and then subtracting 16 by ignoring the carry which occurs. For example, consider the addition of 1 plus 4 in the excess-3 code.

	0100	One
	0111	Four
	————	
	1011	
	1101	
Ignore carry	(1) 1000	Five

When the decimal sum is greater than 10, a decimal carry should be sent to the next higher order. The decimal carry may be sensed conveniently by sensing the carry in the "8's order," because the sum will, in this case, be greater than 15. The decimal carry has the effect of carrying 16, which is 6 too much; therefore, in this case 6 must be added. But it is still necessary to restore the sum to excess-3 code by subtracting 3, so that the net correction should be the addition of 3.

Of course, a carry from the next lower order may be added to the two digits, D_1 and D_2, but this may be done without affecting the nature of the corrections which must be applied.

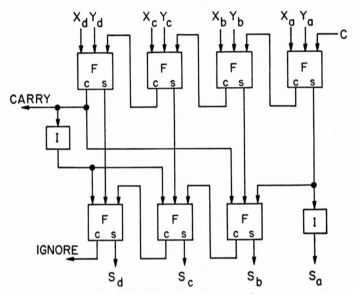

FIG. 8-5. Adder for excess-3 code.

A functional block diagram of a decimal adder for the excess-3 code is shown in Fig. 8-5. Regardless of whether the additive correction is 3 or 13, a 1 will be added into the "1's order." A simple inverter may be used to perform the correction in this order, and the uncorrected sum bit may be used as the carry from this order. The decimal carry may be used for the additive correction bit in the "2's order," and the inverse of the decimal carry may be used for the additive correction bits in the "8's and 4's orders" to effect the addition of 3 or 13 as is required. A total of two inverters and seven full adders are required, except that the carry from full adder which forms the correction in the "8's order" is not used.

Decimal carry propagation is relatively slow in the excess-3 adder because the carry must pass through all four binary orders when the decimal sum is 9. However, it may be made faster by resolving each of the four full adders into two half adders and an "or" switch. The corresponding bits in each binary order are added in one half adder, and the carry from the next lower binary order is added in the second half adder. A five-input "and" switch is then used to sense signals from the sum output lines of the first half adder in each order and the carry from the next lower decimal order. The output of this "and" switch is then combined by means of an "or" switch with the regular decimal carry output line. With this arrangement, when the decimal sum is 9 and a carry is received from the next lower order, it will be transmitted on to the next higher order through only one "and" switch and one "or" switch. The resolving of each full adder into two half adders and an "or" switch is desirable, if not necessary, because the sum output signals of the full adders change during the addition of the carry to a sum of 9.

Adder for 5,4,2,1 Code. The 5,4,2,1 code is another code which is readily adaptable to decimal addition through the use of binary tech-

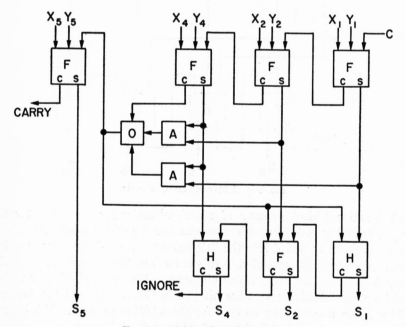

Fig. 8-6. Adder for 5,4,2,1 code.

niques. From the listing of the 5,4,2,1 code in the chapter on decimal codes, it may be observed readily that the 4, 2, and 1-bits are used in the standard binary fashion except that decimal equivalents of 5, 6, and 7 are missing. In the adder, a carry to the "5's order" may be detected either by a carry from the "4's order" or by the simultaneous existence of 1's in the "4's and 2's orders" or the "4's and 1's orders." When such a carry is detected, 3 must be added in some cases and 5 must be subtracted in other cases. The subtraction of the 5 may be accomplished by adding 3 and subtracting 8. The functional arrangement of an adder operating with the 5,4,2,1 code is shown in Fig. 8-6. Notice that it is substantially the same as the 8,4,2,1 decimal adder shown in Fig. 8-2, except that the "adding by 5's" is done in the lowest three orders instead of the highest three orders of binary adders which make up the decimal adder.

Decimal carry propagation may be made faster by sensing by means of an "and" switch signals from the sum output lines of the binary adders in the "4's and 5's orders" and the carry from the next lower decimal order. The output of this "and" switch is then combined by an "or" switch with the carry output from the "5's order." Actually, the full adder in the "5's order" should be resolved into two half adders and an "or" switch, and the sum output from the half adder which adds the two 5-bits should be used, because the sum output of the full adder changes when adding a carry to a sum of 9.

Decimal Adders Employing Miscellaneous Codes. Decimal codes which are not based on the binary number system require a quite different approach in adder design. It is usually necessary to consider the decimal addition table, which is given in Table 8-I.

TABLE 8-I. DECIMAL ADDITION TABLE

Addend Digit

```
            | 0 1 2 3 4 5 6 7 8 9
          --+---------------------
          0 | 0 1 2 3 4 5 6 7 8 9
          1 | 1 2 3 4 5 6 7 8 9|0    Carry
          2 | 2 3 4 5 6 7 8 9|0 1
          3 | 3 4 5 6 7 8 9|0 1 2
 Augend   4 | 4 5 6 7 8 9|0 1 2 3
 Digit    5 | 5 6 7 8 9|0 1 2 3 4
          6 | 6 7 8 9|0 1 2 3 4 5
          7 | 7 8 9|0 1 2 3 4 5 6
          8 | 8 9|0 1 2 3 4 5 6 7
          9 | 9|0 1 2 3 4 5 6 7 8
            |Carry
```

If, for example, a given bit in the code which is chosen is 1 for decimal digits 2, 4, and 9, switching circuits must be designed to detect all pairs of addend and augend digits which yield a sum of 2, 4, or 9, and there are thirty such pairs. Similar switching circuits must be assembled for all of the other bits in the code. Although the design of the switching circuits is straightforward, a large number of switching components are required, and the resulting adder would probably be impractical for most applications. It is usually possible to obtain a reduction in the required number of components by clever rearrangements of the "straightforward" switching functions; however, it is, in general, extremely difficult to find an arrangement which competes well with binary addition techniques when these can be used.

The switching circuits for handling the carry may also require a large number of components when the adder design is built around the decimal addition table. When a carry from the next lower order is received, the sum digit should, of course, be increased by 1. With some codes and types of components this function may be relatively simple, but in other cases it can be quite complex. As indicated in the table, there are forty-five pairs of input digits for which a carry to the next higher is required. When a carry from the next lower order is received, the pairs which otherwise produce a sum of 9 should be included. As with the development of the sum, the development of the carry can be straightforward, but it also may be complex especially when compared with binary techniques.

Redundancy Bits for Checking Addition. In Chapter 6 on decimal codes, the use of redundancy bits was described for checking the transmission of decimal digits. When two decimal digits are added, it would be advantageous if the same redundancy bits could be used to check for errors in the addition process. For this purpose it is necessary to find a relationship between the redundancy bit of the sum and the redundancy bits of the addend and augend digits. Since the sum of the 1's in the sum digit is not equal to the sum of the 1's in the addend and augend digits, the nature of the addition process must be considered in finding the relationship between the redundancy bits. Actually, of course, in determining the redundancy bit it is not necessary to know the sum of the 1's in a digit, but it is sufficient to know only whether the sum of the 1's is odd or even. The redundancy bit is (usually) 0 when the sum of the 1's is odd, and 1 when the sum of the 1's is even.

The use of redundancy bits for checking addition will be described for the 8,4,2,1 code with the addition performed as shown in Fig. 8-2. With binary addition, a sum bit is 0 if the corresponding bits of the addend and augend are both 0 or both 1. For this reason, the number of bits in the sum digit would be odd or even, depending upon whether the number of bits in the addend and augend digits, taken together, is odd or even, except that the binary carries disrupt this simple relationship. For each binary order into which a carry is added, the rule for the sum bit is reversed; that is, the sum bit then becomes 1 when corresponding bits of the addend and augend are both 0 or both 1. Therefore, to determine the redundancy bit for the sum decimal digit it is necessary to examine the carries in the addition process as well as the redundancy bits of the addend and augend. As an example, consider the addition of 6 plus 2 with a carry from the next lower decimal order.

Carries	(1)(1) 1	
Augend	0 1 1 0	1
Addend	0 0 1 0	0 Redundancy
	————	– bits
Sum	1 0 0 1	1

From the redundancy bits, it may be determined that the total number of 1's in the augend and addend is odd. Therefore, there would be an odd number of 1's in the sum if no carries had occurred in the addition. But in this example there was an odd number (three) of carries so that the odd-even status of the 1's in the sum was altered an odd number of times. The net result is that there is an even number of 1's in the sum and its redundancy should therefore be 1.

In those instances where the sum is ten or more and a correction of six is added, the carries which occur during the addition of six should be counted in the same manner.

Counting pulses which occur serially in time is no problem, but it is not obvious how signals which appear in parallel may be counted. One way is through the use of circuits such as those used in forming the sum in either half adders or full adders. Note that with either a half adder or a full adder, the sum bit is 1 if there is an odd number of signals present on the input lines. A half adder is therefore capable of "counting" two signals, and a full adder is capable of "counting" three. If more than three signals are to be "counted," the output of the adder may be used as one of the input signals of another adder. Fig. 8-7(a) shows how a half adder and a full adder may be used to determine whether there is an odd or even number of signals present on four input lines. With an inverter, as shown, this arrangement may be used to generate the redundancy bit of a 4-bit decimal digit.

Another functional arrangement for "parallel counting" is shown in Fig. 8-7(b). Actually, it is only a series of half adders, but the components are arranged in the figure to make their functions more easily understood. With this arrangement, the 8-bit is used as the redundancy bit, but it is inverted or not, according to whether the other bits are 1's or 0's. For example, if the 4-bit is a 0, the 8-bit passes through an "and" and an "or" switch without change. But if the 4-bit is a 1, the 8-bit becomes inverted because its path is then through an inverter. The 8-bit is subject to a second inversion in a similar manner under

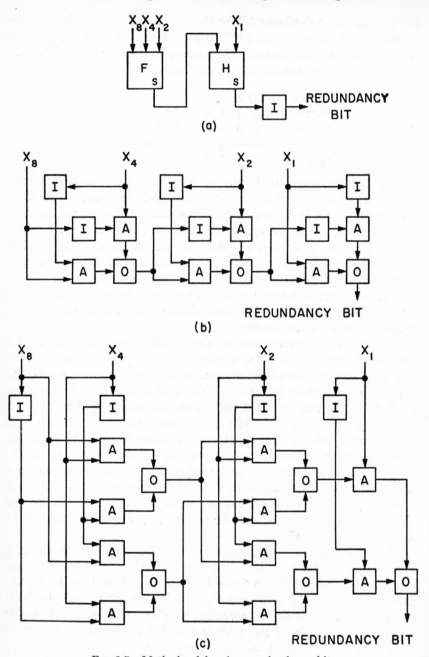

FIG. 8-7. Methods of forming a redundancy bit.

control of the 2-bit. A third inversion, exactly the same as the first two, could be used for the 1-bit, but the redundancy bit so obtained would be 1 when number of 1's in the digit is odd, whereas it is desired (usually) to use the opposite convention. The redundancy bit could be passed through an extra inverter, but the inverter may be eliminated by using the connections as shown in Fig. 8-7(b). The 1-bit causes an inversion if it is 0, but not if it is 1. For purposes of uniformity, the same connections could have been used for the inversion by the 4 and 2-bits.

A somewhat different method for generating the redundancy bit is shown in Fig. 8-7(c). With this arrangement both the 8-bit and its inverse are transmitted through the switching circuits. The 4-bit is used to reverse the lines on which the signals appear. If the 4-bit is 0, the signals pass through the bottom set of "and" switches and are not altered, but if the 4-bit is 1, the signals pass through the top set of "and" switches and are then transmitted on to the next stage on the opposite lines because of the reversed connections to the "or" switches. Similarly, the 2-bit reverses or does not reverse the lines, according to whether it is a 1 or 0, respectively. The 1-bit is used to select one or the other of the lines according to whether this bit is 0 or 1. With the connections shown, the signal appearing on the output line is then the desired redundancy bit. This functional arrangement is similar to the switching circuit which is commonly used to control an ordinary electric light or other electrical device by means of switches at several different locations. Regardless of whether the light is on or off, its status may be changed simply by throwing the switch at any of the locations. Each switch reverses the connections on a pair of wires, with the result that the circuit is closed when an odd number of switches have been changed from their initial "off" setting.

The same type of functional arrangements may be used for "computing" the redundancy bit as were used for forming it from the decimal digit itself. Instead of "counting" the 1's in the sum digit, the redundancy bits of the augend and addend and the carries are "counted." To check the addition, the redundancy bit should be obtained from both sources and compared. The comparison may be performed by means of a half adder, because the sum output of a half adder is 0 when neither or both of the input signals are 1, such as would be the case when the redundancy bits obtained from the two sources are the same. An output of 1 from the half adder would indicate that the bits as obtained from the two sources were not the same and, therefore, that an error had occurred.

However, there are further complications to the problem of checking addition by means of redundancy bits. For one thing, the carries used in computing the redundancy bit should be generated separately from the carries used in computing the sum. Otherwise, an error in one of the carries can cause an error in both the sum and the computed redundancy bit, with the result that the final comparison of redundancy bits may fail to detect the error. The duplication of the carry circuits including the carries which may occur in the adding of the corrective 6 in the 8,4,2,1 code would require that almost the entire adder be

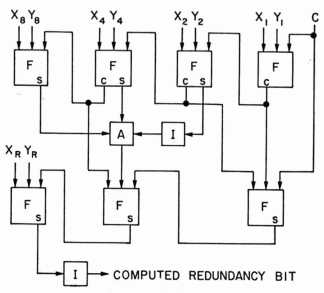

Fɪɢ. 8-8. Method of computing redundancy bit of sum (8,4,2,1 code).

duplicated. However, an examination of all possible cases reveals that the corrective 6 will cause an alteration of the redundancy bit only when added to 12 or 13 (1100 or 1101). Since the corrective 6 will never be added to any of the digits, 4 through 9, the presence of 1's in the 8 and 4-bits and a 0 in the 2-bit of the sum may be used to invert the redundancy bit. In other words, a signal representing the presence of a 12 or 13 is "counted" along with the original redundancy bits and the carries. The resulting functional arrangement for computing the redundancy bit with separate circuits for generating the carries is shown in Fig. 8-8.

Even when the carries are generated separately, some types of errors can escape undetected. As an example, assume that 1 is being added to 3, and there is a failure in the carry.

$$(1)(1)$$

	0 0 1 1		0 0 1 1	Carry
Correct	0 0 0 1		0 0 0 1	fails
	0 1 0 0		0 0 1 0	

Since, in this case, a carry in the 2's order causes a carry in the 4's order, the failure of the carry will reduce the number of carries from two to none. The computed redundancy bit will be the same for the incorrect sum as for the correct sum, and also the number of 1's is the same for the incorrect and correct sums. Therefore, the comparison of the computed redundancy bit with the redundancy bit obtained from the sum digit will fail to detect the error.

Although it is possible to make the checking circuits elaborate enough to detect errors from all sources in the addition process, the number of components necessary to do so is relatively large. If complete checking is required, duplication of the entire adder with comparison of the sums, bit by bit, is probably as attractive as computing the redundancy bit.

Checking Addition Through the Use of an Error-detecting Code. When an error-detecting code is used, the adder itself may provide a means for checking the addition if it is designed properly. As an example, a functional arrangement for an adder employing the biquinary code will be described.

The biquinary code was described briefly in Chapter 6 on decimal codes. As was mentioned there, the code is composed of two parts—the binary part and the quinary part. The two bits in the binary part signify whether the decimal digit is from 0 to 4 or whether it is from 5 to 9, and the bits may be considered as having the weights of 5 and 0. The 5 bits in the quinary part have the weights of 4, 3, 2, 1 and 0. When adding two decimal digits, the binary and quinary parts of the digit codes may be added separately, except that an "internal carry" may occur from the quinary part to the binary part. Mathematically, the addition process is quite simple. The quinary parts of the augend and addend can yield a sum which may be from 0 through 8. When the carry from the next lower decimal order is added, the range may be extended to 9. For sums of 5 through 9, the quinary part is reduced by 5 and an internal carry is sent to the binary part. Therefore, in the binary part, "5's" may be received from three different sources, the binary parts of the augend and addend and the carry from the quinary part. The binary part of the sum and the carry to the next higher decimal order may be generated

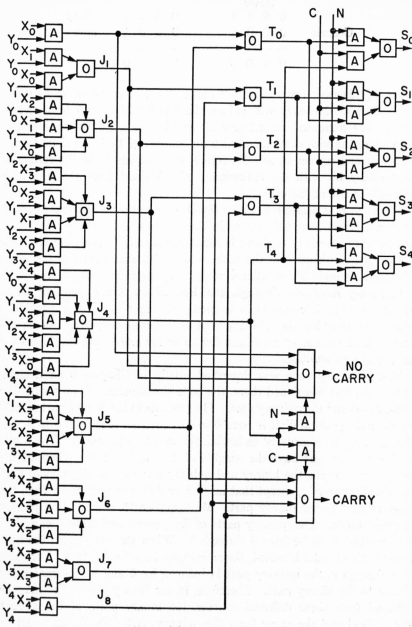

FIG. 8-9.   Error-detecting adder for quinary part of biquinary code.

from the three "5's" in the binary part in the same manner that the sum and carry are generated in ordinary binary addition, which has already been discussed.

Fig. 8-9 shows a functional block diagram for the addition of the quinary part in the biquinary code. The quinary bits of the two decimal digits are X_0 through X_4 and Y_0 through Y_4. Two lines are used for the carry from the next lower decimal order. A signal is obtained on one line, marked C, when a carry is present, and a signal is obtained on the other line, marked N, when no carry is received. To perform addition, the quinary bits of X and Y are applied to a set of "or" and "and" switches, as shown, to form an intermediate sum, J, which may have any value from 0 through 8. A signal is present on the J_1 line, for example, in the case where X is 1 and Y is 0, or in the case where X is 0 and Y is 1. Then in Boolean algebra notation (see Chapter 2), the signals on the nine lines representing the nine possible values of J may be generated as follows:

$$J_0 = X_0Y_0$$

$$J_1 = X_1Y_0 + X_0Y_1$$

$$J_2 = X_2Y_0 + X_1Y_1 + X_0Y_2$$

$$J_3 = X_3Y_0 + X_2Y_1 + X_1Y_2 + X_0Y_3$$

$$J_4 = X_4Y_0 + X_3Y_1 + X_2Y_2 + X_1Y_3 + X_0Y_4$$

$$J_5 = X_4Y_1 + X_3Y_2 + X_2Y_3 + X_1Y_4$$

$$J_6 = X_4Y_2 + X_3Y_3 + X_2Y_4$$

$$J_7 = X_4Y_3 + X_3Y_4$$

$$J_8 = X_4Y_4$$

The lines on which these signals appear are indicated in the figure. The "carry" and "no carry" lines from the quinary part to the binary part, also in Boolean algebra notation, are:

$$\text{Carry} = J_4C + J_5 + J_6 + J_7 + J_8$$

$$\text{No carry} = J_0 + J_1 + J_2 + J_3 + J_4N$$

In forming the quinary part of the sum, a few switching components may be saved if, instead of adding the carry at this point, a tentative sum is formed first and the carry is added as a subsequent step. The five lines in the tentative sum, T, would then be:

$$T_0 = J_0 + J_5$$

$$T_1 = J_1 + J_6$$

$$T_2 = J_2 + J_7$$

$$T_3 = J_3 + J_8$$

$$T_4 = J_4$$

The "final" sum, S, is obtained after adding the "carry" and "no carry" (C and N) signals from the next lower order according to the following arrangement:

$$S_0 = T_0 N + T_4 C$$

$$S_1 = T_1 N + T_0 C$$

$$S_2 = T_2 N + T_1 C$$

$$S_3 = T_3 N + T_2 C$$

$$S_4 = T_4 N + T_3 C$$

The various switching functions set forth above are indicated in Fig. 8-9.

To retain the error-detecting feature of the biquinary code, it is necessary to use both the "carry" and "no carry" signals in forming the sum. Although through the use of an inverter, the "carry" signal would be sufficient to obtain the desired sum, a failure in that part of the adder which handles the carry could go undetected. With the arrangement as shown, if any individual "and" or "or" switch fails or if an improper combination of input signals is applied to the adder, there will be none or two signals present on the five lines carrying the quinary part of the sum digit, or else signals will appear on neither or both of the "carry" and "no carry" output lines. Either of these conditions may be used to detect the presence of an error. However, it would not be possible to correct the error, and it is possible that two or more simultaneous failures in the switches would not be detected.

Any of the arrangements shown in Fig. 8-7 could be used to check the presence of one and only one signal in the five sum lines. Since these arrangements sense the odd-even status of a number of signals, three or five signals would produce the same response as one, but the presence of three or five signals would indicate that two or more errors had occurred. Because the adder is useful in detecting the presence of only one error at a time anyway, the odd-even count is sufficient for checking the sum. If desired, more elaborate checking arrangements may be designed.

A moderate reduction in the number of switching components required for the quinary part of the biquinary adder may be achieved if the J signals are formed according to the following Boolean algebra expressions.

$$J_0 = X_0 Y_0$$

$$J_1 = (X_0 + Y_0)(X_1 + Y_1)$$

$$J_2 = (X_0 + Y_0)(X_2 + Y_2) + X_1 Y_1$$

$$J_3 = (X_0 + Y_0)(X_3 + Y_3) + (X_1 + Y_1)(X_2 + Y_2)$$

$$J_4 = (X_0 + Y_0)(X_4 + Y_4) + (X_1 + Y_1)(X_3 + Y_3) + X_2 Y_2$$

$$J_5 = (X_2 + Y_2)(X_3 + Y_3) + (X_1 + Y_1)(X_4 + Y_4)$$

$$J_6 = (X_2 + Y_2)(X_4 + Y_4) + X_3 Y_3$$

$$J_7 = (X_3 + Y_3)(X_4 + Y_4)$$

$$J_8 = X_4 Y_4$$

That these expressions are equivalent to the previous ones may be understood by expanding them to simple "and-to-or" form and noting

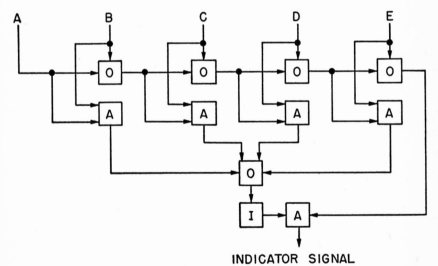

INDICATOR SIGNAL

Fig. 8-10. Functional block diagram for indication of one and only one signal.

that terms such as $X_0 X_1$ may be ignored because only one X signal and one Y signal will be applied at any one time. However, in the event of an error it may happen that signals will appear on three instead of just two of the final output lines representing the sum. An example of this kind of error occurs when one of the "or" switches, say the one for $X_0 + Y_0$, produces an output when it should not.

To check the above form of the adder for errors it is necessary to have a circuit which will indicate the presence of one and only one signal on the five output lines; the simple indication of an odd number of signals is not sufficient. A block diagram of a switching circuit which will provide this function with a reasonable quantity of components is shown in Fig. 8-10. This particular arrangement is useful in that it may be readily expanded in a straightforward manner to sense the presence of one and only one signal on any number of signal lines.

Addition Through the Use of Decimal Digit Counters. Decimal digit counters may be used to effect addition in a manner analogous to the way in which binary counters were used for binary addition. In the case of parallel operation, a decimal digit counter is used for each order in the numbers which are to be added. Each individual digit of a number is transmitted by a series of pulses with the number of pulses equal to the value of the digit. The units, tens, hundreds, and so on, digits are transmitted on separate lines to units, tens, hundreds, and so on, counters, respectively. After the one of the numbers to be added is entered into the counters, and second number is entered in a similar fashion. If, for example, the hundreds digits of two numbers which are being added are 2 and 7, two pulses will be sent to the hundreds counter when the first number is entered, and seven pulses will be sent to the same counter when the second number is entered. The counter will then have received nine pulses and will register the digit 9. A similar process will take place in the counters of all orders. Of course, the sum of the two digits in a given order may be more than ten, in which case the counter will register only the excess above ten, and a pulse must be entered in the counter of the next higher order to increase the digit in that counter by one. This extra pulse is the familiar carry. If a given counter registers a total of 9 and a pulse is received from the next lower order, the counter must not only advance to 0, but it must also cause the carry to propagate to the next higher order. Functionally, the various addition methods employing counters differ, for the most part, only in the manner in which the carries are propagated from order to order.

With the binary system of numbers it was possible to generate the carry signal by comparing the binary digit entered into a counter with the digit in the counter after the entry. If the digit entered was a 1 and the digit in the counter was a 0, the counter must have changed from 1 to 0, and, therefore, a carry should be sent to the next higher order. It is conceivable that an analogous method for transmitting carries could be worked out for the decimal system, but for most applications the idea does not appear to be practical. To generate the carry by this method in the decimal system, it would be necessary to employ almost as much equipment as is required to form a decimal adder, because there are so many digits to be compared. For example, if the digit in the counter is a 3 after entry of the number being added, a carry should be sent to the next higher order if digit entered was any digit from 4 through 9, but no carry should be sent if the digit entered was from 0 through 3. Also, since the digit entered is represented by a series of pulses, it is usually impractical, if not impossible, to make the digit entered available for comparison after the entry.

It is more common, or almost universal, practice to generate the carry by a signal which is obtained from the counter itself when it passes from 9 to 0. Since the counter may pass from 9 to 0 at any time during the entry of the pulses being added, most types of counters are designed to store the carry until the entry of pulses is complete. Subsequently, a "carry pulse" initiates the actual transmission of the carries from order to order. One functional arrangement for accomplishing this result is shown in Fig. 8-11, which illustrates three orders of a parallel accumulator. "Digit pulses," which are the pulses representing the digits being added, are applied to the counters of the orders corresponding to the respective digits; that is, for example, if the number 37 is to be added, three pulses are sent to the tens counter and seven pulses are sent to the units counter. If any decimal digit counter changes to the state representing 0, a pulse-type signal is sent from that counter to its corresponding carry-storage device and turns it from "off" to "on." In the figure this function is represented as a line passing from the 0-output of the counter through a condenser to a binary storage device. The condenser differentiates the otherwise steady-state signal, and "off" and "on" may be considered to correspond to 0 and 1, respectively, in the binary carry-storage device. Before the start of the addition process, all carry-storage triggers had been set to 0 through the action of a pulse on the "carry reset" line.

After all digit pulses have been entered into the counters, a carry pulse is applied to the line indicated. For each order in which a carry had been generated, signals will be present simultaneously on both input lines of the No. 1 "and" switch and the carry pulse will be transmitted through a delay device to the counter in the next higher order. If a counter contains the digit 9, and a carry pulse is received from the next lower order, the carry pulse will be automatically propagated to the next higher order because signals will be applied simultaneously to both input lines of the No. 2 "and" switch. The delay device is necessary in principle to prevent the transition of the counter from one state to the next before the carry pulse has disappeared; otherwise, the carry pulse might be propagated from one order to the next when it should not be. In some cases the decimal digit counters may be slow enough in their counting action to cause the need for a separate delay device to be eliminated.

The carry arrangement shown in Fig. 8-11 is actually no more than the decimal equivalent of a binary carry arrangement which was de-

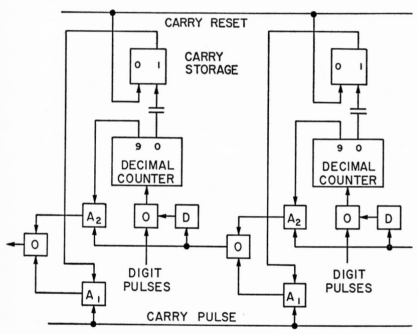

Fig. 8-11.   Parallel decimal accumulator.

scribed in connection with binary addition. In the binary system it was found possible to propagate the carry pulse, as described, or it was possible to apply the signals from the counters to the switches in such a manner that these signals would be propagated, and the carry pulse would then be sent directly to the counters. The same idea may be adopted in the decimal system. One order of a parallel accumulator operating in this fashion is shown in Fig. 8-12. With this arrangement the digit pulses, the counter, and the carry-storage device function as before. The distinguishing feature is that the 1-output of the carry-storage device is sent directly through the "or" switch to the next higher order. Also, in a given order, if such a signal is received from the next lower order and the counter contains the digit 9, the signal will be propagated to the next higher order through the action of the No. 1

Decimal Addition and Subtraction 233

"and" switch. The signal is also applied to one input line of the No. 2 "and" switch; therefore, the carry pulse will pass through the No. 2 "and" switch, through the delay device, and through an "or" switch to the counter regardless of the order in which the carry originated. This arrangement is slightly faster than the one described previously because the propagation of a signal from order to order starts immediately upon entry of the digit pulses instead of upon application of the carry pulse.

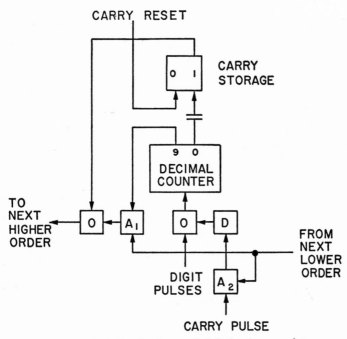

Fig. 8-12. Variation in the parallel decimal accumulator.

Two orders of another type of carry arrangement are shown in Fig. 8-13. After entry of the digits a carry "gate" signal instead of a pulse is applied to transmit the carries. In a given order, the 1-output of the carry-storage device in the next lower order is applied to an "and" switch. When the carry gate is applied, the differentiated output from the "and" switch is entered into the counter as an additional pulse to be counted. If this additional pulse happens to cause the counter to pass from 9 to 0, the carry-storage device will be changed to 1 and a signal will be transmitted to the "and" switch of next higher order. It is assumed that the carry-gate signal is still applied, and therefore a pulse will be entered into the counter of the next higher order. The carry-gate signal must be maintained for a length of time sufficient to allow the propagation of carries through all orders. Since the counters and carry-storage devices must all function one after another, this carry propagation method is relatively slow, but less switching equipment is required than for the other methods. The method also has the advantage that no delay devices are needed, even in principle.

If it is desired to eliminate the carry-storage devices, the carry propagation method shown in Fig. 8-14 may be used. With this arrangement,

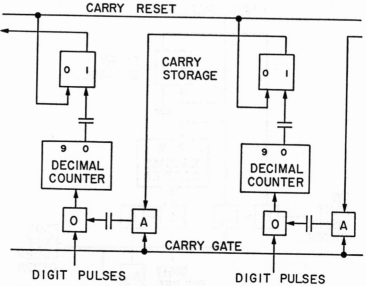

FIG. 8-13. Parallel decimal accumulator employing carry "gates."

carries are sent from one order to the next immediately after a counter passes from 0 to 9 rather than after all digit pulses have been entered. When eliminating the carry-storage devices, two important problems must be solved. One problem arises from the fact that, when a carry occurs in a given order, the counter in the next higher order may be receiving a digit pulse at substantially the same time. Therefore, means must be provided for delaying the carry pulse sufficiently to prevent its interfering with a digit pulse, and yet in the interests of fast operation the delay should not be cumulative as the carry is propagated from order to order. The second problem arises in the attempt to solve the first one. If a given counter contains the digit 9, a carry from the next lower order may be transmitted without substantial delay to the next higher order through the use of an "and" switch with the 9-output signal from the counter used as one input signal for the switch. But when the given counter changes from 9 to 0, a second and unwanted carry sig-

nal will be transmitted to the next higher order unless means are provided to prevent it.

Fig. 8-14 shows one way in which the problems of automatic carry
initiation may be solved. The digit pulses are applied to the No. 1 "and"
switch in a given order as well as to the counter. When the counter
arrives at the state representing 0, a pulse is applied to the other input
line of this "and" switch. It is assumed that there is no delay in the
transfer of the counter from 9 to 0; if there is a substantial delay, a

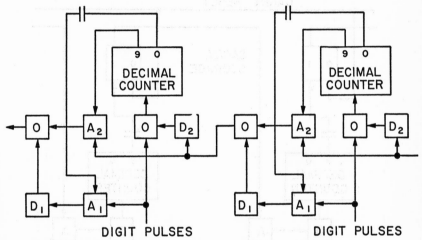

Fɪɢ. 8-14. Parallel decimal accumulator with automatic carry initiation.

compensating delay may be placed in the first input line of the "and"
switch. The coincidence of pulses at the No. 1 "and" switch then causes
a pulse which acts as a carry pulse to be sent through delay device, D_1,
to the next higher order. Delay device, D_1, allows sufficient time to
elapse between the arrival of a digit pulse and the arrival of a carry pulse
to make it possible for the counter to accept both pulses. When a counter
contains the digit, 9, and a carry pulse is received from the next lower
order, the carry will be transmitted to the next higher order through the
No. 2 "and" switch in a manner which has been described previously.
However, when the counter transfers from 9 to 0 upon reception of a
carry pulse, it will not transmit a second pulse to the next higher order
because no digit pulse is being applied to the No. 1 "and" switch at this
time, and therefore the pulse from the 0-output of the counter cannot get
through. Delay device, D_2, allows the carry pulse to die out at the
input of the No. 2 "and" switch before the counter changes state. Note
that when a carry pulse is propagated through many orders, it must pass
through only one D_1 and one D_2 delay device. The outstanding disad-

vantage of this method of carry propagation is that the accumulator is made slower for a given type of components because the time between individual digit pulses must be increased sufficiently to allow for carry propagation after any one of them.

In all of the accumulator arrangements which have been described, the carry was generated by the arrival of the counter at the state representing 0. In many applications it is equally practical or even preferable

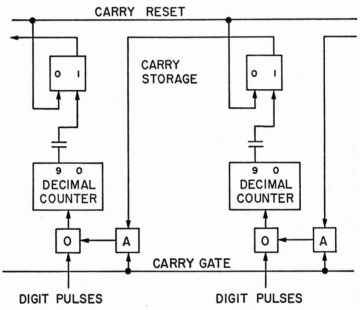

Fig. 8-15. "Leaving 9" carry applied to counters with intermediate stable states.

to use the 9-output signal from the counter to generate the carry. The differentiated 9-output signal will yield a pulse in one direction when the counter arrives at 9 and another pulse, but of opposite polarity, when the counter leaves 9. This opposite polarity "leaving 9" pulse may be used for carry purposes just as well as the "arriving 0" pulse because, if a counter leaves 9, it is known that it will arrive at 0. One advantage of using the "leaving 9" pulse is that the 0-output line from the counter may be eliminated with the 9-output being used both for carry generation and carry propagation.

With some types of digit counter it is necessary to use the "leaving 9" signal in order to obtain satisfactory carry propagation. Included in these types are gas-tube counters, of which there are several varieties. A gas-tube counter requires pulses which have a relatively long duration rather than short "impulse-type" characteristics. The pulse to be counted causes the counter to transfer to one of ten intermediate stable states, and at the termination of the pulse the counter transfers from the intermediate stable state to one of the stable states which represents a digit. The functional arrangement is as shown in Fig. 8-15. The carry pulse which is entered into the counter of a given order is the carry gate combined with the 1-output of the carry-storage device in the next lower order. If the entry of a carry pulse causes the counter to leave 9, the corresponding carry-storage device will be changed from 0 to 1 and a carry pulse will thereby be applied to the counter in the next higher order. At the termination of the carry-gate signal, each counter which has been affected will transfer from an intermediate state to the next digit-representing state.

The "leaving 9" carry is also required for some forms of parallel accumulators employing counters comprised of magnetic cores. The reasons are similar in that the magnetic core counter operates through the use of intermediate stable states, to which the counter transfers when proceeding from one digit-representing state to the next.

Parallel-serial and Serial-parallel Operation. The adders which were described may be used to add decimal digits either in parallel or serially. If they are used in parallel, the operation might be called parallel-parallel, because both the decimal digits and the bits within the digits are handled in parallel. If serial operation is employed, the adder unit itself functions in the same way, except that only one such unit is required to add two decimal numbers, and the carry is stored after the addition of one pair of digits and is added to the next pair of digits along with the addition of those digits. Since the individual bits of the decimal digits are in parallel, this type of operation might be called serial digit, parallel bit.

In the case of the accumulators employing decimal digit counters, the pulses representing the digits were applied in serial fashion even though the operation with regard to the digits was of a parallel nature. Operation of this type might be called parallel digit, serial bit. On the other hand, a single decimal digit counter may be used to add to decimal numbers. First, the units digit of one number may be entered into the counter, and then the units digit of the other number may be entered. The counter would then contain the sum of the two digits; and the carry, if any, may be stored in a separate carry-storage device. The sum may then be removed from the counter, such as by shifting each bit into the first stage of a shifting register. After resetting the counter to zero, the carry from the units order may be entered as one pulse and the counter is ready to accept pulses representing the tens digits of the numbers being added. Since both the digits and pulses representing the digits are applied serially, this mode of operation is serial-serial.

The four types of operation mentioned above do not exhaust the possibilities. In fact, there are many variations in the ways decimal digits may be handled for addition. One variation, which is a form of serial-serial operation, will be described because it illustrates a bit-to-bit carry propagation scheme which has not been described previously. The functional arrangement is shown in Fig. 8-16. An 8,4,2,1 code is used. When adding the decimal digits of corresponding orders of two numbers

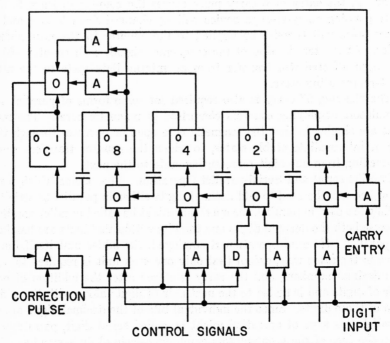

FIG. 8-16. Another arrangement for decimal addition.

the 8,4,2,1 binary digit counters are set to zero. The carry-storage device, indicated by C, contains the carry from the addition of the next lower-order digits. A pulse applied on the "carry entry" line enters the carry in the 1's storage device, and the carry-storage trigger is then reset to zero through means not shown. One of the digits then appears on the "digit input" line in serial form; and, during the same time, control signals are applied on the "control" lines. At the time an 8-bit is to arrive, the 8-control line allows a pulse to be entered into the 8's counter if there is an 8 in the binary coded representation of the digit. The 4, 2, and 1-bits are channeled into the 4's, 2's, and 1's counters in a similar fashion. The digit of the same decimal order in the other number then appears on the "digit input" line and is entered into the storage devices in the same way. If any of the storage devices change from 1 to 0 when the second digit is entered, a pulse will be sent to the counter of the next higher binary order. The distinguishing feature of this method of addition is that no storage devices are required for the binary carries; and the binary carries may be sent directly through an "or" switch because there will be no other bits being entered into the adding device at this time. If the decimal carry-storage device, C, receives a pulse or if the sum contains an 8 and a 4-bit or else an 8 and a 2-bit, a decimal carry is required and 6 should be added to the sum to correct it. Both of these results may be obtained by applying a pulse on the line marked "correction pulse." A pulse will be entered in the 4's counter and subsequently, because of the delay device, into the 2's counter. The binary carries resulting from the addition of 6 will cause the decimal carry-storage device, C, to be changed from 0 to 1 if it was not already at 1. The sum digit is then withdrawn from the binary counters by means not shown; and, after the counters are reset to zero, addition may be performed on the digits of the next higher decimal order.

Decimal Subtraction. As in the case of subtraction in the binary system, there are two general methods of subtracting in the decimal system. One method might be called "direct subtraction," and the other method involves the addition of complements. Either method may be adapted to either decimal adders or decimal counters.

When the decimal digits are coded in the binary 8,4,2,1 code, for example, a sort of hybrid form of subtraction may be used; that is, the decimal digits may be subtracted directly, but the subtraction of the individual digits may be accomplished through the addition of binary complements.

Direct Subtraction. For direct subtraction, a "decimal subtracter" may be used in place of a decimal adder. A decimal subtracter would have a minimum of nine input lines and five output lines, which is the same number as is required for an adder; but borrow signals would be substituted for carry signals, and four of the output lines would represent the difference digit instead of the sum digit. As with adders, there are a great many ways by which a subtracter may be formed, even when the code for representing the decimal digits is specified. When one of the codes with binary properties such as the 8,4,2,1 code or the excess-3 code is employed, binary subtracters, which were described in Chapter 4 on binary addition and subtraction, may be used. The use of the 8,4,2,1 code is particularly simple. The binary bits comprising the coded representations of the decimal digits are merely applied to appropriate input lines of four binary full subtractors. If a borrow signal is obtained from the 8's order, this borrow signal without any corrections to be applied represents the decimal borrow to be sent to the next higher decimal order. However, when a borrow occurs, it is necessary to correct the difference by subtracting 6. For example, when subtracting 7 from 5, the following steps are taken.

Borrows	(1)	(1)(1)				
		0	1	0	1	Five
		0	1	1	1	Seven
		1	1	1	0	
Subtract 6			1	1		
(−)		1	0	0	0	(−) Eight

The result is 8, which is the 10's complement of the correct difference, 2. If 777 were subtracted from 555 by the use of three decimal subtracters in parallel, decimal borrows would be subtracted in the tens and hundreds orders, and the result would be 778, which is the 10's complement of the difference, 222. (Strictly speaking, it would be the 10^n complement, where n is the number of orders, but this term is not usually used.) The 9's complement of the difference may be obtained by using an end-around borrow in the same fashion that an end-around borrow was used in binary arithmetic. (The 9's complement is obtained by subtracting each individual digit in the number from 9.) If desired, conversion from 9's complement representation to true representation may be accomplished as described in Chapter 6 on decimal codes.

When counters are used for direct subtraction, it is necessary that the counter be able to count "backwards." Counting backwards in the decimal system is more of a problem than in the binary system, because a binary digit counter does nothing but transfer back and forth between 0 and 1 regardless of whether it is counting forwards or backwards. For a decimal counter to count backwards, it is necessary that it progress through the ten stable states in the opposite sequence. Of course, if the counter counts only backwards and not forwards, a trivial redefining of the stable states is sufficient to establish backwards operation. When redefining the stable states it should be remembered that the counter should produce a signal (the borrow) when it arrives at 9 instead of when it arrives at 0. Since, in general, it is desired to be able to perform either addition or subtraction, the counter must be capable of operation in either direction.

Many different types of decimal digit counters have been designed which will count either forwards or backwards. However, particularly in the case of counters employing electronic or electromagnetic components, very few of them have ever been adopted for use in practical applications. The reason is not that there is anything inherently wrong with such counters; it just seems to turn out when all details are considered that it is more satisfactory from the standpoint of simplicity to subtract by the addition of complements.

Subtraction by the Addition of Complements. The use of 9's or 10's complements for subtraction in the decimal system corresponds almost exactly to the 1's and 2's complements, respectively, which were used for subtraction in the binary system. However, the important features of the use of complements will be repeated here because it is not particularly convenient to study binary complements when it may be that only the decimal system is of interest.

When subtracting one number, N_1, from another number, N_2, by adding the 10's complement of N_1 to N_2, the result is $10^n - N_1 + N_2$. The addition may have produced a carry in the highest order, or it may not have produced a carry. Since the highest order is the $n - 1$ order (the orders correspond to the range of n from 0 to $n - 1$ inclusive), the carry would be added into the nth order, but this order is presumably nonexistent. The carry, if it occurs, is therefore dropped, and this has the effect of subtracting 10^n, which then yields the difference, $N_2 - N_1$, as desired. If no carry occurs, the 10^n is not dropped and the difference remains $10^n - (N_1 - N_2)$, which is the 10's complement of the difference. Note that a carry will occur whenever $N_1 \leqq N_2$, so that the absence of a carry in the highest order may be used to indicate a negative difference and the fact that the difference is in complement form.

When subtracting from N_2 when N_2 is negative, the result is $10^n - N_1 + 10^n - N_2$, which always causes a carry in the highest order. The dropping of this carry then yields $10^n - (N_1 + N_2)$ for the "difference."

There are three general methods by which the 10's complement of a number may be obtained. One method is the obvious method of subtracting from 10^n. For example, the 10's complement of 3260 is $10,000 - 3260 = 6740$. The second method is to obtain the 9's complement by subtracting each individual digit from 9 and then adding 1. The 9's complement of 3260 is 6739; and, when 1 is added, the same result, 6740 is obtained for the 10's complement. The third method is to use the rule that, when examining the digits in sequence starting with the lowest order, all 0's are unchanged until the first nonzero digit is reached; the first nonzero digit is subtracted from 10 and all subsequent digits are subtracted from 9. Although the three methods are very similar from a mathematical standpoint, the design of the machinery for performing the complementing may be quite different for the three methods.

In many applications it is desirable to use the 9's complement in preference to the 10's complement, because the transfer back and forth between 9's complement and true representation is more straightforward. The 9's complement system does introduce one complication, and that is the requirement of an end-around carry, but this complication is negligible in most parallel systems and is not a great disadvantage even in some serial systems. Since the 9's complement of a number, N, is $10^n - 1 - N$, the subtraction of N_1 from N_2 by the addition of the 9's complement produces the result, $10^n - 1 - N_1 + N_2$. If $N_1 < N_2$ (the case, $N_1 = N_2$, is not included), the result will be equal to or greater than 10^n, which means that a carry will occur in the highest order. The carry is entered, end-around fashion, into the lowest order, and this has the effect of subtracting 10^n and adding 1. The difference is then $N_2 - N_1$ as desired. If $N_1 \geqq N_2$, no carry in the highest order will be obtained, and difference will be $10^n - 1 - (N_1 - N_2)$, which is the desired difference in 9's complement form. As with the 10's complement system, the absence of a carry from the highest order may be used to indicate a negative difference and the fact that the difference is in complement form. Note that a difference of zero will be represented as being negative.

If it is required that zero be represented as a positive quantity, positive numbers may be represented in complement form and negative numbers in true form. To illustrate how this scheme operates, the problem $+ 23 - 50 + 27 - 15 + 81 - 66$ is worked out below.

		Balance
	9999	Zero
Add 23	9976	
	9975	
End-around carry	1	
	9976	+23
Subtract 50	50	
	0026	
End-around carry	1	
	0027	−27
Add 27	9972	
	9999	Zero
Subtract 15	15	
	0014	
End-around carry	1	
	0015	−15
Add 81	9918	
	9933	+66
Subtract 66	0066	
	9999	Zero

Table 8-II shows the rules for determining the sign of the balance in all possible situations.

TABLE 8-II. RULES FOR DETERMINING SIGN OF BALANCE

	End-around Carry	No End-around Carry
Adding to + bal.	+	Capacity exceeded
Subtracting from + bal.	−	+
Adding to − bal.	−	+
Subtracting from − bal.	Capacity exceeded	−

Several variations in the foregoing procedure are possible. One variation of importance should be considered when it is desired to represent all numbers by magnitude and sign, with the magnitude always in true, or always in complement, form. The above procedure may be used for this case if appropriate conversions are made in the accumulator. However, the conversion must be made each time the balance in the accumulator is negative (or each time it is positive, depending on the convention which is used). If the number in the accumulator is always of the same form—that is, always true or always complement—and if the number being entered into the accumulator is entered in the same form when its sign is the same, but in opposite form when its sign is opposite, the balance in the accumulator need be complemented only when balance changes sign. For those systems where the complementing operation requires extra time, this procedure may allow substantial savings in time in many problems because the balance may change sign relatively infrequently compared to the total number of additions and subtractions.

Avoiding the Negative Zero Problem Through the Use of a Subtraction. If it is desired that zero be identified as a positive quantity and it is also desired that positive quantities be represented in true form, the use of subtraction instead of addition may be more convenient. To add, the 9's complement of the number is subtracted; and to subtract, the true value of the number is subtracted. End-around borrow instead of end-around carry is employed. As an example, 6 will be added to zero and then subtracted to obtain a balance of zero.

		Balance
	0000	Zero
Add 6	9993	
	————	
	0007	
End-around borrow	1	
	0006	+6
Subtract 6	0006	
	————	
	0000	Zero

With wheel or ring counters, subtraction is substantially the same as addition; it is only necessary to change the "labels" on the stable states to change from addition to subtraction. However, when the decimal counters are composed of binary counters operating in the 8,4,2,1 code, for example, some actual physical changes in the counters are required when altering them to perform subtraction instead of addition.

Obtaining the 9's Complement. The methods by which digits may be subtracted from 9 in obtaining the 9's complement depend greatly upon the code, the type of computer components, and the type of operation (serial-serial, etc.) being used. A method applicable to the 8,4,2,1 code with bits in parallel was described in Chapter 6 on decimal codes. Also, a scheme adaptable to self-complementing codes was described. Another commonly encountered requirement is the change of a one-out-of-ten timed pulse indication to a series of pulses equal in number to the value of the digit or its 9's complement. A good example of where this requirement is found is in the use of a punched card where a digit is represented by a punching in one of ten locations. If the card is passed by a brush such that the ten locations pass the brush one at a time, the brush will make an electrical contact through the hole at a time corresponding to the digit punched in the card. A functional arrangement for changing the timed pulse to the desired series of pulses is shown in Fig. 8-17. The timed pulse which represents the digit, a control pulse, and a series of nine pulses are applied on the lines shown with the timing as shown in part (b) of the figure. A steady signal is applied on one of the lines marked "True" or "Comp.," according to whether true or complement representation, respectively, is desired. For the true representation of the digit, the binary storage device is changed from 0 to 1 by the control pulse and is changed back to 0 by the timed digit pulse. If the digit is 3, for example, the binary storage device is on 1 for a length of time just sufficient to allow 3 of the nine pulses to pass the "and" switch. For complement representation, the control pulse causes the binary storage device to be changed to 0, but the timed digit pulse changes it to 1, which allows the last 6 of the nine pulses to pass in the case of the digit, 3.

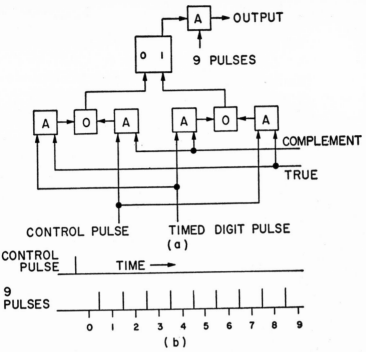

FIG. 8-17. Arrangement for obtaining true or complement representation of a decimal digit.

Self-complementing Counters. A few types of decimal digit counters have been designed whereby the counter itself may be used to create the 9's complement as well as the true representation of a digit. The design is straightforward in the case of electromechanical counters where the value of the digit is indicated by the position of a brush on a commutator. The complement may be obtained by installing a second brush and commutator with appropriate connections to the segments of the commutator. In the case of decimal digit counters composed of four binary digit counters, it is possible to cause the counter to transfer to the 9's complement of the digit it contains by applying a pulse on a special input line. However, for most such counters, the amount of switching components necessary to accomplish this function is prohibitively great, although with a counter that operates in the 2,4,2,1 code or some other self-complementing code, it is sufficient to enter a pulse into each binary digit counter and to prevent propagation of binary carries. Also some types of gas-tube counters and magnetic-core counters have been designed and constructed which have self-complementing features.

When self-complementing counters are employed in a parallel accumulator, the number in the accumulator (the augend) instead of the addend may be transposed to 9's complement form. The addition with end-around carry may proceed as before except that, whenever the sign of the difference is the same as the previous augend, the difference will appear in 9's complement form. The difference may be removed from the counters in either true or 9's complement form through the use of the same self-complementing properties of the counters.

The Storage of Positive and Negative Numbers. When choosing the convention to be used with regard to the form of positive and negative numbers in the storage part of a computer, substantially the same factors must be considered in the decimal system as in the binary system. If 10's and 9's complements are substituted for 2's and 1's complements, respectively, the section at the end of Chapter 4 on binary addition and subtraction may be applied directly to the decimal system.

Chapter 9

DECIMAL MULTIPLICATION AND DIVISION

Multiplication and division methods as used by machines working in the decimal system are usually considerably more involved than the same operations in binary machines. It is possible to perform decimal multiplication and division by a relatively straightforward series of additions and subtractions, but this "straightforward" method is frequently deemed not satisfactory because of speed considerations. To increase the speed of these operations, a variety of refinements have been worked out, although, in general, speed is gained only at the expense of further complexities in the computing machinery. Nevertheless, the high-speed multiplication and division methods may be attractive, particularly in large-scale computers where the arithmetic circuits are a relatively small portion of the entire machine.

Most of the important ideas pertaining to the execution of multiplication and division in a computing machine are related to the way in which the decimal digits are manipulated mathematically in forming the product or the quotient. The means for manipulating the digits are, of course, important too, but for the most part the means are merely an assemblage (often elaborate) of switches, storage devices, counters, shifting registers, and other components which have been discussed previously. A considerable length of text and extensive block diagrams would be required to explain a complete functional arrangement in reasonable detail. Since going into such detail would be beyond present purposes, attention in this chapter will be centered on the arithmetic of multiplication and division rather than the actual circuits except in a few instances where the circuits are of particular interest.

The Decimal Multiplication Table. The pencil-and-paper method of multiplication involves the use of the familiar multiplication table, which is usually memorized. A multiplication table type of operation is employed in some computers, as well. The digits of the multiplier are examined one at a time, and each digit of the multiplicand is compared with the multiplier digit. The product of each pair of digits is then obtained either from a digit-storage device that effectively stores the multiplication table, or, which mathematically amounts to the same thing, the product of each pair of digits is formed by an array of switching circuits.

The multiplication table may be employed in any of a variety of ways. One way, which corresponds closely to the pencil-and-paper multiplication method, is to compare each digit of the multiplicand with each digit of the multiplier and obtain the corresponding two-digit products in sequence. The individual products are then accumulated in the appropriate orders of an accumulator to form the desired product of the multiplier and multiplicand. For a 10-digit multiplicand and an 8-digit multiplier, for example, 80 operations would be required. Although this mode of operation has actually been employed in some computers, it is probably more common practice to separate the multiplication table into two parts, the left component and the right component, and to use a somewhat different procedure.

The decimal multiplication table separated into its two components is shown in Table 9-I. The left-component digit of the product is the

TABLE 9-I. DECIMAL MULTIPLICATION TABLE

Left Component											Right Component										
0	1	2	3	4	5	6	7	8	9		0	1	2	3	4	5	6	7	8	9	
0	0	0	0	0	0	0	0	0	0		0	0	0	0	0	0	0	0	0	0	
1	0	0	0	0	0	0	0	0	0		1	0	1	2	3	4	5	6	7	8	9
2	0	0	0	0	0	1	1	1	1		2	0	2	4	6	8	0	2	4	6	8
3	0	0	0	0	1	1	1	2	2		3	0	3	6	9	2	5	8	1	4	7
4	0	0	0	1	1	2	2	2	3		4	0	4	8	2	6	0	4	8	2	6
5	0	0	1	1	2	2	3	3	4		5	0	5	0	5	0	5	0	5	0	5
6	0	0	1	1	2	3	3	4	4	5	6	0	6	2	8	4	0	6	2	8	4
7	0	0	1	2	2	3	4	4	5	6	7	0	7	4	1	8	5	2	9	6	3
8	0	0	1	2	3	4	4	5	6	7	8	0	8	6	4	2	0	8	6	4	2
9	0	0	1	2	3	4	5	6	7	8	9	0	9	8	7	6	5	4	3	2	1

tens digit and the right-component digit is the units digit if the digits in the two factors being multiplied are both in the units order. Multiplication usually proceeds with the multiplier digits handled one at a time and with the lowest-order multiplier digit taken first. The entire multiplicand is brought into the computation once for each multiplier digit. The multiplicand digits may appear one at a time or simultaneously, that is, either serially or in parallel, but in the following explanation it will be assumed that the multiplicand digits are in parallel. As an example, consider the multiplication of 916 by 93.

916	Multiplicand
93	Multiplier
738	Right components
201	Left components
2748	Partial product
194	Right components
805	Left components
85188	Product

The first step is to compare the first digit of the multiplier, which is 3 in this example, with each digit of the multiplicand. From the multiplication table it is found that the right components are 8, 3, and 7 for the units, tens, and hundreds orders, respectively. The order of any particular component digit depends, of course, on the orders of the digits in the multiplier and multiplicand which make up that component digit, but the rules for determining the orders are the same as in the familiar pencil-and-paper multiplication procedure. The left-component digits for the first multiplier digit are 1, 0, and 2 and should be added in the tens, hundreds, and thousands orders, respectively. The partial product obtained from the first multiplier digit is then 2,748. The second multiplier digit (9) is handled in the same fashion except that the component digits are all shifted to positions corresponding to orders one higher than before because this multiplier digit is in the next higher order. After adding the left and right components, the final product of 85,188 is obtained.

If the right- and left-component digits are accumulated as separate numbers with carries added in after each addition, no particular problems are encountered with the above procedure. However, two adding operations (accumulation operations) for each multiplier digit are required, and to increase the speed of multiplication it is desirable to reduce the number of required additions. It is not convenient to add both the left and right components before adding in the carries which result, because in a given order a carry of 2 may be necessary. In the previous example this situation occurred in the hundreds order when adding the left and right components obtained from the second multiplier digit. Nevertheless, time can be saved by accumulating the left and right components in separate accumulators and combining the two sums in one of the accumulators as a last step in forming the product.

$$916 \quad \text{Multiplicand}$$
$$93 \quad \text{Multiplier}$$

Left-components Accumulator	Right-components Accumulator
2010	
80500	738
———	1940
82510	———
2678 ←	2678
———	
85188	

In the illustration the right components are added into the accumulator holding the left components, but the opposite procedure would serve just as well. Since the accumulation of the left and right components can proceed simultaneously, the number of additions required to complete a multiplication is only one greater than the number of digits in the multiplier. The fraction of the time saved increases with increasing number of digits in the multiplier and approaches 50% for multipliers of many digits.

Multiplication by Over-and-over Addition. Although it does not correspond as closely to the pencil-and-paper type of operation, the simplest form of multiplication to incorporate into a computing machine is probably over-and-over addition. With this type of multiplication the digits of the multiplier are examined one at a time, as before, but instead of using a multiplication table to obtain the partial products, the multiplicand is added a number of times equal to the value of the multiplier digit. It is common practice to place the multiplier digit in a decimal digit counter which counts backwards toward zero (or the complement is placed in a counter which counts forwards), and before each step in the multiplication process the counter is sensed. If the counter is not at zero, the multiplicand is added and a pulse is entered into the counter to subtract 1 from the digit it contains. The multiplicand is added repeatedly until the digit in the counter is reduced to zero. At this point, the next multiplier digit is placed in the counter and the over-and-over addition of the multiplicand is carried out in a similar fashion except that the orders into which the multiplicand is added are shifted according to the order of the multiplier digit. As an example, 916 is multiplied by 23.

Accumulator.	*Multiplier*
000	23
916	
916	22
916	
1832	21
916	
2748	20
916	
11908	10
916	
21068	00

The number of additions required to perform multiplication by this method is clearly equal to the sum of the digits in the multiplier. If the multiplier digits are of random values, an average of $4\frac{1}{2}$ additions per multiplier digit are required.

Including Subtraction in the Multiplication Procedure. The over-and-over addition method of multiplication may be improved upon from the standpoint of speed if provision for subtraction is included. With subtraction facilities, multiplier digits, 6 through 9, are handled by subtracting the multiplicand a number of times equal to the 10's complement of the digit and then adding 1 to the next higher-order multiplier digit. The adding of 1 to the next higher-order multiplier digit has the effect of adding the multiplicand ten times. To illustrate the process, 1567 will be multiplied by 7918 as a multiplier. The equivalent multiplier is 1 2 1 2 2, where the underlined digits are negative.

Sub.
```
0 0 0 0 0 0 0 0
        1 5 6 7
```

Sub.
```
(−) 9 9 9 9 8 4 3 3
          1 5 6 7
```

Add
```
(−) 9 9 9 9 6 8 6 6
          1 5 6 7
```

Add
```
0 0 0 1 2 5 3 6
      1 5 6 7
```

Sub.
```
0 0 0 2 8 2 0 6
      1 5 6 7
```

Sub.
```
(−) 9 9 8 7 1 5 0 6
          1 5 6 7
```

Sub.
```
(−) 9 8 3 0 4 5 0 6
          1 5 6 7
```

Add
```
(−) 9 6 7 3 7 5 0 6
    1 5 6 7
```

```
1 2 4 0 7 5 0 6
```

By considering the number of additions or subtractions required for each of the ten decimal digits, it may be determined that the average number of additions or subtractions required per multiplier digit is 2.5 if the "carry" to the next higher multiplier digit is left out of the computations. The "carry" to the next higher multiplier digit increases by 1 the number of operations required for that digit if it is from 0 through 4, but decreases by 1 the number of operation required if that digit is from 5 through 9. Therefore, except for the "carry" which may be caused by the highest-order multiplier digit, 2.5 is the correct figure for the average number of operations required per digit when the multiplier is composed of random digits.

Doubling. With many types of components and decimal codes, doubling is a relatively simple operation. If the doubled multiplicand as well as the multiplicand itself is available for use in multiplication, the number of additions required to complete a multiplication operation may be reduced when compared with the straightforward over-and-over addi-

Decimal Multiplication and Division 253

tion method. The additions necessary for each multiplier digit would then be as follows.

Multiplier Digit	Add	Number of Additions
0	Nothing	0
1	1	1
2	2	1
3	2 + 1	2
4	2 + 2	2
5	2 + 2 + 1	3
6	2 + 2 + 2	3
7	2 + 2 + 2 + 1	4
8	2 + 2 + 2 + 2	4
9	2 + 2 + 2 + 2 + 1	5

The digits in the add column indicate the number of times the multiplicand or the doubled multiplicand are added in the formation of the partial product. The number of additions required for random multiplier digits is 2.5 per multiplier digit on the average.

In the binary system of numbers, doubling may be accomplished simply by shifting each binary digit to the next higher order. If the 8,4,2,1 decimal code is used, the same shifting procedure may be used except that, when the doubled digit is ten or greater, a decimal carry with a correction of +6 is required for the same reasons that they were required when adding two decimal digits in the 8,4,2,1 code. Doubling with this code may be accomplished by the use of binary adders as shown in Fig. 9-1(a). However, it is possible to accomplish doubling with less equipment. The functional arrangement may be derived by noting that signals are never present on the 8 and 4 lines simultaneously or on the 8 and 2 lines simultaneously and that, when a correction is added, it is always added in the 4 and 2-orders simultaneously. Another way of deriving a functional arrangement requiring less components is writing down each decimal digit and its doubled value in the 8,4,2,1 code and observing the conditions in the original digit that create 1's in the respective bits of the doubled digit. By either procedure, the following Boolean algebra expressions may be obtained for the bits (indicated by D) in the doubled digit. The carry from the next lower order is C, and the carry to the next higher order is C_a. The digit being doubled is X.

$$C_a = X_8 + X_4X_2 + X_4X_1$$
$$D_8 = X_8X_1 + X_4\overline{C_a}$$
$$D_4 = X_2\overline{C_a} + X_2X_1 + X_8\overline{X_1}$$
$$D_2 = X_1\overline{C_a} + \overline{X_1}C_a$$
$$D_1 = C$$

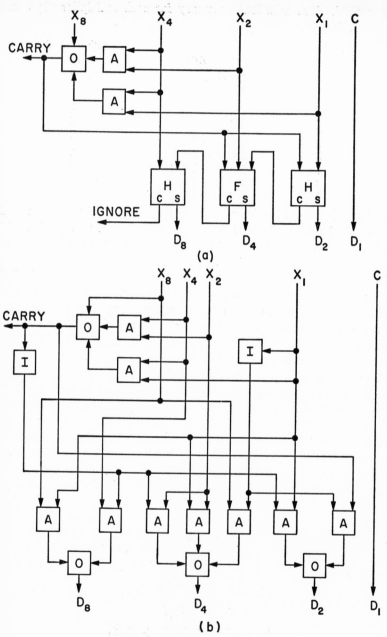

FIG. 9-1. Doubling with 8,4,2,1 code.

This arrangement is shown in Fig. 9-1(b). Many variations in the arrangement are possible.

Quintupling. Another relatively simple operation is quintupling. There are two useful ways of viewing the operation of quintupling. One is a straight multiplication by 5, in which case the resulting right-component digit is either a 0 or a 5, but the carry (left-component digit) may have any value from 0 to 4. From the other viewpoint, quintupling is a division by 2 combined with a multiplication by 10. When dividing by 2, the "carry" to the next lower order is either 0 if the digit is even or 5 if the digit is odd. This "carry" is added to the next lower-order digit after it is divided by 2. The multiplication by 10 is accomplished by shifting each decimal digit to the next higher decimal order. Mathematically there is no difference between the two viewpoints, but when adapting them to machine computations there is sometimes an important difference. When multiplying by 5 the digits are handled in increasing order of significance and it is necessary to use three bits for representing the carry; when dividing by 2 and multiplying by 10 the digits are handled in decreasing order of significance but only one bit for the "carry" is required.

With the 8,4,2,1 code, quintupling is readily accomplished by using the 1-bit to indicate whether the right-component digit is 0 or 5 and the 8, 4, and 2-bits may be used without modification for the carry. Note that the entering of the 8, 4, and 2-bits into the 4, 2, and 1-binary orders in the next higher-decimal order gives the effect of dividing these bits by 2 and multiplying them by 10, which amounts to a multiplication by 5. The functional arrangement for quintupling in this manner is shown in Fig. 9-2(a). Again, by noting that certain combinations of signals are never present simultaneously or by studying the bits in the quintupled digit as a function of the 1-bit and the bits in the carry, the following Boolean algebra expressions may be obtained for the bits in the quintupled digit. The symbols, C_4, C_2, and C_1, refer to the 4, 2, and 1-bits, respectively, in the "carry" from the next lower order, and Q refers to the quintupled digit.

$$Q_8 = X_1 C_4 + X_1 C_1 C_2$$

$$Q_4 = (X_1 + C_4)\overline{Q_8} = X_1 \overline{Q_8} + C_4 \overline{Q_8}$$

$$Q_2 = (C_2 + X_1 C_1)\overline{Q_8} = C_2 \overline{Q_8} + X_1 C_1 \overline{Q_8}$$

$$Q_1 = (X_1 + C_1)\overline{(X_1 C_1)}$$

The functional arrangement for quintupling by this method is shown in Fig. 9-2(b).

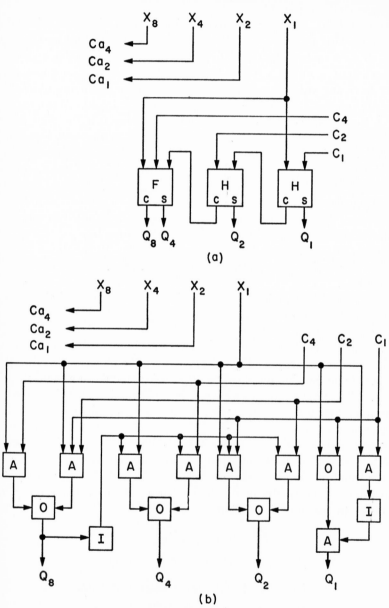

Fig. 9-2. Quintupling with 8,4,2,1 code.

Quintupling may be combined with over-and-over addition to reduce the number of additions required in multiplication. For example, for a multiplier digit of 7, the multiplicand would be added twice and the quintupled multiplicand would be added once. For random multiplier digits, an average number of 2.5 additions per digit are required.

"N-tupling." The obtaining of all multiples of the multiplicand from the first through the ninth is here called "N-tupling." For multiplication purposes, N-tupling is similar to using a multiplication table, but there is a distinction between the two methods. The use of a multiplication table implies that the product of every possible pair of digits is actually stored by some means or other in the computer. For N-tupling, no products of digits are stored; instead, the various multiples of the multiplicand are generated each time the multiplicand is passed through the generating device.

The complications involved in designing a switching circuit for generating the 3rd, 4th, 6th, 7th, 8th, or 9th multiples of a number are substantially greater than are found in obtaining the 2nd or 5th multiples. The reason is that, when the carries are added into a given order, the value of the carry to be sent to the next higher order may be affected. For example, when multiplying 68 by 3 the product of the 3 and 8 is 4 with a 2 to be carried to the tens order. The product of 6 and 3 is 8 with a 1 to be carried to the hundreds order, but when the carry from the units order is added the result is a product digit of 0 with the carry to the hundreds order increased from 1 to 2. Such a situation cannot arise when obtaining the 2nd or 5th multiples, as may be understood from a study of the left and right components in Table 9-I. For these two multiples the sum of any left-component digit and any right-component digit can never be greater than 9, but the sum may be greater than 9 for all other multiplier digits (except 0 and 1, of course).

Although a "tripler" may be relatively difficult to design, the tripled value of a number can be obtained readily through the use of a doubler and an adder. The adder is used to add the doubled value to the number itself. The quadrupled value of a number may be obtained by connecting two doublers in tandem. Similarly, the 6th and higher multiples can be obtained by doubling or adding together appropriate lower multiples. For the case of serial digit, parallel bit operation, an arrangement for obtaining all nine multiples is shown in Fig. 9-3. In this figure a line implies four wires in parallel to transmit the four bits of a decimal digit, and the digits appear serially, one after the other. The carries are sent through one-digit delay devices to be returned and added to the next higher-order digit.

Except in the serial-parallel multiplication scheme to be described later, it is generally not necessary to have all nine multiples of the multiplicand available simultaneously. In fact, with the ordinary N-tupling method of multiplication, only one multiple at a time is required, and in this case, it is possible to achieve a substantial saving in equipment. From Fig. 9-3 it may be observed that no more than one adder is re-

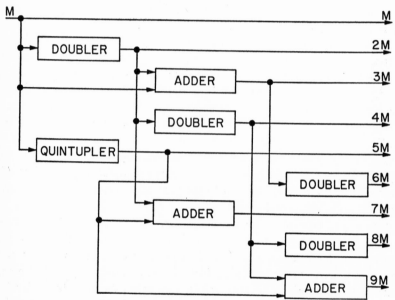

FIG. 9-3. An arrangement for obtaining the 9 multiples of the multiplicand.

quired for any given multiple. Then, if one adder is provided, it is possible to generate any one of the nine multiples through the use of this adder, two doublers, and a quintupler by switching these components into various arrays under the control of the multiplier digit.

There is a multitude of variations in the ways by which the adder, the two doublers, and the quintupler may be switched. While it is not difficult to derive a workable arrangement, the finding of the one that requires the minimum number of components is a rather tricky puzzle, and no method of solution except cut-and-try is known. One particular arrangement which employs the 8,4,2,1 code for the multiplier digit and which is reasonably conserving of equipment will be described.

If the two inputs to the adder are labeled X and Y, the multiples of the multiplicand as obtained from the doublers ($4M$ is obtained from the two doublers in tandem) and the quintupler according to the following pattern:

Multiplier Digit	X Adder Input	Y Adder Input
0	—	—
1	1M	—
2	—	2M
3	1M	2M
4	4M	—
5	5M	—
6	4M	2M
7	5M	2M
8	4M	4M
9	5M	4M

The control signals obtained from the 4 bits of the multiplier digit, R, may be represented in Boolean algebra by the equations,

$$M_x = R_1\overline{R}_4\overline{R}_8 \qquad\qquad 2M_y = R_2$$

$$4M_x = \overline{R}_1(R_4 + R_8) \qquad 4M_y = R_8$$

$$5M_x = R_1(R_4 + R_8)$$

where the term $4M_x$, for example, signifies a control signal to be combined with the $4M$ lines in a set of "and" switches. When a signal is present on the $4M_x$ control line (as it will be when the multiplier digit is 4, 6, or 8 in this arrangement), the 4th multiple of the multiplicand will be entered into the X input of the adder.

Fig. 9-4 shows the functional block diagram of this N-tupling scheme. A heavy line indicates four parallel wires, which means that there are actually four times as many "and" and "or" switches as indicated in the corresponding circuits.

The adder used for accumulating the partial products is, of course, separate from the one indicated in Fig. 9-4. Since one accumulation of a partial product is required for each multiplier digit except zero, an average of 0.9 operation per multiplier digit is required for random multiplier digits.

The Use of Counters. The properties described in the previous sections concerning the sum of the left- and right-component digits are of particular interest when accumulators employing counters are used to assemble the partial products in the formation of a product. When performing an accumulating function in an ordinary manner, a counter in a parallel accumulator receives a maximum of 9 pulses (for the digit

9) plus a carry pulse from the next lower order. With only minor modifications the accumulator may be adapted to receive both the left and right components in the same addition operation if the multiplier digit is 1, 2, or 5. With other multiplier digits, the sum of the left- and right-component digits in a given order may be greater than 9; and this would not only require that extra time be used to enter the two digits,

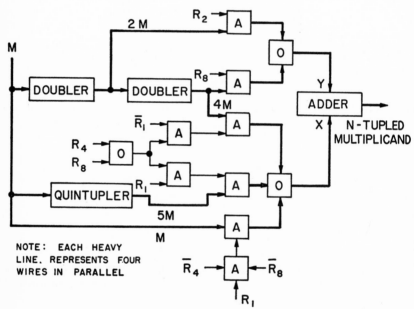

Fig. 9-4. N-tupler (multiplier digit in 8,4,2,1 code).

but also the counter may arrive at 0 twice during the entry of the pulses and therefore require that two carry pulses be entered into the next higher order.

The adding of the left and right components of the 1, 2, and 5 multiples of the multiplicand into an accumulator in a single operation has been adapted to at least one electromechanical computer (IBM's type 602A Computing Punch).

Combinations of Subtraction, Doubling, and Quintupling. Addition, subtraction, doubling, and quintupling may be combined in a variety of ways to obtain further reductions in the number of operations required to perform multiplication. If all four processes are used, the number of operations per multiplier digit can be reduced to 1.3 by handling the multiplier digits in the following manner.

Multiplier Digit	Operations
0	—
1	+1
2	+2
3	+2 + 1 or +5 − 2
4	+2 + 2 or +5 − 1
5	+5
6	+5 + 1 or −2 − 2
7	+5 + 2 or −2 − 1
8	−2
9	−1

In the above listing, 1 must be added to the next higher-order multiplier digit when subtraction is used for multiplier digits 6 through 9, but not for multiplier digits 3 or 4.

Table 9-II lists the average number of operations required per multiplier digit when various combinations of addition, subtraction, doubling, and quintupling are employed in multiplication. Random multiplier digits are assumed. When subtraction is employed the figure given is only an approximation; the correct figure is slightly greater with the amount of error decreasing with an increasing number of digits in the multiplier.

TABLE 9-II. NUMBER OF OPERATIONS REQUIRED FOR MULTIPLICATION

Functions	Operations per Multiplier Digit
Addition Only	4.5
Addition and Subtraction	2.5
Addition and Doubling	2.5
Addition and Quintupling	2.5
Addition, Doubling, and Quintupling	1.7
Addition, Subtraction, and Doubling	1.5
Addition, Subtraction, and Quintupling	1.7
Addition, Subtraction, Doubling, and Quintupling	1.3
Addition, Subtraction, Doubling, and Quadrupling	1.2
Addition, Doubling, Quadrupling, and Quintupling	1.4
N-tupling	0.9

In the table, figures involving quadrupling were included because reasonably fast multiplication speed may be obtained through the use of quadrupling. Although quadrupling by itself is usually not a particularly simple operation, it can sometimes be achieved readily through two doubling operations.

Handling the Multiplier Digits in Opposite Sequence. Except when subtraction was involved, the multiplication methods which have been described could be used with the multiplier digits appearing in any desired sequence. It is necessary only that the multiplicand or its appropriate multiple be entered into the proper orders in the accumulation of the partial products. However, when the lowest-order multiplier digit is used first and the other multiplier digits are used in ascending sequence, the "length" of the accumulator need not exceed the length of the multiplicand since one product digit is definitely determined and may be shifted out of the accumulator after each multiplier digit is used. When the multiplier digits are used in the opposite sequence, the length of the accumulator must be as great as the length of the product, because of the carries which may occur in the accumulation of the partial products.

One scheme for saving a few operations in the multiplication process when the multiplier digits are used in descending sequence is to add the multiplicand according to the following pattern.

Multiplier Digit	
0	—
1	+1
2	+2
3	+5 − 2
4	+5 and subtract 9's complement of succeeding multiplier digit
5	+5
6	+5 + 1
7	+5 + 2
8	+10 − 2
9	+10 and subtract 9's complement of succeeding multiplier digit

Doubling, quintupling, and subtraction are employed. In the case of digits 8 and 9, the tens multiple of the multiplicand is obtained by adding the multiplicand itself shifted one order rather than by adding 1 to the next higher multiplier digit (which has already been used). The reduction in the number of operations is achieved when the multiplier digit is 4 or 9. In these two cases, after an initial addition of 5 or 10 times, respectively, of the multiplicand, the succeeding digits are sensed in 9's complement form and subtracted. The subtraction of 9's complement is continued until the last multiplier digit is reached when the 10's complement is subtracted or until a 4 or a 9 is to be subtracted, in which case the procedure reverts to addition of the multiplicand. The following example is presented to illustrate the process more clearly; the number, 5,461,023,972, is the multiplier, and M is the multiplicand.

	5	Add 5 $\times$ $10^9 M$
	4	Add 5 $\times$ $10^8 M$
(Sense as 3)	6	Sub. 5 $\times$ $10^7 M$; Add 2 $\times$ $10^7 M$
(Sense as 8)	1	Sub. 1 $\times$ $10^7 M$; Add 2 $\times$ $10^6 M$
(Sense as 9)	0	Sub. 1 $\times$ $10^6 M$
	2	Add 2 $\times$ $10^4 M$
	3	Add 5 $\times$ $10^3 M$; Sub. 2 $\times$ $10^3 M$
	9	Add 1 $\times$ $10^3 M$
(Sense as 2)	7	Sub. 2 $\times$ $10^1 M$
(Sense as 8)	2	Sub. 1 $\times$ $10^1 M$; Add 2 $\times$ $10^0 M$

The above procedure is used in IBM's type 602A Computing Punch.

Error-detecting Multiplier. One way to detect errors in multiplication is to employ ordinary over-and-over addition with an error-detecting code in an error-detecting adder. In the case of the biquinary code, at least, error-detecting doublers and quintuplers are relatively easy to design, and these may be used to increase the speed of multiplication.

Also, through the use of the biquinary code, it is possible to form an N-tupler which has error-detecting properties; and one way of doing this will be described. The multiplier digit, R, is applied to one set of input lines, and the digits of the multiplicand M are applied one after the other to another set of input lines. Both the right- and left-component digits will be generated; the right-component digit, P, will be used as the partial product digit to be accumulated in the formation of the final product, and the left-component digit, C_a, will function like a carry to be added into the N-tupler in the formation of the next higher-order right- and left-component digits. If the digits of M and R are broken up into their binary and quinary parts, indicated by the subscripts b and q, respectively, the product of the two digits is

$$(M_b + M_q)(R_b + R_q) = M_b R_b + M_b R_q + R_b M_q + M_q R_q$$

In Fig. 9-5, the four parts of the product are generated in the E, G, and J boxes. The $M_b R_b$ part has a weight of 0 or 25 and the output lines from this box may be (in Boolean algebra notation) as follows in terms of the input signals.

$$E_0 = M_0 + R_0$$

$$E_{25} = M_5 R_5$$

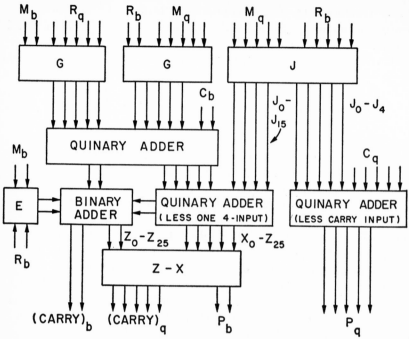

Fig. 9-5.   Error-detecting biquinary multiplier.

The M_bR_q and R_bM_q parts may have a weight of 0, 5, 10, 15, or 20.   The G box for the M_bR_q part may function as follows (the G box for the R_bM_q part would be the same functionally).

$$G_0 = M_0 + R_0$$

$$G_5 = M_5R_1$$

$$G_{10} = M_5R_2$$

$$G_{15} = M_5R_3$$

$$G_{20} = M_5R_4$$

The J box for the M_qR_q part is substantially a 5 by 5 multiplication table.   The output of the J box can have a weight up to 16, but this may be divided into "binary" part with weights of 0, 5, 10, or 15 and a quinary part with a weight of 0, 1, 2, 3 or 4.   The respective output signals may be generated according to these functional relationships.

$$J_0 = M_0 + M_1 + R_0 + R_1 + M_2R_2$$

$$J_5 = M_3R_2 + M_4R_2 + M_2R_3 + M_3R_3 + M_2R_4$$

$$J_{10} = M_3R_4 + M_4R_3$$

$$J_{15} = M_4R_4$$

$$J_0 = M_0 + R_0$$

$$J_1 = M_1R_1 + M_3R_2 + M_2R_3 + M_4R_4$$

$$J_2 = M_1R_2 + M_2R_1 + M_3R_4 + M_4R_3$$

$$J_3 = M_1R_3 + M_3R_1 + M_2R_4 + M_4R_2$$

$$J_4 = M_1R_4 + M_4R_1 + M_2R_2 + M_3R_3$$

Note that there are two J_0 output signals, but this should not be confusing because the biquinary code itself has a binary zero and a quinary zero.

The "carry," C (the left-component digit from the next lower order), must be added to the signals generated by the E, G, and J boxes. The quinary part, C_q, is added to the quinary part of J in an error-detecting quinary adder. The "carry input" part of this adder is not used. The output of this adder is the desired quinary part, P_q, of the partial product. The carry output of this adder has a weight of 0 or 5 and must be added to the quinary part of J as well as to C_b and the output signals from the G boxes. Fig. 9-5 shows one way of performing the necessary additions; the input lines on the right-hand ends of the adder boxes represent the carry input lines.

The carry output lines from the binary adder in the figure have a weight of 0 or 50 and may be used as the desired $(C_a)_b$ signals. The Z and X lines in the figure must be translated according to the following relationships to get the desired P_b and $(C_a)_q$ signals.

$$P_0 = Z_0(X_0 + X_{10} + X_{20}) + Z_{25}(X_5 + X_{15})$$

$$P_5 = Z_0(X_5 + X_{15}) + Z_{25}(X_0 + X_{10} + X_{20})$$

$$(C_a)_0 = Z_0(X_0 + X_5)$$

$$(C_a)_{10} = Z_0(X_{10} + X_{15})$$

$$(C_a)_{20} = Z_0X_{20} + Z_{25}X_0$$

$$(C_a)_{30} = Z_{25}(X_5 + X_{10})$$

$$(C_a)_{40} = Z(X_{15} + X_{20})$$

The arrangement has error-detecting properties because every set of binary or quinary signal lines normally transmits one and only one signal, and each output signal in any "box" is generated independently of all other output signals. It is not necessary to apply checking circuits to all of the lines between boxes; instead, it is sufficient to check the product digit P because an error anywhere in the circuit will eventually be transmitted to P. An error in C_a will be detected in the next higher order P digit since the C_a becomes the C of that order.

Serial-parallel Multiplication. One of the fastest known methods of multiplication operates with one factor (the multiplicand) presented in serial form and the other factor (the multiplier) in parallel. The individual bits in the digits may, in principle, be in either serial or parallel form, although parallel bit operation appears more practical. The method is analogous to the serial-parallel scheme described for binary multiplication except that the decimal system introduces substantial complications.

Although the 9 multiples of the multiplicand are being generated by means such as indicated in Fig. 9-3, the arrangement shown in Fig. 9-6 is used to assemble them under the control of the multiplier digits. The lowest-order multiplier digit, R_0, causes the appropriate multiple of the multiplicand to be sent to one set of input lines to one of the decimal adders. The first (lowest-order) digit of this multiple is the correct digit for the final product, and it appears on the output lines of this adder. At the same time, the next higher-order multiplier digit, R_1, causes its corresponding multiple of the multiplicand to be entered into the next decimal adder. The output lines from this adder are sent to the other set of input lines of the first adder, but through delay devices which cause the lowest-order digit of this multiple to be added to the second digit of the multiple obtained through control by R_0. The addition of these two digits may create a carry which is returned to the adder to be added to the sum of the third digit arriving from the multiple obtained through control by R_0 and the second digit arriving from the next adder. Note that the second digit from this next adder is now the sum of the second digit obtained through control by R_1 and the first digit of the multiple obtained through control by R_2.

The process continues in an analogous manner for all orders of the multiplier and multiplicand. A new product digit is determined after each "cycle" of operation; therefore, the time required for multiplication is equal to the number of digits in the product times the time required for one "cycle," and this is simply the time required to transmit the product in serial form.

Although the operation of division will be described in more detail in subsequent paragraphs, it will be mentioned here that no method is known for reversing this method of multiplication to obtain division.

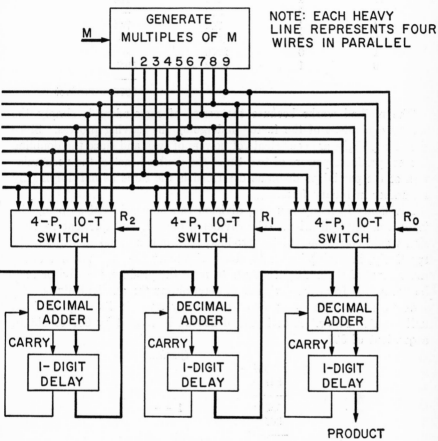

Fig. 9-6. Serial-parallel multiplication.

Multiplication by "Duplation." A frequently discussed but seldom used method of multiplication involves the process sometimes known as "duplation." In this method, one factor is repeatedly halved and the other is repeatedly doubled. Each time a remainder of 1 is obtained from the halving process, the appropriate multiple of the other factor is accumulated in the formation of the product. As example, consider the multiplication of 93 by 75.

268 Arithmetic Operations in Digital Computers

Halved Factor	Remainder	Doubled Factor	Partial Products
75			
37	1	93	93
18	1	186	186
9	0	372	—
4	1	744	744
2	0	1488	—
1	0	2976	—
0	1	5952	5952

6975 = Product

The method works because the series of remainders is simply the binary equivalent of the factor undergoing the halving process. Since the binary digits are coefficients of powers of two, and since the doubling process produces powers of two times the doubled factor, the accumulation of the partial products as described is the same as multiplying by a number in binary form.

Division. In many respects, division can be considered as being the inverse of multiplication. The dividend, divisor, and quotient in division would correspond to the product, multiplicand, and multiplier, respectively, in multiplicand. Instead of adding the multiplicand under the control of the multiplier digits to form the product, the divisor may be subtracted from the dividend in determining the quotient digits. An example of division by over-and-over subtraction in its simplest form is illustrated below. A dividend of 292034 is divided by 967 to obtain a quotient of 302.

	Quotient
292034	
967	
195334	1 – –
967	
98634	2 – –
967	
1934	3 – –
967	
967	3 0 1
967	
0	3 0 2

Each time the divisor is subtracted from the dividend, a 1 is added into the appropriate order of the quotient.

In spite of the many similarities between multiplication and division, there are some difficulties encountered in the division process which are not found in multiplication and which cause division to be a substantially more complex operation than multiplication. The difficulties are of such magnitude that in many computing machines it has been found advantageous to incorporate methods of division which bear little resemblance to the inverse of the multiplication procedure in use.

The first difficulty involves the determination of the proper orders from which to subtract the divisor the first time. In the above example, if the divisor had been 002 instead of 967, the units order of the divisor should have been subtracted from ("lined up with") the hundred-thousands order instead of the hundreds order of the dividend. When employing the usual pencil-and-paper methods of arithmetic, the proper orders from which to make the first subtraction may be readily determined by inspection. However, "inspection" is not necessarily a simple operation to incorporate into a machine. In floating-point computers the problem is not usually serious, because automatic means are provided to cause the digit in each number to be shifted so that the highest-order nonzero digit appears on the left. In fixed-point computers it is necessary that the approximate relative magnitudes of the dividend and divisor be known or that means be installed which will, in effect, determine the approximate relative magnitudes. The sensing of zeros in orders higher than the highest-order nonzero digit in the dividend and in the divisor will yield most of the necessary information. For example, when dividing 008726 by 093, the 9 in the divisor should be lined up with the 7 in the dividend, but if the divisor had been 043, the 4 in the divisor should have been lined up with the 8 in the dividend. To handle all possible combinations of numbers, it is sufficient to line up the highest-order nonzero digit in the divisor with the highest-order nonzero digit in the dividend. In some cases (as in the above example when the divisor is 093), the first quotient digit will be 0, but this does not affect the correctness of the quotient. Of course, it is possible to start the division process with the lowest-order divisor digit lined up with the highest-order dividend digit, regardless of the values of any of the individual digits. However, this process consumes an excessive amount of time for many applications, and the large number of zeros which will be obtained before the first nonzero quotient digit in most practical problems will cause complications in the efficient utilization of the significant digits in the quotient.

The second difficulty encountered in division is the determination of when to subtract the divisor from the dividend. Probably the most straightforward way to make this determination is actually to perform the subtraction and then to add the divisor if the subtraction caused a negative remainder. The division of 292034 by 967 would then be accomplished by the following steps.

			Quotient
Sub.		292034 967	
		———	
Sub.		195334 967	1 – –
		———	
Sub.		98634 967	2 – –
		———	
Sub.		01934 967	3 – –
		———	
Add	(−)	05234 967	3 – –
		———	
Sub.		01934 967	3 – –
		———	
Add	(−)	92264 967	3 0 –
		———	
Sub.		01934 967	3 0 –
		———	
Sub.		00967 00967	3 0 1
		———	
Sub.		00000 967	3 0 2
		———	
Add	(−)	99033 967	3 0 2
		———	
		00000	3 0 2

The appropriate digit in the quotient is increased by 1 only when the subtraction of the divisor does not cause the remainder to become negative. The number of operations (additions and subtractions) required for each quotient digit is two greater than the value of the digit. The quotient digit of 0, for example, requires two operations—a subtraction to determine that the digit should be 0 and an addition to correct the negative remainder which is obtained. The quotient digit, 9, is an exception to the rule. If the remainder has not become negative after a series of nine subtractions, it is known that the corresponding quotient digit must be 9 unless an error has been made at an earlier point in the division operation or unless the divisor was not correctly lined up with the dividend at the start of the operation. The tenth subtraction should always cause a negative remainder; therefore, the tenth subsequent corrective addition may be eliminated. An average of 6.3 operations per quotient digit are required for random quotient digits.

A third difficulty encountered in division involves the final remainder. In cases where the dividend is not an exact multiple of the divisor, the division process may yield an endless series of digits for the quotient. It is customary to obtain one more quotient digit than is desired and then to round off the quotient so that the digits retained will represent a quantity which is as close to the exact quotient as it is possible to represent with the number of quotient digits retained. Round-off procedures will be discussed in more detail in a later paragraph.

Increasing the Speed of the Division Process. There are a few available tricks that may be employed to improve upon the speed of the division process. One such trick is to shift and perform over-and-over addition when the remainder becomes negative instead of adding the divisor and then shifting. This variation may be used because the subtraction which caused the remainder to become negative has the same effect as ten subtractions in the determination of the next lower-order quotient digit. The next lower-order quotient digit therefore may be determined by noting which addition operation causes the remainder to become positive again. Consider the division of 201,136 by 967 according to this method.

		Quotient
	201136	
Sub.	967	
	104436	1 – –
Sub.	967	
	007736	2 – –
Sub.	967	
	(−) 911036	2 (10) –
Add	967	
	(−) 920706	2 9 –
Add	967	
	(−) 930376	2 8 –
Add	967	
	(−) 940046	2 7 –
Add	967	
	(−) 949716	2 6 –
Add	967	
	(−) 959386	2 5 –
Add	967	
	(−) 969056	2 4 –
Add	967	
	(−) 978726	2 3 –
Add	967	
	(−) 988396	2 2 –
Add	967	
	(−) 998066	2 0 (10)
Add	967	
	(−) 999033	2 0 9
Add	967	
	(+) 000000	2 0 8

In the determination of the second quotient digit (0 in this example), the 9th addition of the divisor still did not cause the remainder to become positive. Since the 10th addition must necessarily cause the remainder to become positive, it need not be executed; instead the divisor may be shifted to the right and the determination of the next quotient digit may be commenced immediately. The number of operations required for each quotient digit is as follows.

Quotient Digit	When Subtracting	When Adding
0	1	9
1	2	9
2	3	8
3	4	7
4	5	6
5	6	5
6	7	4
7	8	3
8	9	2
9	9	1

For random digits in the quotient, an average of 5.4 operations per quotient digit are required.

The use of doubling and quintupling is not as fruitful for division as it is for multiplication, although some gain in speed may be achieved. For example the quintupled divisor may be subtracted to determine whether the quotient digit is equal to 5 or greater, or whether it is less than 5. However, if a negative remainder is corrected simply by adding back the quintupled divisor, little is saved. For example, if the quotient digit happens to be 0, four operations are required. After subtracting and adding the quintupled divisor, it is still necessary to subtract and add the divisor itself in determining the 0. For random digits in the quotient it turns out that, as with the division method described above, 5.4 operations per quotient digit are required on the average.

If the divisor and its quintupled value (indicated by a 5 and a 1, respectively) are handled according to the following pattern, with shifting and addition when a negative balance is obtained, a reduction to 3.8 operations per quotient digit may be achieved.

Quotient Digit	When "Subtracting"	When "Adding"
0	−5 +1 +1 +1 +1 (N)	+5 +1 +1 +1 +1 (N)
1	−5 +1 +1 +1 +1	+5 +1 +1 +1 +1
2	−5 +1 +1 +1	+5 +1 +1 +1
3	−5 +1 +1	+5 +1 +1
4	−5 +1	+5 +1
5	−5 −1 (N)	+5 −1 (N)
6	−5 −1 −1 (N)	+5 −1 −1 (N)
7	−5 −1 −1 −1 (N)	+5 −1 −1 −1 (N)
8	−5 −1 −1 −1 −1 (N)	+5 −1 −1 −1 −1 (N)
9	−5 −1 −1 −1 −1	+5 −1 −1 −1 −1

The letter, N, indicates the cases when the remainder is negative and "addition" should be used to obtain the next quotient digit. Note that it is for the quotient digits 0, 5, 6, 7, or 8 whether that particular digit was obtained by a "subtraction" or addition process.

If doubling is combined with addition and subtraction according to the following pattern, an average of 4.0 operations per quotient digit are required.

Quotient Digit	When "Subtracting"		When "Adding"	
0	−2 +1	(N)	+2 +2 +2 +2 +2 −1	(N)
1	−2 +1		+2 +2 +2 +2 +2 −1	
2	−2 −2 +1	(N)	+2 +2 +2 +2 −1	(N)
3	−2 −2 +1		+2 +2 +2 +2 −1	
4	−2 −2 −2 +1	(N)	+2 +2 +2 −1	(N)
5	−2 −2 −2 +1		+2 +2 +2 −1	
6	−2 −2 −2 −2 +1	(N)	+2 +2 −1	(N)
7	−2 −2 −2 −2 +1		+2 +2 −1	
8	−2 −2 −2 −2 −2 +1	(N)	+2 −1	(N)
9	−2 −2 −2 −2 −2 +1		+2 −1	

By combining doubling and quintupling with addition and subtraction, the required number of operations for division is reduced to 3.4 per quotient digit. The steps required for each quotient digit are as follows.

Quotient Digit	When "Subtracting"		When "Adding"	
0	−5 +2 +2	(N)	+5 +2 +2	(N)
1	−5 +2 +2 −1	(N)	+5 +2 +2 −1	(N)
2	−5 +2 +2 −1		+5 +2 +2 −1	
3	−5 +2 −1	(N)	+5 +2 −1	(N)
4	−5 +2 −1		+5 +2 −1	
5	−5 −2 +1	(N)	+5 −2 +1	(N)
6	−5 −2 +1		+5 −2 +1	
7	−5 −2 −2 +1	(N)	+5 −2 −2 +1	(N)
8	−5 −2 −2 +1		+5 −2 −2 +1	
9	−5 −2 −2		+5 −2 −2	

If the first quotient digit is 1, for example, the subtraction of the quintupled divisor will cause a negative remainder. The addition of the doubled divisor will not cause the remainder to become positive again, but the second addition of the doubled divisor will create a positive remainder. At this point it is known that the quotient digit is either 1 or 2. A subtraction of the divisor will then create a negative remainder to provide the final determination. Since the remainder is negative, the next quotient digit should be determined by an "adding" process. If the remainder had remained negative after the second addition of the doubled divisor, a quotient digit of 0 would have been indicated. The other quotient digits are determined in an analogous manner.

By making all nine multiples of the divisor available, such as with the arrangement shown in Fig. 9-3, a much faster division method is possible. Each multiple (appropriately lined up) is compared with the dividend or the remainder by means of nine separate comparing circuits. Each comparing circuit may consist of means for performing a subtraction, but since only the carries are needed to determine the sign of the difference, the portions of the circuits which generate the difference digits may be eliminated. The largest multiple which leaves a positive remainder after subtraction is noted because it determines the quotient digit, and then this multiple is actually subtracted. For the determination of the next quotient digit, the nine multiples of the divisor are compared with the new remainder. In computers where the digits are handled serially, the comparison for the determination of the new quotient digit may proceed at substantially the same time as the subtraction of the divisor multiple corresponding to the previous quotient digit because the digits of the new remainder are made available for the comparison as rapidly as the subtraction progresses. With this method of operation, division may proceed at the rate of 1.0 operation per quotient digit.

Division by "Duplation." It is possible to reverse the "duplation" process which was described for multiplication and obtain another method of division except that it is necessary as a first step to find the largest power of two times the divisor which can be subtracted from the dividend. Since this determination of the starting point requires approximately the same amount of time (unless a very elaborate system of doubling and comparing circuits is employed) as the division process itself, the method is not particularly attractive.

The initial doubling procedure may be avoided if the decimal point of either the dividend or the divisor is shifted in a manner to make the dividend no greater than twice the divisor. The divisor is repeatedly halved; each time it is less than the dividend (or remainder) a subtraction is performed. Concurrently, the digit, 1, is halved; and each time a subtraction is performed the corresponding fractional part of 1 is accumulated to form the quotient. To illustrate the process, 6,557 is divided by 79.

Divisor	Dividend		
79	65.57	1.0	
	39.5		
	———		
39.5	26.07	0.5	0.5
	19.75		
	———		
19.75	6.32	0.25	0.25
9.875		0.125	
	4.9375		
	———		
4.9375	1.3825	0.0625	0.0625
2.46875		0.03125	
	1.234375		
	———		
1.234375	0.148125	0.015625	0.015625
0.6171875		0.0078125	
0.30859375		0.00390625	
			———
			0.828125
			Quotient

Since the decimal point was shifted two places to the left in the dividend, it must be shifted two places to the right in the quotient. The quotient, 82.8125, is only an approximation to the correct quotient, which is 83. The process could be continued to yield a more accurate approximation, but the exact value could never be found in this example because, in reality, a conversion between a binary fraction and a decimal fraction is being made. This division method can produce an exact representation of the quotient only in those instances where the quotient (expressed as a quantity less than 1) can be represented exactly in both the binary and decimal number systems.

Division Through the Use of Trial Quotient Digits. In some computing machines a division process somewhat similar to the pencil-and-paper method has been incorporated. The divisor is "compared" with the dividend or remainder and a trial quotient digit is selected. The divisor is multiplied by the trial quotient digit and then subtracted from the appropriate orders of the dividend. If the remainder is positive and less than the divisor, the trial quotient digit is the correct quotient digit. In the pencil-and-paper method, if these conditions are not satisfied, the work is erased and another trial quotient digit is selected. In a computer, the speed of division may be increased by comparing the divisor with the new remainder and proceeding in a similar manner regardless of the magnitude or sign of the new remainder. Appropriate amounts are added or subtracted from the quotient digits as they are developed.

The comparison of the divisor and the dividend can be made in a variety of ways. By making a very elaborate comparison, a very good determination of the trial quotient digit may be made. In a sense, the comparing of all nine multiples of the divisor with the dividend (described in a previous paragraph) is the carrying of this process to its extreme. At the other end of the scale, only the highest-order digit of the divisor need be compared with only the highest-order digit of the dividend. At least one computer (IBM's Type 602A) operates in this fashion. The trial multiplier digit is selected according to Table 9-III. Note that only the 1st, 2nd, and 5th multiples of the divisor are

TABLE 9-III. ONE SYSTEM FOR DETERMINATION OF TRIAL MULTIPLIER DIGIT

		Highest-order Dividend Digit								
		1	2	3	4	5	6	7	8	9
Highest-order Divisor Digit	1	1	2	2	2	5	5	5	5	5
	2	.5	1	1	2	2	2	2	2	5
	3	.5	.5	1	1	2	2	2	2	2
	4	.2	.5	1	1	1	1	2	2	2
	5	.2	.5	.5	1	1	1	1	2	2
	6	.2	.5	.5	.5	1	1	1	1	1
	7	.2	.2	.5	.5	.5	1	1	1	1
	8	.2	.2	.5	.5	.5	1	1	1	1
	9	.2	.2	.5	.5	.5	.5	1	1	1

employed. The 0.2 and 0.5 multiples are the same as the 2nd and 5th multiples, respectively, except that each digit in the multiple is shifted to the next lower order. To illustrate the division process more clearly, the division of 206,362 by 473 will be worked out as an example.

		206362	*Quotient* 0000
473		206362	0000
Sub.		2365	+0.5
	(−)	30138	500
Add		473	−1
	(+)	17162	400
Sub.		946	+0.2
	(+)	7702	420
Sub.		946	+2
	(−)	1758	440
Add		946	−0.2
	(−)	812	438
Add		946	2
	(+)	134	436

In the determination of the trial multiplier digit, the divisor in this example is considered as being divided into the first three nonzero dividend
digits. For this reason, the first trial multiplier digit is 0.5 in the thousands order instead of 5 in the hundreds order. As the division operation progresses, the determination of each trial multiplier digit is made
by comparing the highest-order divisor digit (4 in this example) with
the highest-order nonzero digit in the remainder occurring at the corresponding point in the process. If the final remainder should happen to
be negative, the situation may be corrected by adding the divisor and
subtracting 1 from the quotient.

In another computer (IBM's Type 602), all nine multiples of the
divisor are available so that the trial multiplier digit may have any
value from 1 through 9. Also, the first two digits of the divisor are
compared with the first two digits of the multiplicand, and the trial
multiplier digit is selected in accordance with a relatively complex selection table. Twenty-three different combinations of the first two digits
of the dividend and of the divisor are utilized in the table. If the first
two digits do not happen to be one of these twenty-three combinations,
the next higher valued combination in the twenty-three is used. With
this arrangement, the trial quotient digit may be in error by 1. If this
is the case, the machine senses the fact after the subtraction of the multiple of the divisor from the dividend, and it then corrects the quotient
digit by an appropriate addition or subtraction of the divisor and a
decrease or increase of the quotient digit depending upon whether the
trial digit was too great or too small.

Decimal Multiplication and Division   279

Division by Iteration—First Method. There are several different methods available for performing division whereby the desired result is obtained through a series of successively better approximations rather than by a straightforward determination of the quotient digits one at a time. One such method was mentioned in connection with binary division. In this method, division is performed by first obtaining the reciprocal of the divisor through an iterative process and then multiplying this reciprocal by the dividend. Two different formulas for obtaining the reciprocal are, in decimal notation,

$$b_{k+1} = b_k(2 - xb_k)$$

$$b_{k+1} = b_k[3(1 - xb_k) + (xb_k)^2]$$

where x is the number for which the reciprocal is being obtained and the b_k are the successive approximations to the reciprocal. The first approximation, b_0, may be chosen in an arbitrary manner provided that it is greater than zero and less than $2/x$; if b_0 is outside of this range, the series will not converge. The first equation given above is "second order" and the other equation is "third order," which means that once a reasonably close approximation is obtained, the number of correct digits in the approximation is doubled and tripled, respectively, upon each application of the equation.

One straightforward way of determining how many applications of the equation are required for finding the reciprocal is to compare each $b_k + 1$ with b_k by means of a subtraction. If the difference between the two successive approximations is less than the allowed error for the reciprocal, the process is complete.

It is possible to design a computer which performs division according to this process, but the process is probably of more interest in connection with the performing of division on a computer in which division is not a built-in operation. The various operations in the iterative process would be executed by means of an appropriate program which would be a part or a sub-program of the main program for solving the problem in which the division operation is one step.

Division by Iteration—Second Method. The division method used in the Harvard Mark IV computer makes use of the iterative equation,

$$\frac{N_{i+1}}{D_{i+1}} = \frac{(2 - D_i)N_i}{(2 - D_i)D_i}$$

where N_0 is the dividend and D_0 is the divisor. If D_0 is made less than 1, then it can be shown that

$$D_0 < D_1 < 1$$

In practice, the divisor is multiplied by an appropriate power of ten to cause D_0 to be equal to, or greater than, 0.1 but less than 1. After repeated applications of the iterative equation, D_i approaches 1. Further, N_i approaches the quotient because the ratio between N_i and D_i is not changed when both the numerator and the denominator are multiplied by the same factor, $2 - D_i$.

By employing only approximations to the quantities, $2 - D_i$, the speed of the division process may be increased.   If d_i is taken to be the highest-order nonzero digit of $1 - D_i$ (that is: $d_i \simeq 1 - D_i$), then $1 + d_i \simeq 2 - D_i$. The digit, d_i, is readily determined by taking the 9's complement of the highest-order nonnine digit in D_i. Although the use of this approximation increases the number of times the iterative equation must be applied to obtain a given number of significant digits in the quotient, the multiplications are rendered so much simpler that there is a net saving in division time.   When the approximation, $1 + d_i$, is used, each multiplication involves a multiplication by only one digit plus one addition operation.

At the start of the division process, N_0 is placed in a register with its highest-order nonzero digit in the second highest order of the register. The reason for this step is that the multiplications by the $1 + d_i$ may cause carries into the highest order. Either N_0 or D_0, or both may have been shifted in the initial steps of the division operation, and it is necessary to record these shifts so that the decimal point may be properly placed in the quotient. It is desirable to make the digit capacity of the registers holding N_i and D_i one or two digits greater than the number

TABLE 9-IV.   EXAMPLE OF DIVISION BY ITERATION (SECOND METHOD)

i	N_i	D_i	$1 + d_i$
0	0359	.273	1.7
1	06103	.4641	1.5
2	091545	.69615	1.3
3	1190085	.904995	1.09
4	129719265	.98644455	1.01
5	13101645765	.9963089955	1.003
6	13140950702295	.9992979224865	1.0007
7	1315014936778660	.9999974319322405	1.000002
8	1315017566808534	.9999994310271026	1.0000005
9	1315018224317317	.9999999310268181	1.00000006
10	1315018303218411	.9999999910268139	1.000000008
11	1315018313738557	.9999999990268139	1.0000000009
12	1315018314922073		1.00000000007
13	1315018315014125		1.000000000003
14	1315018315018070		

$$\tfrac{359}{273} = 1.315018315018315\cdots$$

of digits to be retained in the quotient in order to reduce the effect of round-off errors.

As D_i approaches 1, a point will be reached (depending upon the number of digits retained) where subsequent multiplications by $1 + d_i$ will have no more effect than to cause the digits of D_i to change to 9, one at a time. At this point, multiplications of D_i by $1 + d_i$ may be stopped with each subsequent d_i digit determined by taking the 9's of the appropriate digit in D_i. The division of 359 by 273 is set forth in Table 9-IV as an example.

Division by Iteration—Third Method. Many variations to the above method of division may be worked out. One such variation which has several points of difference will be described as an example. In order to obtain the first correct quotient digit in less steps, both the dividend and divisor are initially multiplied by a factor which causes the first two digits in the divisor to be either 0.9 or 1.0. Note that the ratio between the dividend and divisor, and therefore the quotient, is not changed by this operation. In the division of 359 by 273 as illustrated in Table 9-V, a multiplier of 4 brings the divisor into the desired range;

TABLE 9-V. EXAMPLE OF DIVISION BY ITERATION (THIRD METHOD)

i	N_i	D_i	$2 - D_i$
—	0.359	0.273	
0	1.436	1.092	$1 - 0.09$
1	1.30676	0.9̄9̄372	$1 + 0.0063$
2	1.314992588	0.999̄9̄80436	$1 + 0.00001957$
3	1.3150183224049476	1.00000000561713252	$1 - 0.0000000056171325$
4	1.31501831501831500		

for some divisors a two-digit multiplier is necessary. The term, D_0, is now equal to 1.092 and N_0 is equal to 1.436.

Here, D_0 happens to be greater than 1, but in this case

$$D_0 > D_1 > 1$$

and the D_i approach unity just the same.

The next step in the division process is to examine the second digit to the right of the decimal point in the divisor. This second digit is used as an approximation for $D_0 - 1$. If this quantity is subtracted from 1, the result is approximately $2 - D_0$, which is the multiplier desired for obtaining N_1 and D_1. In the example, the second digit is 9, but instead of using a multiplier of 0.91, the term, D_1, is obtained by subtracting $0.09D_0$ from D_0, and N_1 is obtained in a similar manner.

To obtain an approximation for $D_1 - 1$, the third and fourth digits to the right of the decimal point in D_1 may be used. In the example, D_1 happens to be less than 1 with the result that the approximation to $2 - D_1$ is 1.0063 since the third and fourth digits are 37. The multiplier for D_2 is obtained in a similar manner except that the fifth through the seventh digits to the right of the point in D_2 are used. In the table, the digits used for obtaining the multiplier are indicated by underlining. For each D_i, twice as many digits are used in the approximation as in the immediately preceding step, and the highest-order digit in the group is in the order one lower than the lowest-order digit of the previous group.

The D_i may oscillate above and below 1; each time D_i is less than 1, the 10's complement of the digits used in the approximation are employed as the multiplier, but when D_i is greater than 1 the true value of the digits are used. In the table each approximation to $2 - D_i$ is recorded as shown, because in those cases where it is less than 1 the multiplications can be performed more rapidly in two parts with one multiplier being simply unity and with a negative quantity for the other multiplier.

Note that the number of successive 0's or 9's to the right of the point in D_i is an indication of the number of correct quotient digits in the corresponding N_i. The speed of the division operation may be increased by sensing the 0's or 9's in the D_i and employing an equal number of digits to the right for use in the approximation to $2 - D_i$. The increase in speed so obtained can be quite great for some examples but would be relatively small on the average. In the example presented, there would be no increase at all in speed.

Round-off Procedures. In multiplication, the number of significant digits in the product is, in general, equal to the number of significant digits in the multiplier or the multiplicand, whichever has the least. Similarly, in division, the number of significant digits in the quotient is no greater than the number of significant digits in the divisor or the dividend, whichever has the least. It is usually desirable that the non-significant digits be discarded, but it is often also desirable that the retained digits be the number with the greatest probability of being the closest possible approximation to the exact value (which may or may not be determinable) of the quantity being represented. For example, if 0.573 is multiplied by 0.605, the product is 0.346665. However, if only three digits in each factor are significant, it is implied that there is some doubt about the accuracy of the third digit in each factor, and only three digits in the product should be retained. If the accuracy of the factors is ±0.0005, the exact value of the product could be any value in the range from 0.34607625 to 0.34725425. The three-digit number which is the closest approximation to the exact value of the product depends upon what the exact values of the factors happen to be, and it could be either 0.346 to 0.347, but the number with the greater probability of being the closest approximation is 0.347 (unless, of course, it is known that the -0.0005 tolerance limit is more likely to apply than the $+0.0005$ tolerance limit).

Also, even though certain digits may be significant in the mathematical sense, it may be desirable for one reason or another to ignore them. One example occurs in accounting problems where money quantities are not represented more accurately than can be represented by the money system in use. Examples of this type occur particularly frequently in interest and other problems where percentages are involved. Consider the problem of finding 1.5% of $614.12. The 1.5% is usually assumed to be exact, which means that it contains an infinite number of significant digits; in other words, all zeros to the right of the 5 are significant. Since there are five significant digits in $614.12, the product of the two numbers has five mathematically significant digits, but not more than three ($9.21) are desired in this case, because the fourth and lower-order digits correspond to money values less than can be represented in the dollars-and-cents system. Another example of where mathematically significant digits are dropped occurs even in purely mathematical problems. Consider the division of 2 by 3 where the 2 and 3 are integers. The quotient contains an infinite number of significant digits, but for purely practical reasons only a finite number of them can be retained. In both examples it is desired that the retained digits represent the exact quantity with the minimum amount of error.

The eliminating of the lower-order digits in a number is known as round-off. Whenever digits are discarded for any of the reasons mentioned above, the desired result with regard to the accuracy of the approximation can usually be achieved by using a round-off procedure whereby 1 is added to the lowest-order retained digit if the highest-order digit which is discarded is 5 or greater. Then, for example, when rounding $0.3695\cdots$ to a 3-digit number, the result would be 0.370, and $0.3692\cdots$ would be rounded to 0.369.

If the number to be rounded were exactly 0.3695, either 0.369 or 0.370 would be equally desirable from the standpoint of accuracy, but it is customary to use the next higher value, or 0.370 in this case. When rounding 4-digit numbers, which are exact representations, to 3-digit numbers, the average error for a large number of round-off operations will not be zero, but will be equivalent to $+5$ in the 5th order if the digits are random. When rounding 5-digit numbers to 3-digit numbers, the average round-off error will be $+5$ in the 6th order. The average

284 Arithmetic Operations in Digital Computers

error for a large number of round-off operations depends upon the number of digits required to give exact representations of the quantities involved and approaches zero as this number of digits approaches infinity.

When the above round-off procedure is applied to negative numbers represented in complement form, a number such as 0.3695 will be rounded the wrong way if it is an exact representation. For example, the 10's complement of the number is 0.6305, and this will become 0.631 after round-off. The result in true form is equivalent to 0.369 instead of 0.370. The most straightforward way out of the difficulty is to convert all numbers to true form before applying the round-off procedure. When 9's complements are employed, it happens that the difficulty may be avoided by subtracting 1 from the lowest-order retained digit when the highest-order discarded digit is 0 through 4. With this system the 9's complement of 0.3695 is 0.6304, which becomes 0.629, and is equivalent to 0.370 in true form, as desired.

In a computer the sensing of the highest digit which is to be discarded may not be a convenient operation. It may be more convenient to place the number to be rounded into an accumulator and to add a 5 into the highest order to be dropped. A carry from this order to higher orders will then occur if the digit already there is 5 or greater. The resulting digit will be incorrect, but it is to be discarded anyway, and the carry causes the desired 1 to be added to the retained digits. A variation in the procedure is to double the highest-order digit to be discarded. The doubled digit will be 10 or greater only if the original digit was 5 or greater and the carry so produced may be used in the same way.

In the case of division where the quotient is being built up in a register which does not have facilities for handling carries, a somewhat different round-off procedure is sometimes useful. Instead of adding 5 to the highest-order quotient digit to be dropped, 5 times the divisor is added to the corresponding orders of the dividend before the actual division process is started. The effect on the retained digits in the rounded quotient is the same and all carry problems are handled in the register which holds the dividend, where carry-handling facilities are needed for the regular division process.

In cases where the major requirement is that the rounded number have equal probability of being greater than, or smaller than, the exact value, certain other round-off procedures may be used which may be more readily incorporated into a computer. One such procedure is to make the lowest or retained digit a 5 regardless of the correct value of that digit and digits in lower orders. With this procedure the rounded number may be too large by as much as 5 in the lowest order retained, or may be as much as 4.999··· too small, but the error averaged over a large number of round-off operations is approximately zero if random digits are assumed.

Another procedure which has been used is to add (with carries) a 0 or a 1 in a random fashion into the lowest retained order regardless of the values of the digits in the number being rounded. It is difficult to repeat computations for checking purposes when numbers are rounded in this way, but the maximum error is reduced to the range of $+1$ and $-0.999\cdots$ in the lowest retained order, and the average error is still approximately zero. Neither of these two procedures yield results that are as accurate as those obtainable with the previously described procedures, where the range of error was from $+0.5$ to $-0.4999\cdots$.

A slightly different round-off procedure is to add 1 to the lowest-order retained digit when it is even and add nothing when it is odd. When the digits are represented in the 8,4,2,1 code, as an example, this procedure is particularly simple because it can be accomplished merely by making the 1-bit of the lowest order a 1 regardless of whether it was originally a 1 or a 0. The rounded number may be as much as 1 greater than or $0.999\cdots$ less than the exact representation. One disadvantage of the procedure is that zero will never be obtained as a result regardless of the factors which entered into the computation. This disadvantage may be avoided by modifying the procedure to the adding of the 1 when the lowest-order digit is odd instead of even. However, in this case it is necessary to provide for the propagation of the carry which will occur when the lowest-order digit is 9.

Chapter 10

MISCELLANEOUS OPERATIONS

Decimal-to-Binary Conversion. In many cases where a binary computer is employed it is desired to retain the decimal system for the representation of the input data and the computed results. For this purpose it is necessary that means be provided for converting numbers from one system to the other. While the conversion is not at all difficult, it is, at the same time, not as simple an operation as one might imagine at first glance. A machine of substantial complexity is required. Frequently, it is found advantageous to use the binary computer itself to perform the conversion. The decimal numbers may be entered into the computer as sets of 1's and 0's in any appropriate decimal code. The computer is then caused to operate upon the sets of 1's and 0's as though they were binary numbers, and through a suitable program of operations the computer converts the coded decimal numbers to true binary numbers.

A great variety of mathematical procedures may be used to perform the conversion. The particular scheme chosen in a given instance is usually dependent on the characteristics and special features of the machine in question. However, in practically all cases the conversion procedure is a variation of one of the several basic procedures described below.

One of the simplest pencil-and-paper methods of converting an integer in the decimal system to its representation in the binary system is repeated division of the decimal number by 2. Each time that a remainder of 1 occurs in the division process, a 1 is entered in the appropriate order of the binary number. For example, if the first division by 2 produces a remainder of 1, the lowest-order binary digit is 1. That this is so may be understood by observing that the remainder determines whether the decimal number was odd or even, and in a binary number the value of the lowest-order digit determines whether it is odd or even. The remainders from the second and succeeding divisions by 2 determine whether the decimal number is made up of odd or even quantities of 2's, 4's, 8's, etc.; and this information is exactly the same as is contained in the respective digits of a binary number.

If the decimal number is a fraction instead of an integer, it should be repeatedly multiplied by 2 instead of divided by 2, and each time a carry into the units order occurs, the corresponding digit is 1 in the binary representation. For example, when the decimal fraction is 0.5 or greater, the first multiplication by 2 will cause a carry and indicate that 1 is the correct digit in the first position to the right of the point in the binary number. The second multiplication by 2 will produce a carry if the decimal fraction contained an amount equal to or greater than 0.25 in excess of 0.0 or 0.5, whichever the case may be. The second digit to the right of the point in the binary number is 1 or 0 depending upon whether or not there is a carry from the second multiplication. Succeeding binary digits are determined one at a time in an analogous maner.

To illustrate these methods of conversion, the steps involved in converting the decimal integer, 243, and the decimal fraction, 0.413, are given below.

Integer			Fraction	
243			0.413	
121	1		0.826	0.0
60	11		1.652	0.01
30	011		1.304	0.011
15	0011		0.608	0.0110
7	10011		1.216	0.01101
3	110011		0.432	0.011010
1	1110011		0.864	0.0110100
0	11110011		1.728	0.01101001
			1.456	0.011010011
			0.912	0.0110100110

Note that a decimal integer always has an exact representation in the binary system. A fraction may not have an exact representation, but the binary equivalent may be determined to any desired degree of accuracy through the determination of a sufficient number of binary digits.

A second method of converting a decimal number to its binary equivalent is to subtract powers of 2 (in decimal notation) from the given number. The powers of 2 are subtracted in sequence starting with the largest power of 2 which is less than the given number. Each power of 2 which would produce a negative difference is not subtracted, and the corresponding digit in the binary number is 1 or 0, depending upon whether the subtraction is or is not performed. This method, as applied to the same examples, is set forth below.

	243			0.413	
2^7	128	1-------	2^{-2}	0.25	0.01
	115			0.163	
2^6	64	11------	2^{-3}	0.125	0.011
	51			0.038	
2^5	32	111-----	2^{-5}	0.03125	0.01101
	19			0.00675	
2^4	16	1111----	2^{-8}	0.00390625	0.01101001
	3			0.00284375	
2^1	2	1111001-			
	1				
2^0	1	11110011			
	0				

For most applications this method does not appear particularly attractive, because the powers of 2 in the decimal system are rather awkward to handle and because it is not always a simple matter to mechanize the determination of which powers of 2 should be subtracted and which should not be subtracted.

The conversion methods described above employed the decimal system, but it is possible to execute the conversion with the binary system, if desired. One such procedure is to examine the digits in the decimal number, one at a time, starting with the highest order if the number is an integer. The binary equivalent of the highest-order digit is recorded in the lowest four binary orders to the left of the point. This amount is then multiplied by 1010 (decimal ten) and the binary equivalent of the next decimal digit is added to the product. This process is repeated for each digit in the decimal number. If the number to be converted is a fraction, the digits are handled in the opposite sequence, and the intermediate results are divided by 1010 instead of multiplied by 1010. Note the binary equivalents of 0.1, 0.2, etc., must be represented in binary form by at least as many binary digits as are desired in the final converted number. The sample conversions by this procedure are as follows.

Integer 243

Add 0010 (2)	0010
Multiply by 1010	10100
Add 0100 (4)	11000
Multiply by 1010	11110000
Add 0011 (3)	11110011

Fraction 0.413

Add 0.010011001101 (0.3)	0.010011001101
Divide by 1010	0.000001111011
Add 0.00011011010 (0.1)	0.001000010101
Divide by 1010	0.000000110101
Add 0.011001100110 (0.4)	0.011010011011

Another conversion procedure employing the binary system is the over-and-over addition of the binary equivalents of one, ten, one hundred, etc., in the case of integers and one tenth, one hundredth, etc., in the case of fractions. When using this method of conversion the steps would be as follows.

Integer 243

Add 1100100 (decimal 100) twice	11001000
Add 1010 (decimal 10) four times	11110000
Add 1 (decimal 1) three times	11110011

Fraction 0.413

Add 0.000110011010 (decimal 0.1) four times	0.011001101000
Add 0.000000101001 (decimal 0.01) once	0.011010010001
Add 0.000000000100 (decimal 0.001) three times	0.011010011101

The reason that the lower-order digits in the binary representations of the fractional example do not agree is that the round-off errors are not the same in the different conversion methods. The round-off error is likely to be particularly great with the last-described conversion method; on the other hand, this method is adaptable to a simple binary accumulator and the round-off error can be minimized by using a few extra orders in the accumulator.

Binary-to-Decimal Conversion. To obtain results in decimal form when a binary computer is used, a binary-to-decimal conversion is, of course, necessary. The computer itself may in some cases be used to perform the conversion by properly manipulating the binary digits in the numbers to cause them to represent decimal digits according to a suitable code. In other cases a separate machine for the conversion may be desired. Each of the four methods described for decimal-to-binary conversion has its direct counterpart in binary-to-decimal conversion.

For binary integers the conversion to decimal form can be made by repeated division by 1010 (decimal ten), and the remainder after each division operation indicates the corresponding decimal digit. For example, in converting 11110011 to decimal form, a division by 1010 yields a quotient of 11000 and a remainder of 0011. The 0011 is the lowest-order digit, 3, in the decimal equivalent. The higher-order decimal digits are found, one at a time, by similar division operations.

The counterpart of the second conversion method which was described for decimal-to-binary operation would be the over-and-over subtraction of powers of ten from the binary number to be converted.

One way of performing the conversion in the decimal system would be to examine the binary digits, one at a time, in sequence, with the highest-order digit examined first. The decimal number is then developed by alternately adding the binary digits and doubling.

Another method of conversion using the decimal system is simply the accumulation of the decimal equivalents of each of the binary digits in the binary number.

Although the binary-to-decimal conversion procedures as outlined above are for integers, the procedures may be modified for fractions in substantially the same manner as the procedures were modified for fractions in decimal-to-binary conversion. The same problems with regard to round-off are encountered.

Comparison. When performing arithmetic by the pencil-and-paper method, the comparison of two numbers is no problem because it is easy to determine at a glance whether or not the two numbers are equal; and, if they are not equal, to determine which is the larger. The operation of comparison is not difficult to mechanize, but it is frequently more complex than a simple "inspection."

Probably the most direct method to use for the determination of relative magnitudes of two numbers in a computer is to subtract one from the other and sense the sign of the difference. The method is particularly convenient in most computers because the same circuits and components used for subtraction may be used for comparison. However, the method leaves something to be desired in the case where the two numbers are equal. For example, if X is being compared with Y and the comparison is made by subtracting X from Y, a positive difference indicates $X \leq Y$ and a negative difference indicates $X \geq Y$. If the comparison is made by subtracting Y from X, a positive difference indicates $X \geq Y$. To make the determination that $X = Y$, it is necessary to perform both subtractions and to sense that the difference is positive each time.

As an alternative to performing the two subtractions it is usually found desirable to install in the computer means for determining that a number is zero. Zero-detection circuits may take on a variety of forms. When electromagnetic components are used, it is generally a relatively simple matter to design the digit-storage devices to include contacts which close when the device contains the digit 0. If several such contacts are connected in series, a closed circuit through the group is an indication that all the digits in the group are 0. With other types of components the physical realization of zero-detection circuits may not be so obvious but, in principle, all that is required is an "and" switch which will produce an output only when each individual digit-storage device contains zero. When decimal digits are being stored through the use of some code, such as the 8,4,2,1 code, it is necessary to sense all four of the individual binary digits to determine that the decimal digit is zero; with the 1-out-of-10 code the sensing of the binary digit corresponding to zero would, of course, be sufficient. In some cases where it is necessary to sense all binary digits it may be more convenient to use an "or" switch which will yield a signal whenever the number is not zero.

Another zero-detection method which is sometimes useful is to convert the number to complement form and add 1. For example, in the decimal system zero $(00\cdots0)$ would be converted to 9's complement form $(99\cdots9)$ and the addition of 1 would cause a carry in the highest order. If the number were any value other than zero, the addition of 1 would not have caused the carry. The presence of the carry in the highest order can therefore be used as an indication that each digit in the original number was a zero.

If desired, circuits may be designed which will compare two numbers without actually performing any subtraction or zero-detection operations. For example, to determine that two numbers are equal the corresponding bits of each number may be compared in a set of half adders (sum parts only). If the outputs of all half adders as sensed by an "and" switch are zero, the two numbers are equal circuits for the determination of which of two numbers is larger may be designed in exactly the same manner as the borrow portion of a subtracter would be designed; the difference portion is not required.

Although the operation of comparison is not as complex as many of the other arithmetic operations in a digital computer, its importance should not be overlooked. Through the comparison of numbers in a sequence of computations, the computer can be caused to proceed automatically through one of two or more different routines of computation. Since the person preparing the problem does not know in advance the results of the comparison, the computer can be caused to proceed through the proper routine without the operator's knowing which routine is being followed. This principle may be applied to many types of mathematical problems in elaborate and complex ways; in fact, it is this principle which makes digital computers the flexible and powerful mathematical tools that they are.

Extracting the Square Root. The extraction of the square root is most often accomplished in a computer through the use of a programmed sequence of the more basic operations which were discussed in previous chapters. It is possible to program the computer to follow paper-and-pencil square-rooting methods, but it is probably much more common practice to employ an iterative routine of some sort.

Two reasonably simple iterative formulas for the square root are:

$$b_{k+1} = \frac{1}{2}\left(\frac{x}{b_k} + b_k\right)$$

$$b_{k+1} = \frac{b_k}{2}\left(3 - \frac{b_k^2}{x}\right)$$

where x is the number for which the square is sought, and b_k is the kth approximation to the square root. In the first formula, the initial approximation, b_0, may have any positive or negative value except zero; in the second formula the magnitude of b_0 must be less than $(5x)^{1/2}$. Both formulas are "second-order," which means that once a moderately accurate determination of the square root has been made, the number of significant digits in the approximation is doubled upon each application of the formula. Note that in the case of the first formula a division operation is required for each successive approximation, but for the second formula the determination of the reciprocal of x is the only division required regardless of the number of times the formula is applied. This feature is of particular importance when considering computers for which division is not a built-in operation. On the other hand, a more accurate "first guess" is required for the second formula.

One way to determine when the iteration process should be terminated is to subtract successive approximations, one from the other, and observe whether or not the difference is less than the tolerable error.

Two third-order iterative formulas for extracting the square root are as follows:

$$b_{k+1} = \frac{1}{8}\left(3b_k + \frac{6x}{b_k} - \frac{x^2}{b_k^3}\right)$$

$$b_{k+1} = \frac{b_k}{8}\left(15 - \frac{10b_k^2}{x} + \frac{3b_k^4}{x^2}\right)$$

When a computer is being designed for a specific application where it is known that the extraction of the square root will be a frequent requirement (of which communications and electrical power network problems are notable examples), it may prove advantageous to incorporate the square-rooting process as a machine function. However, the iterative formulas are not particularly convenient for building into a machine, and it is probably more practical in most cases to employ a square-rooting method which is more closely related to the pencil-and-paper process.

The pencil-and-paper method of extracting the square root is similar to division in many respects but, of course, with some important differences. A number of minor variations in the method can be worked out; the basic steps in one particular variation will be explained by extracting the square root of 184,729 as an example.

$$4\sqrt{\begin{array}{ccc} 4 & 2 & 9 \\ \hline 18 & 47 & 29.00 \end{array}}$$

$$
\begin{array}{r}
4\overline{)}\quad 18\ 47\ 29.00 \\
16 \\
\hline
8\ 2 \quad 2\ 47\ 29 \\
1\ 64 \\
\hline
84\ 9 \quad 83\ 29 \\
76\ 41 \\
\hline
6\ 88
\end{array}
$$

First, the digits of 184729 are set off in pairs starting from the decimal point. The highest-order pair (18 in this case) is then examined, and the largest digit for which the square is equal to or less than these two digits is ascertained. The digit is 4 in this example. The fact is noted on paper, as indicated, and the square of 4 is subtracted from the 18. The first digit of the square root has now been determined. The second digit is obtained by doubling the first digit and using it in the "tens" order of a sort of "divisor" where the units digit is not fixed but is the same as the trial square-root digit. In the above example, the doubled digit is 8 (designated by an underline), and the next digit of the square root is 2. Note that when the product of 2 and 82 is subtracted from the previous remainder, the new remainder is 83. This fact does not mean that the square-root digit should be 3 instead of 2 because, if the product of 3 and 83 is subtracted a negative remainder will result. In a similar manner the third digit of the square root is obtained by doubling the first two digits to obtain 84 and using these as the tens and hundreds orders of a new "divisor." In general, the square root will not be an integer, but the round-off procedures which may be used are substantially the same as described previously in connection with multiplication and division.

To adapt this method of square rooting to machine computations, some means other than "inspection" must be found to enable the machine to make the appropriate initial choices for the trial square-root digits and then to select the correct one. One such means may be derived from the fact that the squares of integers may be obtained by adding the series of odd numbers, for example the square of 4 is $1 + 3 + 5 + 7 = 16$.

The odd numbers may be generated readily in a computer by setting an accumulator or a counter to 1 and successively adding 2. Then, to obtain the first digit of the square root, the series of odd numbers is subtracted from the appropriate orders of the number for which the square root is desired until a negative remainder is obtained. When the remainder becomes negative, it is corrected by adding the last odd number which was subtracted. For successive digits of the square root, the accumulator or counter in which the series of odd numbers is being built up should be set to the value obtained by doubling the previously determined square-root digits. For the second square-root digit in the above example, the numbers, 81, 83, 85, 87, 89, 91, ··· would be subtracted until the remainder becomes negative. To clarify the procedure, the steps a computer would take in determining the first two digits of the square root of 184,729 are indicated below.

		Square Root
18 47 29		
1		
17		1 - -
3		
14		2 - -
5		
9		3 - -
7		
2		4 - -
9		
−93		
Add 9		
+ 2 47 29		
2 47 29		
81		
1 66		41 -
83		
83		42 -
85		
− 998		
Add 85		
+ 83		

Although there are complications not previously encountered, the operation of extracting the square root can be accomplished much more rapidly in a computer by techniques similar to those used for division. However, since the incorporation of square rooting as a built-in operation is relatively rare, the problem of increasing the speed of the process seems to have received little attention.

The description of the square-rooting operation has been given in terms of the decimal system only; nevertheless, the principles apply equally well to the binary system. Actually, extracting the square root is very much simpler in the binary system because the largest digit in the square root is 1 and therefore the "series" of odd numbers degenerates to one term, 1. Not only is the necessity eliminated for building up the series of odd numbers, but also no carries are involved in building up the trial "divisor." The trial divisor may be obtained simply by shifting the previously determined square-root digits to the appropriate orders (a shift to the left of one order is a multiplication by 2) and by placing a 1 in the "units" order.

Sorting. Sorting is the process of arranging a set of numbers in a uniform sequence as determined by the magnitudes of the individual numbers. As an example, consider the problem of sorting a group of numbers where each number is in the range of 000 to 999. Although it is not necessary, it is convenient for illustrative purposes to assume that each number is recorded on a separate piece of paper or a card. A person faced with this problem is most likely to follow one of two lines of attack.

A rather obvious method of sorting would be to examine each card and place all those numbers in the range 000 to 099 in one pile, all those in the range 100 to 199 in another pile, and so on. After completing this step, each pile would be divided into ten smaller piles according to the digit in tens order, and a final subdivision would then be made as guided by the digit in the units order.

With the above procedure, it is necessary to handle each card three times; and it may be found that the manipulating of the various piles is awkward, particularly with the lower-order digits because the various individual piles must be kept separate by some means or other. These difficulties may be circumvented by using a different sorting procedure, which involves the building up of the sorted set in its final form one card at a time. That is, if the first card examined has the number 805, it is placed in a file as a sorted set of one card. If the second card has the number 920, it is placed behind the first. A third number of 259 would be placed in front of both. A fourth number of 809 would be placed between the first and second, and so on.

When a method of sorting is to be adapted to machine operation, neither of the above manual methods is found to be convenient. The first method may be altered to one applicable to machine operation simply by reversing the sequence in which the orders are examined. After sorting according to the digits in the units order, the ten piles are appropriately reassembled, and a sort is then made on the tens digit. This process is continued through the digits of all orders. To illustrate the process more clearly, the arrangements of ten 3-digit numbers after the various steps in the sorting process is presented.

After Sorting on

Random Sequence	Units Order	Tens Order	Hundreds Order
823	060	609	038
059	823	823	059
673	673	229	060
158	653	038	158
229	177	653	177
038	158	158	229
177	038	059	609
653	059	060	653
609	229	673	673
060	609	177	823

For purposes of computing the speed of the sorting operation, it may be observed that the number of passes of cards through the digit sensing device is equal to the product of the number of cards and the number of orders on which the sort must be made.

The sorting method just described is convenient for sorting cards, but it has important disadvantages for certain machine applications. In particular, it may be very inefficient when the cards or numbers to be sorted are already in a known orderly arrangement. A common example of this situation is the sorting of numbers when they are initially in two groups with the numbers within each group properly sorted. A sorting operation in this special case is frequently called "merging" two sets of numbers. Another disadvantage of the previously described sorting method lies in the fact that ten separate hoppers or storage locations must be provided with each one large enough to hold the entire file of numbers (unless a chance is taken with regard to the randomness of the digits or unless special provisions are made to handle overflows).

A sorting procedure which minimizes both of these disadvantages is known as sorting by "collating." When sorting by collating, the various numbers to be sorted are compared with one another and distributed into one of two storage locations according to the results of the comparison. Three numbers at a time are considered in each comparison operation, and the rules for the operation are indicated below, where X and Y are two of the numbers from the list to be sorted, and L is the last number which was placed in one or the other of the two storage locations.

If $X > Y > L$, store Y in same location as L.
If $Y > X > L$, store X in same location as L.
If $X > L > Y$, store X in same location as L.
If $Y > L > X$, store Y in same location as L.
If $L > X > Y$, store Y in opposite location from L.
If $L > Y > X$, store X in opposite location from L.

When starting the operation, X and Y are the first two numbers in the list. The smaller of the two is stored in one of the two locations, and for the next step it is replaced by the next number in the list.

After proceeding through the entire list, the numbers in the two storage locations, which will be called A and B, are then transferred to two new storage locations, C and D, by following a similar comparison procedure. When starting this part of the process, X and Y are the first numbers in A and B, respectively. The smaller of the two is placed in one of the two locations, say C, and for the next step this number is then replaced by the next one in the storage location from which it came. After transferring the entire file to C and D, it is then placed back in A and B by following the same comparison rules. This procedure of sending the numbers back and forth between the A and B storage locations and the C and D locations is continued until the numbers are properly sorted. Only four storage locations are required because the file may be initially stored in C, for example. To illustrate the process of sorting by collating, the steps involved in sorting one particular file of random numbers will be set forth. The numbers in parentheses indicate the order in which the numbers are transferred from one storage location or pair of storage locations to the next.

C	A	B	C	D	A	B
823 (3)	059 (1)	158 (2)	059	038	038	—
059 (1)	673 (4)	229 (3)	158	060	059	—
673 (2)	823 (5)	060 (7)	229	177	060	—
158 (4)	038 (6)	452 (9)	673	452	158	
229 (7)	177 (8)		823	609	177	
038 (5)	609 (10)			653	229	
177 (6)	653 (11)			920	452	
653 (9)	920 (12)				609	
609 (8)					653	
060 (11)					673	
920 (10)					823	
452 (12)					920	

The number of operations or the time required to sort a list of numbers by this method depends upon the initial arrangement of the numbers. The worst possible case occurs when the numbers are initially in the exact opposite order from that desired. In this case it is not difficult to show that the number of times the file must be transferred from one place to another is $(\log_2 N)_{int}$, where N is the number of numbers in the file and the subscript on the logarithm indicates the next larger integral value of $\log_2 N$.

When the numbers initially have a random distribution, the determination of the number of transfers is a difficult problem in the theory of probability and, so far as is known, a solution has not been worked out. However, if a group of consecutive numbers in the proper order is called a "sequence," the number of sequences, S, in the initial arrangement may be used in the expression, $1 + (\log_2 S)_{int}$, to obtain the maximum possible number of times that the file must be transferred. In the example which was worked out, the sequences are indicated by brackets. Since there were seven sequences in the initial arrangement, a maximum of four transfers may have been required. The formula indicates only the maximum and not the actual number of transfers, because a phenomenon called "accidental merging" sometimes occurs during a transfer. That is, successive sequences in a storage location may happen to be continuations of one another and therefore produce an effectual reduction in the number of sequences. The first transfer may not produce any reduction in the number of sequences (as may be observed by sorting the series of one-digit numbers, 7, 8, 5, 6, 3, 4, 1, 2), but in general each successive transfer reduces the number of sequences at least by a factor of two. The file is sorted when the number of sequences is reduced to one.

In actual practice, the possibility of having two or more numbers equal to each other usually must be taken into consideration. No severe complications are introduced. If $X = Y$, an arbitrary choice may be made as to which is stored. If X or Y is equal to L, the one which is equal to L should be stored in the same location as L.

This method of sorting by collating may be expanded to two sets of three or more storage locations. An analogous set of rules is followed. In general, the numbers are transferred to the same storage location as L as long as a sequence can be built up. When all numbers in a comparison are less than L, the storage locations are switched in a rotational pattern. The comparisons are somewhat more complex in that one number from each storage location and L must enter into the comparing operations, but the maximum number of transfers is reduced to $(\log_n N)_{int}$, where n is the number of storage locations in each group.

Sorting by collation is particularly well adapted to situations where the numbers appear on magnetic or punched paper tape instead of on cards, although card collators are found to have wide application also. The comparison operation which must be performed in collating is, of course, more complex than the simple digit-sensing procedure used in the previously described sorting method, and this factor must be considered when designing a sorting machine. This problem is not so great when sorting is to be accomplished on a computer where the basic operations of addition and subtraction have already been incorporated.

Checking by "Casting Out 9's." A method of checking arithmetic operations performed in the decimal system is known as "casting out 9's." The method involves the use of the "residue modulus nine," or RMN, of the factors entering into the calculations. The RMN of a number is the remainder after dividing by 9; for example, the RMN of 392,971 is 4.

To check an addition, the RMN's of the two numbers are added in a modulus nine fashion and the result is compared with the RMN computed from the sum. As an example, consider the addition of the following two numbers:

		RMN
	392,971	4
	189,078	6
Sum	582,049	1

Although the sum of 4 and 6 is 10, the remainder after a division by 9 is 1, which checks with the RMN of the sum. If the second number had been subtracted from, instead of added to, the first, the difference would have been 203,893 which has an RMN of 7. This result checks with the modulus nine difference of the RMN's because, when subtracting 6 from 4, a 9 must be added to the 4 to avoid a negative result.

When using the casting out 9's method to check a multiplication, the RMN of one factor is added in modulus nine fashion a number of times equal to the RMN of the other factor, and the result is checked against the RMN of the product. The same result may be obtained by finding the RMN of the product of the RMN's. If the individual RMN's are 4 and 6, respectively, as in the previous example, the product of the two is 24, which has an RMN of 6, which will check with the RMN of the product of the original numbers being multiplied.

For division, the RMN of the quotient is subtracted in modulus nine fashion from the RMN of the dividend a number of times equal to the RMN of the divisor, and the result is checked against the RMN of the remainder. Actually, the roles of the quotient and divisor may be interchanged in this process.

In some applications, particularly when adapting the casting out 9's checking method to machine operation, it may be preferable to use a different method for finding the RMN of a number. It may be shown that the RMN of the sum of the digits of a number is equal to the RMN of the number itself. In the example of 392,971, the sum of the digits is 31 which has an RMN of 4. Of course, when adding the digits, the 9's may be disregarded if desired. In a computer, the RMN may be determined by adding the digits in the usual decimal fashion except that each time a carry is obtained it is added with the other digits. Then, when the digits in the example are considered (disregarding 9's), the RMN would be found according to the following steps:

$$1 + 7 = 8$$

$$8 + 2 = 0 \text{ with a carry of } 1$$

$$1 + 0 = 1$$

$$3 + 1 = 4 = \text{RMN}$$

In the binary system of numbers a "casting out 1's" process would be meaningless. However, an analogous checking process may be formed by considering the binary digits in groups of three, for example, and casting out 7's as in an octonary system.

Trigonometric and Other Transcendental Functions. In the design of a computer, it is necessary to "draw a line" between those arithmetic operations which are to be built-in functions and those which are to be performed through a programmed sequence of the built-in ones. The advantage in omitting any given operation is, of course, that a simpler and less expensive machine may be realized. On the other hand, the inclusion of an operation will make it possible for the computer to function faster and with less complications in the program for those problems which require the operation. The frequency with which the various operations must be performed in the problems to be solved by the computer is the outstanding factor to be considered in determining the ones to be included. Unfortunately, the problems which will be applied to the computer are often not known.

Although it is possible to perform all arithmetic operations with simple counting as the only built-in operation, the operations of addition, subtraction, and multiplication are almost always incorporated in any machine which is called a computer in the usual sense of the word. Division is an operation which is included in most general-purpose computers, but because of the existence of a simple iterative formula for finding reciprocals, division is frequently omitted, especially when computer cost is particularly important. The operation of extracting the square root is rarely incorporated in a computer, but it has been done in a few instances where it was known that the problems to be solved by the computer required this operation frequently.

The computation of trigonometric and other transcendental functions is definitely on the side of the line where the desired results are achieved through programmed sequences of more basic operations rather than through designing the computing machinery especially for the purpose. Possibly some exceptions to this general rule could be found, such as the means for generating sines and cosines which will be described in the section on digital differential analyzers. However, even the exceptions usually amount to an assemblage of the more basic operations through wiring if not through programming.

The programs which may be used for the computation of trigonometric and other transcendental functions may be any one of at least three different forms. First of all, a table of values may be stored, and the function of an argument value which is not in the table may be computed through the use of interpolation formulas. A second method of approach is through the use of various infinite series forms of the function. Any desired degree of accuracy may be obtained by employing a sufficient number of terms in the series. A third method is frequently useful particularly when the function is needed only over a limited range of the argument. The desired function may be approximated by a polynomial expression. The complexity of the polynomial depends upon the extent of the range and the required accuracy.

The particular method of computation to be used in any given instance can be the subject for intensive mathematical study. Many factors must be considered in view of the many possible variations. One type of variation, for example, is encountered when using the interpolation method. It must be decided whether to store the function in large steps and use a complex interpolation procedure or to store the function in smaller increments of the argument and use a simpler interpolation procedure. Among the important factors to be considered are the amount of storage capacity available in the computer, the time required for access to any one storage location, the speed of each individual operation, and the difficulty in preparing the program. Since the mathematical procedures which are involved are well known to mathematicians and are not peculiar to computing machinery, they will not be described in more detail here.

It is interesting to note that during the early development of computers it was a widely held view that the computers would be used largely for the preparation of extensive tables of complicated functions compiled to a high degree of accuracy. Although computers are used for this purpose to some extent, emphasis has been shifted away from this application. It has become possible to make machines perform arithmetic operations extremely fast relative to the speed of access to the large-capacity storage media. For this reason it is often more practical to compute a value of a function when it is needed in the course of other computations rather than to select the value from a table.

Integration and Differentiation. When evaluating an integral, a person employing pencil-and-paper mathematics would attempt to find a function which represents the integral of the given function. If such a function can be found, the value of the integral may be determined by inserting the limits of the variable. For example, when finding the integral of the function, cotangent of x, with x varying from $\pi/4$ to $\pi/3$, it would be determined by some means or other (probably from a table of integrals in this case) that the desired function is the logarithm of the sine of x. Then, by using tables of logarithms and sines, the value of the function at the limits may be determined, and the value of the integral would be the difference between these two quantities. Differentiation, similarly, is accomplished by finding a function which represents the derivative of the given function. The derivative at any desired value of the variable would, of course, be obtained by evaluating the deriative function with the desired value of the variable inserted in the function.

So far as is known, no computer has ever been worked out which integrates and differentiates through the process of determining integrated or differentiated functions. Instead, a "numerical" approach is followed. Since integration is substantially a matter of finding the area under a curve, it is possible to evaluate the integral by evaluating the given function at the end points and a number of intermediate points and then computing the area by summing a series of incremental areas. Any desired accuracy in the result may achieved by dividing the desired area into a sufficiently large number of incremental areas appropriately distributed as dictated by the variations in the function. Many refinements to this procedure have been worked out and are well known to mathematicians. Among them are the trapezoidal rule, Simpson's rule, and method of Gauss for more accurately evaluating an incremental area with a given change in the variable. Further, it is sometimes possible to simplify the computations by using the first and higher-order derivatives of a function to determine successive values of the function over a limited range of the variable. A first derivative may be computed numerically to any required accuracy by evaluating the given function at two values of the variable which are sufficiently close to the value for which the derivative is desired. The derivative is then the ratio between the change in the value of the function and the change in the value of the variable.

As was the case with trigonometric functions, the numerical processes for evaluating derivatives and integrals are usually accomplished in a computer by programmed sequences of the more basic arithmetic operations rather than by building integration and differentiation into the computer circuits. For this reason, the subject fits better in the realm of mathematics than it does in the realm of computers. There is one important exception to the rule, however, and that is in connection with a type of machine known as a digital differential analyzer. The principle of operation of this type of machine is explained in the next section.

Digital Differential Analyzer. The digital differential analyzer is a digital adaptation of an analog type of machine, the principles of which were first described by Lord Kelvin in 1876. Apparently the work of Kelvin became obscured, and it was not until 1931 that Vannevar Bush published a description of the first differential analyzer ever to be built. Since that time many variations and improvements have appeared, with the emphasis gradually shifting from mechanical through electromechanical to electronic components. The digital version was worked out shortly after World War II by a group of engineers who, at the time, were with the Northrop Aircraft Corporation.

Although the principal purpose of the differential analyzer is to solve differential equations, it is composed mainly of a set of units which perform an integrating function. Each such unit is called an integrator. The integrators in the digital differential analyzer are functionally analogous to the integrators found in analog machines; but, since there are so many points of difference, the description here will be given only in terms of digital devices.

The basic integrator circuit may be considered as consisting of an accumulator register, R, and an addend register, Y, together with means for adding the contents of Y to R. The arrangement is shown in Fig. 10-1(a). The addition occurs each time a pulse is applied to the line marked dx. As the number in Y is repeatedly added to R, the R register will overflow from time to time, and each time an overflow occurs a

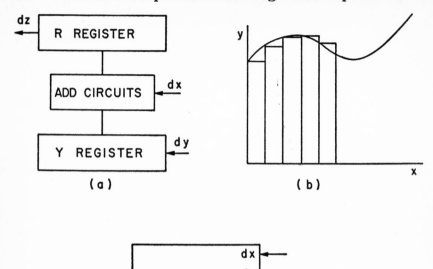

FIG. 10-1.   Integrator arrangement and symbol.

pulse will appear on the dz output line.   The rate at which the overflow occur will, of course, be dependent on the magnitude of the number in Y; that is, the relationship between the number of dz pulses and dx pulses will be

$$dz = \frac{1}{r^n} \, y \, dx$$

where y is the number in Y, r is the radix of the number system in use, and n is the number of orders in the registers.   It may be helpful in visualizing the operation of the integrator to consider the time rates, dz/dt and dx/dt, of the pulses as represented by the equation,

$$\frac{dz}{dt} = Ky \frac{dx}{dt}$$

This equation states that the rate of appearance of the dz pulses is proportional to y and to the rate of application of the dx pulses.   However, it should be understood that time does not directly affect the operation of this digital integrator; it may function at any speed.   The dy input in Fig. 10-1 (a) is for altering the value of y.   The dy signal may be either a single pulse to add unity to y or it may be a number of substantial magnitude to be added to y. The counter or adder circuits necessary to effect the alteration are not shown in the figure. That this arrangement represents an integration type of operation may be observed by noting that the dz output represents an area. The incremental areas which are summed are indicated by the vertical strips in Fig. 10-1(b). Each dx pulse, which may represent one unit of x, causes the corresponding value of y to be accumulated. Means must, of course, be provided to cause y to vary in accordance with the desired functional relationship with x. If a suitable constant of proportionality, K, is chosen, a count of the dz pulses will be a measure of the area under the curve. Figure 10-1(c) shows a simplified symbol for the integrator.

As has been mentioned, differential equations are solved through appropriate interconnections among an assembly of integrator units of the type just described. As a particularly simple illustration of the method, consider the differential equation,

$$\frac{dy}{y} = dx$$

which can be solved with just one integrator. For this equation the dz output is connected to the dy input as in Fig. 10-2. The result is (ignore K, for the moment):

$$dz = dy = ydx$$

The solution to this equation is $y = e^x$, and therefore $dy = e^x dx$. Since e^x plays the role of y in this case, an initial value of x may be assumed

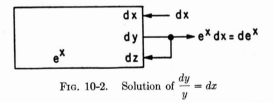

FIG. 10-2. Solution of $\dfrac{dy}{y} = dx$

and a number representing e^x may be placed in the Y part of the integrator. Then, as dx pulses are applied, which represent increases in x and which cause successive additions of Y to R, the number in Y will vary as e^x and yield the result, $y = e^x$. In other words, the rate of pulses on the dz output is e^x times the rate of dx input pulses.

Before proceeding further with the discussion of integrator connections, the problem of signs will be described. Clearly, in the general case, it will be desirable to allow y to increase or decrease. Because in many applications the dy input of one integrator will be obtained from the dz output of another integrator; and, for other reasons, means must be provided for causing dz to indicate a subtraction. One ingenious system uses the absence of a pulse to indicate that subtraction should be performed. With this system, zero in a Y register is represented by a 1 for a sign digit, and the sign digit is placed to the left of the highest-order digit of the number. Then, if zero represented in this way is repeatedly added to the R register, the R register will overflow on each alternate addition operation. The dz output when applied as an input to another integrator will therefore cause alternate additions and subtractions, with a net effect of zero. If the number in the Y register is some positive quantity, the R register will overflow more often than not, with the result that more additions than subtractions will be signaled. When the contents of Y are negative, a zero will appear in the sign position and the number will be in complement form. Consequently, the R register will overflow less than half the time so that more subtractions than additions will be caused by the dz output. When y has a maximum negative value, all digits of y will be zero; and, in this case, R will never overflow, with the result that dz will initiate a continuous series of subtractions.

An alternate system for handling negative numbers involves the use of two wires for each signal line. A pulse on one wire is used to signify addition, and a pulse on the opposite wire signifies subtraction. With this system, the numbers in the registers may be handled in a more straightforward manner, but if the R register overflows in the negative direction either from subtracting a positive y or adding a negative y, the dz output will appear on the line signifying subtraction. Note that the dz output in this system or in the system described in the previous paragraph may be used either as the dx or the dy input of another integrator.

In some applications it is desired to use the negative of the dz output. The means that may be used for inverting dz depend upon the system of negative numbers in use. With the two-wire system, for example, inversion of dz may be accomplished simply by interchanging the signals on the two wires. In the symbol for an integrator, an encircled minus sign signifies that the negative of dz is appearing on the output.

As a further illustration of the use of the differential analyzer, consider the differential equation,

$$\frac{d^2w}{dt^2} = -w$$

The required connections between the integrators may be worked out by noting the following relationships:

$$d\left(\frac{d^2w}{dt^2}\right) = -dw = -\left(\frac{dw}{dt}\right)dt$$

$$d\left(\frac{dw}{dt}\right) = \frac{d^2w}{dt^2}\,dt$$

If d^2w/dt^2 is placed in the Y part of one integrator and dt is used for the dx input, the dz output will be $d(dw/dt)$ and the required dy input will be $-(dw/dt)dt$. These quantities form the dy input and dz output, respec-

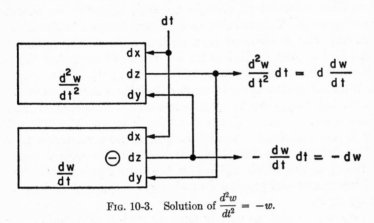

Fig. 10-3.   Solution of $\dfrac{d^2w}{dt^2} = -w$.

tively, of a second integrator, with dy/dt in the Y part and with dt as the dx input. The resulting arrangement is shown in Fig. 10-3. The output of the second integrator yields pulses at a rate which, when compared with the rate of dt input pulses, gives w as a function of t.

Since the solution being sought in the above example may be written as

$$w = A \sin t + B \cos t$$

where A and B are arbitrary constants, it is apparent that the form of the solution depends upon the initial conditions entered into the Y parts of the integrators. With appropriate initial conditions the output of either integrator may be used to generate sine or cosine functions. Actually, the differential equation under discussion is so simple that a machine would probably not be used for its solution. Nevertheless, this particular method of generating sines and cosines is useful in the solving of more complicated differential equations which involve these functions.

The usefulness of a differential analyzer type of computer can be appreciated more fully through a study of a somewhat more complicated example. Consider the differential equation,

$$\frac{d^2w}{dt^2} - w\frac{dw}{dt} - \sin w = 0$$

The interconnections which will be required between integrators may be found quickly by rewriting the equation as follows:

$$d\left(\frac{d^2w}{dt^2}\right) = d\left(w\frac{dw}{dt}\right) + d(\sin w) = wd\left(\frac{dw}{dt}\right) + \frac{dw}{dt}dw + d(\sin w)$$

The "dy input" to the integrator containing d^2w/dt^2 will consist of the sum of three terms which must be obtained from the "dz outputs" of other integrators. The resulting configuration is shown in Fig. 10-4. The $wd(dw/dt)$ term is obtained from an integrator which contains w and which has $d(dw/dt)$ applied to the dx input. Observe that the output of the first integrator is $(d^2w/dt^2)\,dt = d(dw/dt)$. The $(dw/dt)dw$ term is manufactured in an integrator containing dw/dt. The dw that is needed in both of these integrators is obtained from another integrator containing dw/dt, but which has dt as the dx input. The differential of $\sin w$ is obtained from two additional integrators connected as in the previous example. In Fig. 10-4, the block labeled with a summation sign is any device which will collect the output pulses from the indicated integrators and produce a number in an appropriate form for use as a dy input.

It may appear that an unduly large amount of arithmetic equipment would be required for all the integrators which would be required to solve a differential equation of reasonable complexity. However, by using a serial system it is possible to perform all arithmetic operations with only one set of arithmetic circuits. In such a system the integrators are merely storage locations, the contents of which are passed in serial fashion through the arithmetic and control parts of the computer. A type of storage medium well adapted to this application is the magnetic drum. The Y and R portions of each integrator are stored side-by-side in two parallel tracks, with the Y portions of all integrators in one track and the R portions of all integrators on the other track. With this arrangement the two magnetic heads sense all integrators in sequence, and the contents of Y may be altered in accordance with the dy input and Y may be added to R or subtracted from R in accordance with the dx input. The new values for Y and R may be recorded on the drum through a separate pair of magnetic heads.

The interconnections between integrators are, of course, not wires with this serial system, but the effect of interconnections may be achieved with a precessing storage track on the drum. If a series of integrators, each requiring N pulse times, pass by the sensing heads on the drum, a short track of $N - 1$ pulse times can be used to produce the desired precessing action. The short track is formed by using two magnetic heads, one for recording and one for sensing, spaced a distance from each other

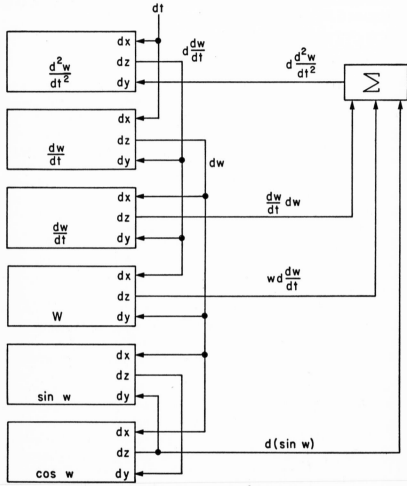

FIG. 10-4. Connections for solution of $\dfrac{d^2w}{dt^2} - w\dfrac{dw}{dt} - \sin w = 0$.

on the circumference of the drum such that $N - 1$ pulse times pass during the traversal of a magnetized spot from the recording head to the sensing head. The sensed information is immediately returned to the drum through the recording head, with the result that the information in the track continually recirculates.

This precessing track, called the Z track, is used for temporarily storing the dz outputs of the integrators. The dz output signal from an integrator occurs during the last pulse time of the integrator (or at least nearly the last depending upon the detailed nature of the machine), and it is placed in the Z track in the position which is under the record head at the time. Assume this position is the number 1 position. Since each integrator requires N pulse times and the Z track is only $N - 1$ pulse times in length, the dz output of the second integrator will be placed in the number 2 position, and so on. The problem is now to select, for each integrator, the desired dz outputs and apply them as dx and dy inputs to other integrators.

Note that, during the passage of any given integrator, the entire Z track will pass under the sense head. Through the use of information stored on a fourth track, the L track, it is possible to select by means of an "and" switch the appropriate dz signals as required for the dy inputs by the differential equation being solved. The information in the L track provides the "interconnections" and remains unchanged throughout the solution of any given equation. Of course, while a given integrator is passing under the magnetic head, it is too late to use any of the Z track data for this particular integrator, but during this time the Z track data are gathered for use with the next integrator. The dy input of an integrator may be the dz output of one integrator or it may be the sum of the dz outputs of several integrators. For this reason it is necessary to employ a counter to count the dz signals called for by the information in the L track. The total is then shifted into a register for addition as the dy input to the Y part of the next integrator, and the counter then proceeds to gather the dz data for the integrator after the next one.

The dx inputs may be obtained from the dz outputs by another track similar to the L track. However, since each dx input is in nearly all cases obtained from only one source instead of the sum of several sources, it may be preferable to use a different scheme for the dx inputs. When the number of integrators in the computer is not the same as the number of pulse times in the Z track it is necessary to use a somewhat more complex control system than the simple one which has been outlined. Then it may happen that certain pulse times are available for storing a number with each integrator, and this number may be placed in a counter which will find the proper dz signal in the Z track by a counting action. The dz signal when used as the dx input will control the addition or subtraction of Y and R in the next integrator to pass under the sensing heads.

Many more details must be taken into consideration before a complete and useful digital differential analyzer can be assembled; it has been the purpose here to present only the basic principles of operation. However, one detail deserves further mention, and that is the constant of proportionality, K, which was previously ignored. If the numbers in the Y parts of the integrators are all assumed to be fractions instead of integers, K becomes unity. Nevertheless, it is desirable to alter the ratio of output to input pulses in order to fit the integrators to the requirements of each individual problem being solved. In particular, the requirements on accuracy of the solution is different in various applications. One way to alter K is to enter the dy input to orders in the Y register other than the lowest orders. With this system each Y register contains a marker pulse in one of the orders, and dy is not added to y until this marker pulse is sensed by the magnetic heads. Alternatively, means may be incorporated for multiplying the dz outputs, each by a different factor.

Conversions Between Conventional Binary and Reflected Binary Codes. As was mentioned in the first chapter, the reflected binary code is frequently found useful for input-output mechanisms because the representations for any two successive quantities differ by only one digit. Since the reflected binary system is awkward to use when arithmetic operations are involved, a scheme for translation between the two number systems is needed.

Although there is a mathematical relationship between the values of the digits in the two systems, the equipment necessary to perform the conversions can probably be determined most readily through an inspection of the representations for a list of integers as given below.

Decimal	Conventional Binary B_5 B_4 B_3 B_2 B_1	Reflected Binary R_5 R_4 R_3 R_2 R_1
0	0 0 0 0	0 0 0 0
1	0 0 0 1	0 0 0 1
2	0 0 1 0	0 0 1 1
3	0 0 1 1	0 0 1 0
4	0 1 0 0	0 1 1 0
5	0 1 0 1	0 1 1 1
6	0 1 1 0	0 1 0 1
7	0 1 1 1	0 1 0 0
8	1 0 0 0	1 1 0 0
9	1 0 0 1	1 1 0 1
10	1 0 1 0	1 1 1 1
11	1 0 1 1	1 1 1 0
12	1 1 0 0	1 0 1 0
13	1 1 0 1	1 0 1 1
14	1 1 1 0	1 0 0 1
15	1 1 1 1	1 0 0 0
16	1 0 0 0 0	1 1 0 0 0

When converting from the conventional binary to the reflected binary system, it may be observed that the value of any given digit in the reflected code is dependent upon the digits which are in the corresponding and the next higher order of the conventional code. The translation scheme may be represented in Boolean algebra notation as follows, where B and R represent conventional binary and reflected binary, respectively, and n represents the highest order in use.

$$R_n = B_n$$
$$R_{n-1} = (B_n + B_{n-1})\overline{B_n B_{n-1}}$$
$$R_{n-2} = (B_{n-1} + B_{n-2})\overline{B_{n-1} B_{n-2}}$$
$$\cdot$$
$$\cdot$$
$$\cdot$$
$$R_0 = (B_1 + B_0)\overline{B_1 B_0}$$

The functions involved are the same as for the sum part of a half adder, and a block diagram of the arrangement in terms of half adders is shown in Fig. 10-5(a).

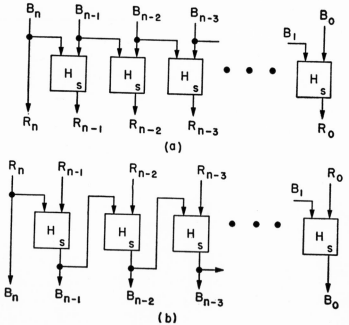

(a)

(b)

Fig. 10-5.   Arrangements for conversions between reflected binary and conventional binary codes.

In the conversion from the reflected to the conventional code, the value of any given conventional code digit is dependent upon the value of the corresponding reflected code digit and the digits of all higher orders as well. However, a conventional binary digit may be used in the development of the next lower order digit according to the following scheme, which is illustrated in Fig. 10-5(b).

$$B_n = R_n$$

$$B_{n-1} = (B_n + R_{n-1})\overline{R_n R_{n-1}}$$

$$B_{n-2} = (B_{n-1} + R_{n-2})\overline{B_{n-1} R_{n-2}}$$

$$\cdot$$
$$\cdot$$
$$\cdot$$

$$B_0 = (B_1 + R_0)\overline{B_1 R_0}$$

Chapter 11

COMPUTER ORGANIZATION AND CONTROL

The first serious thought involving the use of machinery to perform computations seems to be credited to Blaise Pascal, who in about the year 1642 built some elementary machines to assist in the computation of taxes. In succeeding years various other mathematicians pondered the problems of reducing the drudgery of routine computing and of increasing the speed and accuracy of the work. A few of them reached the stage of constructing models, but it was some 200 years after Pascal's first work that the production of computing machinery was placed on a commercial basis. Punched-card accounting and computing equipment had its beginnings in the 1890 census, although punched cards had been used years previously in the control of weaving complex patterns on looms. After about 1890, the development of adding machines, desk computers, bookkeeping machines, and punched-card accounting equipment proceeded at a rapid pace. Even so, the machines appearing on the market as late as the 1920's might be considered crude compared with the advanced models available today.

Some of the ideas presented in the various chapters of this book pertain in a vague fashion to adding machines, desk computers, and machines of similar categories, but for the most part an entirely new class of machines has been in mind. Scientific and accounting problems of any complexity require long sequences of operations in order to reduce the input data to computed results in the desired form. With the desk computer category of equipment, substantially only one operation at a time can be performed. For each addition, subtraction, multiplication, or other operation, the operator must depress some keys on the keyboard. The results of intermediate computations must be recorded externally to the machine. Furthermore, the operator must make all decisions regarding the selection of alternate computing routines when the arithmetic operations to be performed are dependent on the nature of the data or the values obtained at intermediate points in the computations. With punched-card equipment many of these decisions can be mechanized through the use of sorters and collators, but even then the operator must at least handle the cards at each step in the process. The outstanding feature of the computers which are the real subject of this book is their ability to perform long sequences of arithmetic operations and "logical decisions" in an automatic manner.

The construction of the first successful computer capable of performing long sequences of operations was started in 1939 by the International Business Machines Corporation in cooperation with Harvard University and was completed in 1944. It is known as the Automatic Sequence Controlled Computer or the Harvard Mark I. One previous attempt at the construction of such a machine had been made by the now-famous Charles Babbage of England at the incredibly early period of approximately 1830 to 1840. Parts of Babbage's machine were completed and made to work, but the project as a whole failed largely because it was too ambitious in view of the relatively primitive engineering techniques available at the time. In spite of the facts that rather detailed descriptions of Babbage's work had been recorded and that substantial parts of his incompleted machine had been preserved, the passage of the years caused his ideas to be largely forgotten. It is believed that the Automatic Sequence Controlled Computer owes its existence to a study of Babbage's work and to a recognition that components and engineering techniques had been developed to a point where a large-scale computer would be feasible.

Most of the components in the Automatic Sequence Controlled Computer were developed by IBM for their regular line of business machines and were electromechanical in nature. Although very useful large-scale computers can be assembled with mechanical or electromechanical components, the more outstanding achievements in computer technology have been made through the use of electronic components because of the extremely high speeds of operation which are attainable electronically. The first electronic computer, known as the ENIAC, was built at the Moore School of Engineering in Philadelphia and was completed in 1946. The construction of the ENIAC must have required great courage for it was started at a time when the electronics industry was having considerable difficulty making the approximately 100 tubes in a radar set function simultaneously for long enough periods to be useful. From tube life data available at the time, it was a simple problem in arithmetic to prove that tubes in a large-scale computer would fail faster than the defective tubes could be found and replaced. Nevertheless, in spite of its 18,000 tubes, the ENIAC did operate successfully.

A basic requirement of sequenced computers is the ability to store numbers and other information. Even in the more elementary sequenced machines, the storage of intermediate results must be accomplished by some means or other; in the more sophisticated computers, number storage is used for a variety of purposes. In the ENIAC, a bistable circuit known as the Eccles-Jordan trigger or flip-flop, which was first described in 1919, was employed as the storage means. The very large number of tubes used in the ENIAC was largely a consequence of the fact that only one binary digit can be stored in one flip-flop.

During the summer of 1946 the Moore School held a special course on the subject of digital computers, and lecturers and students from a variety of organizations interested in the field were invited to participate. In this course the idea was presented that the information concerning the sequencing of operations was data that could be entered into the computer and stored through the use of the same components employed for the entry and storage of the numbers undergoing the computations. This concept contained a number of attractive features, the most outstanding of which was the possibility of using the program to alter itself. (Here, the "program" means the series of operations which the computer is to perform.) Through the use of a "stored program" computer, as this type of machine is called, a great variety of tricks could be performed which would aid in the solution of many kinds of problems. In particular, the using of portions of the program over and over (subroutines) became easy to accomplish, whereas this result had been achievable only with considerable difficulty on previously existing computer designs. Further, new means of electronic storage, such as ultrasonic delay lines, magnetic drums, and electrostatic storage tubes had been recently invented, and the practicability of using large amounts of electronic storage for programming was thereby enhanced immeasurably. It is hardly possible to give an accurate estimate of the amount of influence that the summer course had on progress in computers; nevertheless, shortly afterward several projects were organized for building computers along the lines which had been described.

The first stored-program machine to be completed was built by a group headed by M. V. Wilkes at Cambridge University in England. Although their machine, known as the EDSAC, was modest in size and capabilities when compared with other large-scale electronic computers being built at the time, Wilkes and his associates are well known for their contributions to programming techniques and procedures. Specifically they were the first to make extensive use of a library of sub-routines with a system for easily assembling them to make programs for the solution of new problems.

Another pioneering organization in the field of digital computers was the Bell Telephone Laboratories. It was found that many of the components developed by the telephone and telegraph industry were suitable for the construction of a computing machine. The arithmetic and control portions could be comprised largely of relays and other pieces of telephone switching equipment, whereas teletype machines with their associated punched-paper-tape facilities served well for input and output equipment. As early as 1940, Bell Laboratories had completed a small computer specifically intended to perform computations with complex numbers, which arise frequently in telephone engineering problems. Subsequently, a series of larger, more versatile, machines were built, with the last one, known as Model VI, being completed in 1950. All were of a type described as "relay computers" because, of course, of the extensive use of relays in their design. An outstanding feature of Models II to VI of the series was the elaborate error-detecting facilities which were incorporated into them. Although components would occasionally fail, the errors created could almost always be detected automatically. Upon sensing an error the machine would stop so that appropriate corrections or repairs could be made by the operator. The machines gained an excellent reputation from the standpoint of reliability of the computed results. Also, the floating-decimal-point idea seems to have appeared first in the Bell Laboratories Model V, which was completed in 1946.

Although relays and other electromechanical components are still used in certain portions, notably the input and output mechanisms, of most computers, interest in the design of new "relay computers" has diminished almost to the vanishing point, especially in the realm of the so-called large-scale computers. The reason is a simple economic one; for a given amount of money more computing can be accomplished with electronic computers because of the much higher speeds which are attainable. However, even the electronic computers are composed largely of components which were developed by another industry, the radio communications industry. In fact, it is literally true that, with a little ingenuity, a quantity of radio sets could be disassembled and then reassembled in the form of a computer of quite respectable abilities. Although the designs of many electronic components have been altered to suit the needs and some new components such as magnetic drums and magnetic storage cores have appeared, the debt of the computer industry to the communications industry is great indeed.

Externally Programmed Computers. The phrase "externally programmed" is intended to mean that each operation which the computer is to perform is under the control of some device external to the components and wiring of the computer itself. It is in contrast to plugged program or stored program computers, which will be discussed in later sections. Examples of external programming means are punched cards and punched-paper tape. In the case of cards, one instruction might be punched in each card in a coded form of some sort. Then, with the deck of program cards in the hopper, the computer would cause a new card to be sensed for each successive operation to be performed. To anyone at all familiar with more sophisticated methods of operation it will be clear that external programming of this nature has severe limitations. However, because the method has considerable historical interest and because the idea still has usefulness in some special applications, it will be described briefly.

Any computer that is to perform long sequences of arithmetic operations must be capable of storing a multiplicity of numbers which are the initial data, the intermediate results, and the final results. Conceivably, this storage could be entirely in the form of punched cards or tape of the same type as used for program controls. In some of the earlier machines, punched cards or tapes were used for auxiliary storage (later machines use the higher-speed magnetic tape), but they all employed at least some "built-in" storage. In the earlier machines the built-in storage was made up of decimal registers, each consisting of a set of decimal counters in parallel.

In order to perform addition, at least one, and frequently several, of the storage registers were equipped with carry-handling facilities to form parallel accumulators, as described in Chapter 8 on decimal addition and subtraction. To add two numbers, it was necessary to place at least one of the numbers in one of the accumulator-type registers and then cause the other number to be sent to this same accumulator. For shifting, multiplication, division, and other more complex operations, the numbers were sent to one of a set of arithmetic units specially designed for the purpose, and the result of the operation was then returned to one of the storage registers.

The job of the program cards or tape was, therefore, largely reduced to a matter of controlling the transfer of numbers from one place to another. The problem is somewhat similar to the problem of telephone switching; it must be possible to connect any unit (phone) to any other unit. However, there is one important difference. In a telephone system it is desirable to allow several conversations simultaneously, but in the computer the program cards call for only one operation at a time. Therefore, a common set of wires, or "bus," may be used to connect all storage registers and arithmetic units. Each must be equipped with an "in" switch and an "out" switch. An instruction on the program card, therefore, causes one "in" and one "out" switch to be closed. Then when the storage registers are sensed, such as by applying ten pulses to each counter and thereby rolling it around through zero to its original state, a set of pulses representing the digits are caused to appear on the bus from the unit which has its "out" switch closed and be transmitted to the unit which has its "in" switch closed.

Many, many more details must, of course, be considered in order to gain a thorough understanding of the system, but more important than the details is an appreciation of the limitations of programming by external means. In the preparation of programs it is frequently desirable to repeat some of the operations a number of times. A typical example of this requirement is the computation of some quantity by an iterative process. The portion of the program can be repeated easily as many times as desired merely by punching enough program cards or tape, but this procedure is clearly unattractive. It is particularly unattractive when the number of times the iterative process is to be applied is not known in advance. The automatic returning of cards to the hopper or the back-spacing of tape by the required amount would accomplish the desired result, although apparently no one has ever considered this solution practical enough to build the required mechanism. Another solution is to put the part of the program which is to be repeated on a separate piece of program tape with ends joined to form a loop. This tape loop may be placed on a separate tape reader which is called into operation by the main program tape, and control is returned to the main tape when the computed results indicate that a sufficient number of iterations of the loop have been completed. This "sub-routine" tape may, if desired, control other sub-routine tape loops as sub-sub-routines. Clearly, when many sub-routines are involved, the controls become complex, and the number of tape reading units can become prohibitively great.

A more severe limitation of external programming is encountered when the sequence of operations is not continuous, but instead, it "branches" according to the results obtained at intermediate points in the computations. Many examples are encountered where one set of arithmetic operations is desired if a given number is positive and a partly or entirely different set is desired when it is negative. Simple cases can be handled by a multiplicity of tape readers; but, as more complex cases of branching are considered, this solution rapidly becomes impractical.

Further, it is not possible for the program to alter itself in the same sense that it is possible in a stored program machine. Many useful programming tricks, some of which are explained in Chapter 12 on programming, are thereby not available on externally programmed computers.

Plugged-program Computers. A second general method for controlling the sequencing of operations is through the use of a plugboard (control panel). With a plugboard the actual physical wiring of the computer is changed for each new set of computations to be performed by the machine. Clearly, it is important to devise a systematic arrangement for connecting the various plug hubs by means of plug wires in order to reduce the required time and the likelihood for mistakes when preparing the plugboard for a given sequence of operations. Even with the best designs, the amount of effort required to prepare a plugboard is likely to be excessive when compared with inserting a deck of program cards especially in commercial applications where the same array of connections must be assembled and disassembled frequently. IBM solved this problem by making the entire plugboard removable, and for each sequence of computations which might be repeated frequently, a separate plugboard is maintained with all plug wires in place. The outstanding limitation of a plugged program computer is the limitation on the number of steps which can be accommodated in the sequence. The limitation is a practical one and not a theoretical one; for many steps (say much over 100), the amount of equipment becomes excessive and the mass of plug wires required becomes unwieldy.

In explaining how a plugged program computer functions, no attempt will be made to describe some imaginary "generalized" computer. Instead, one specific design of machine, IBM's Type 604, will be used as a pattern, although liberal variations in the details and nomenclature will be made in an effort to illustrate the basic principles with a minimum of confusion from information that is not pertinent. However, it should be understood that the 604 arrangement is by no means the only one possible. Any group of imaginative engineers at the task of designing their own machine would probably incorporate many of their own ideas and arrive at a design substantially different from this one.

A block diagram of the major units in the arithmetic and storage portions of the computer is shown in Fig. 11-1. There are two eight-wire number busses (each indicated by a single line) in the system. One is used for entering numbers into the various registers, and this operation is called "read-in," which is abbreviated to RI. The other bus is for "read-out," which is abbreviated RO. Besides the registers intended specifically for storage, there are two special registers—one, the multiplier-quotient (M-Q) register; and the other, the accumulator. As the name implies, the M-Q register is for storing the multiplicand when multiplying and for storing the digits of the quotient as they are generated when dividing; however, this register may be used for ordinary storage if desired. All actual arithmetic is performed in the accumulator. The accumulator is similar in many respects to the other registers except that facilities for handling decimal carries are included. The decimal digit-storage devices in all registers are electronic decimal counters made up of four binary flip-flops with connections to eliminate six of the

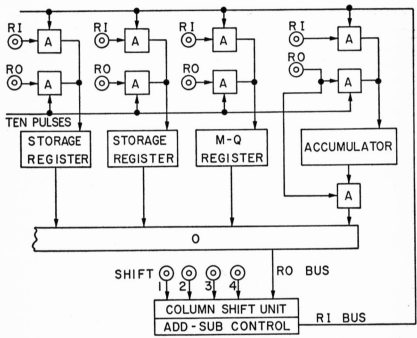

FIG. 11-1. Organization for plugged-program computer.

sixteen possible stable states in accordance with one of the schemes on counting described in Chapter 7. Then, to read-in a digit, a number of pulses equal to the value of the digit are applied to the counter. To read-out a digit, ten pulses are applied to the counter, and a pulse is caused to appear on the corresponding wire of the RO bus at the time the counter arrives at zero. After the tenth pulse the counter is, of course, back in its original state.

All arithmetic operations involve the transferring of numbers from one register to another, and all transfers occur through the "column-shift unit" and the "add-subtract control." The column-shift unit is a switching network capable of shifting the connections between the RO and RI busses under the control of external signals which are applied to it. For example, if a shift of two places is called for, the units RO signal will appear on the hundreds RI wire, the tens RO signal on the thousands RI wire, etc. The add-subtract control converts the timed pulses on the RO bus wires to series of pulses which the counters can count on the RI bus wires. Either the true or 9's complement representation can be obtained for addition and subtraction purposes in the manner described in Chapter 8 on decimal addition and subtraction. To cause a number to transfer from one register to another it is necessary to apply a steady-state signal to one RI plug hub and one RO plug hub during the time of the transfer. In Fig. 11-1 each "and" and "or" switch actually represents eight such switches because of the eight wires in the bus. Also, control signals must be applied to the column-shift unit to indicate the desired shift and to the add-subtract unit to indicate whether an addition or subtraction is to be performed. The set of "and" switches on the output side of the accumulator is for the purpose of preventing output pulses from reaching the RO bus when reading into the accumulator. Corresponding "and" switches are not needed on the outputs of the other registers because these other registers are always reset to zero before reading into them, with the result that the counters will never go past nine during read-in.

The basic source of pulses in the machine is a continuously running multivibrator which drives a 23-stage ring counter. The signals obtained from the various stages in the ring are used either directly or in conjunction with other flip-flops to generate control pulses and "gate" signals which may be needed throughout the computer. This ring circuit, together with its associated equipment, is sometimes referred to as the "clock." Time is measured with respect to the status of the ring. The instant when the last trigger in the ring goes off and the first one comes on is known as 1-time. The time of the second trigger's coming on is 2-time; the third, 3-time, and so on. The pulses generated from 1-time to 10-time are used for a variety of purposes including the resetting to zero of the appropriate storage registers, multiplication and division control, and others. The ten pulses used for the transfer of one storage location to another are generated from 11-time to 20-time, inclusively, and the carry-gate signal occurs from 21-time to 1-time of the next cycle. Although a more detailed understanding of the "clock" would be desirable for some purposes, it will not be described further because an understanding of the sequencing of arithmetic operations does not depend upon it.

The signals controlling the sequencing of operations are obtained from another ring counter, called the "program ring." The program ring may have as many stages as desired with one stage, or step, being required for each operation. The program ring gets its stepping pulses from the first stage in the clock ring, with the result that each time the clock ring goes through one complete cycle of operations the program ring is advanced one step. The output signals from the program ring are brought out to hubs on the plugboard. Therefore, during each entire arithmetic operation (during each program step) a steady-state type of

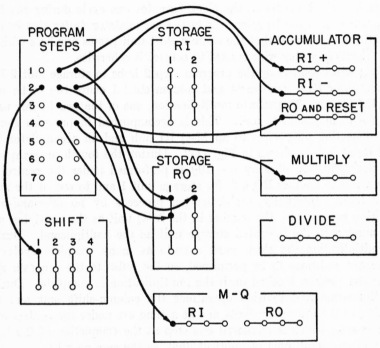

FIG. 11-2. Plugboard wiring for computing $x(x - 10y)$.

signal is available to control the various functions in the computer. Actually, each output from the program ring is brought to three separate hubs, called the program-exit hubs, and each connection is made through a separate electronic driving tube in order to prevent back circuits. The reason for the three output hubs is that it is frequently necessary to control three things during one program step.

To illustrate the functioning of a plugged program computer, a simplified plugboard wired to do the computation, $x(x - 10y)$, is shown in Fig. 11-2. Assume that x is initially in storage register 1, and y is in storage register 2. During the first program step, steady-state signals appear on the three program-exit hubs corresponding to this step. A plugged connection is made from one of these hubs to one of the storage

RO hubs corresponding to storage register 1. Note that there are four of these latter hubs shown in the figure. The line connecting them indicates that they are electrically wired together beyond the plugboard. This arrangement allows the convenient plugging of this RO function four times in the preparation of the plugboard. The same remarks apply to other hubs which are similarly connected. A second plug wire is used to connect program step 1 to an accumulator RI+ (add) hub. The operation which occurs as the clock executes one cycle during the first program step is the transfer of x to the accumulator (refer also to Fig. 11-1). It is assumed that the column-shift unit passes numbers without a shift unless a plug wire is used to control it otherwise.

Plug wires connecting the program step 2 hubs to storage unit 2 RO, accumulator RI− (subtract) and column shift 1 cause $10y$ to be subtracted from x. To perform multiplication, one of the two factors must be placed in the M-Q unit. This is accomplished in program step 3 by connecting plug wires to an M-Q RI hub and an accumulator RO and Reset hub as shown in Fig. 11-2. During the fourth program step the multiplication of x by $x - 10y$ is performed under the control of plug wires to another RO hub for storage unit 1 and to one of the multiply hubs. Internally, multiplication proceeds by an over-and-over addition process with the number in the M-Q unit as the multiplier and the number in the indicated storage unit as the multiplicand. During a multiplication the clock must execute as many complete cycles as there are additions to be performed, so the pulse to the program ring from the clock is blocked until the multiplication is complete. During multiplication and division operations the column-shift unit and the sensing of the multiplier digits one at a time are under the control of a ring counter which is advanced one step at the completion of the handling of each multiplier or quotient digit, as the case may be.

As might be expected, any practical plugboard arrangement would contain many more features than the basic ones which have been described. Of these other features, the most important ones are the means for causing the computer to proceed through different sequences of operations under the control of intermediate results and to repeat certain sequences as required in iterative processes. One system for accomplishing these results involves the suppression of certain program steps. Along with the three program-exit hubs on the plugboard corresponding to each program step there is a fourth hub called the program-suppress hub. When a signal is applied to this hub through a plug wire from any other source, the program step will not be executed because signals will be prevented from appearing on the program-exit hubs. In most cases the computations can be arranged so that the determination of which sequence to be followed is dependent on the sign of a number in the accumulator. Therefore, the accumulator sign flip-flop can be used to supply accumulator-plus and accumulator-minus signals which may be used for suppressing unwanted program steps. Other sources of program suppress signals may, of course, be used if desired. To repeat a portion of the program using this system it is necessary to repeat the entire program while suppressing all program steps except the portion to be repeated. To facilitate the suppression of so many steps and for other purposes, a "group suppression" feature has been devised. A binary storage device is used to control the suppression of any desired group of program steps through the use of appropriate hubs and wires on the plugboard. The steps in the group are suppressed or not, according to the status of the bistable device, which may be an electronic flip-flop or a relay, and which may be turned "on" or "off" by signals from any of a variety of sources in the computer. By supplying a multiplicity of group suppression devices, considerable flexibility may be achieved in the altering and repeating of sequenced operations. This system is used on IBM's type 607 computer and the "Card Programmed Calculator."

More flexible and higher-speed methods of altering and repeating programs may be worked out, usually at the expense of additional equipment. One such method involves the elimination of the "ring" feature of the program counter. Instead of proceeding from step to step in a uniform sequence, each program step is provided with an "in" hub to which a signal must be applied to initiate the action called for by the plug wires of that step. Also, with each program step there is an "out" hub on which a signal appears when that particular step has completed its operation. A plug wire must then be used to connect the "out" hub of each step to the "in" hub of the step which is to follow. When the selection of the next step is to depend upon the status of some condition in the computer (such as the plus-or-minus condition of the number in the accumulator), a group of pluggable "and" and "or" switches are needed. For example, assume that the program steps are executed in a uniform sequence through step number 15, but after step 15 the next step should be 16 if the number in the accumulator is plus or step 7 if it is minus. To accomplish this result, the outputs of the accumulator sign flip-flop are combined by means of plug wires in "and" switches with the "out" signal from program step 15. The outputs from the "and" switches are plugged to the "in" hubs of steps 7 and 16, respectively, with the result that, upon completion of step 15, a signal will be routed to step 7 or 16 in accordance with the status of the sign flip-flop. The "or" function is needed at the input of step 7 because this step may be initiated from step 6 or step 15. Since there are no restrictions on which step may be the "next" one, the altering and repeating of sequences are accomplished in the same way.

Storage Devices. Before proceeding to stored-program computers, a few points concerning the devices used in them for number storage should be understood. Although the counters used for storage in the earlier externally programmed and plugged-program computers could be used in a stored-program fashion, they are not nearly as practical as the storage devices which have been developed specially for the purpose. The organizations which have been worked out for stored-program machines depend in large measure upon the nature of the storage medium which is chosen.

Of the various storage devices that have been considered for computer applications, five have emerged as being acceptable from engineering and commercial standpoints. They are: magnetic cores, electrostatic storage tubes, acoustic delay lines, magnetic drums, and magnetic tapes. The differences in these storage devices are not only in the physical mechanism of storage, but also in the means used for gaining access to the individual storage bits. In fact, from the standpoint of computer organization, the access properties have a far greater effect on design than the storage mechanism itself. Naturally, cost has an important bearing also.

Magnetic Cores. Of the five, magnetic cores are the most recent to become successful, and it is with them that the shortest access times are possible. The storage principle of magnetic cores is simple enough. A toroidal-shaped piece of ferromagnetic material with a nearly square hysteresis loop is caused to be magnetized to saturation with the lines of flux passing in one direction or the other around the toroid. The remanent flux represents the storage of a binary 1 if it is in one direction, and 0 if it is in the other direction. The problem of gaining access in a practical manner to a specific core in an array is more difficult. In general, the means which are employed make use of the fact that, with a square hysteresis loop, it is possible to apply a magnetic field of strength H_0 which will have no effect where a field of $2H_0$ is sufficient to cause the flux to change completely from one state to the other. Then, in a rectangular array of cores, a current in a wire which passes through all cores in one column combined with a current in a wire which passes through all cores in one row can be used to selectively magnetize the core at the intersection of the row and column. To sense the status of the core, it is necessary to magnetize the core by the same procedure but in the opposite direction and to use a third wire through the core, which acts like a secondary winding of a transformer. A pulse or no pulse appears in the secondary, depending upon whether the flux was changed or not when sensing. Therefore, the problem of selecting a given core reduces to a problem of selecting two wires (one for row and one for column) to which pulses of current should be applied. When the number of cores is so great that one array is not practical, it is necessary to select one of a third group of wires to select the desired array. When each individual core is specified by a number which is stored in a set of flip-flops, it is possible to select the desired wires through the use of matrices as described in the chapter on switching networks.

Electrostatic Storage. With electrostatic storage the 1's and 0's are stored in small charged areas on the face of a cathode-ray tube; if a given area is left charged positively or negatively, a 1 or a 0, respectively, may be stored. Here, positive and negative are relative to each other and not to ground. There are several different ways by which the electron beam (cathode rays) can be used to create the desired charge pattern. The most successful, at least in terms of amount of use it has received, is known as the Williams tube system. With this system ordinary cathode-ray tubes developed for oscilloscopes and television sets can be used, although better results are obtained when certain design parameters are changed.

The feature in common with most electrostatic storage systems is the use of deflection plates to deflect the electron beam to the desired area on the tube face for access purposes. To gain access to a given spot, a voltage which is one of a multiplicity of discrete values is applied to the horizontal deflection plates and another voltage which is one of a different set of discrete values is applied to the vertical deflection plates. If a number representing the location of the desired spot is stored in a register composed of a set of flip-flops, it is necessary to convert these binary voltages to a sort of "semi-analog" voltages to be applied to the deflection plates. This effect is usually accomplished through current summing circuits comprised of precision resistors with values appropriately chosen. The summed currents are passed through other resistors to develop the stepped voltages which are then amplified and applied to the deflection plates.

The time required for access with electrostatic storage is slightly greater than for magnetic cores. The reason is largely in the fact that it takes some time to develop the deflection voltages to the accuracy necessary for the beam to hit the desired spot on the tube face within the tolerance required for reliable operation. With either cores or electrostatic storage, the sensing of information destroys it and it must be re-recorded if its continued storage is desired. In the case of Williams tubes, all stored information must be re-recorded periodically whether it is used or not, because otherwise the charge pattern would gradually disappear because of ohmic leakage. As a result, with this type of storage in some applications, a certain amount of time is required for regenerating storage and is not available for calculating.

Acoustic Delay Lines. With acoustic delay lines the storage mechanism is the presence or absence of mechanical vibrations traveling along the length of some material, usually a column of mercury. The term, "acoustic," is somewhat of a misnomer in that the frequency of the vibrations is well above the range of hearing; in fact, the pulse repetition rate may be as high as 2 megacycles or more, and the major frequency components of the individual pulses are even higher. To convert the electrical signals from the computer to mechanical vibrations in the mercury, a quartz crystal is mounted at one end of the column with the vibrations being induced by virtue of the piezoelectric properties of the quartz. Another quartz crystal is used at the far end of the line to sense the pulses as they arrive and convert them back to electrical signals. Of course, the amplitude and shape of the pulses are deteriorated when passed along the delay line. Therefore, for continued storage of information they are not returned directly to be recirculated; instead, they are used to gate fresh pulses into the line. This procedure is possible because it is the time of the pulse in the line which is of consequence in identifying it with a particular binary digit. The practicality of acoustic delay lines lies in the fact that it is possible to store several hundred binary digits of information in one line.

The means used for gaining access to a given bit in a delay line is quite different from the means used for cores or electrostatic storage. Once a pulse is sent down the delay line it cannot be sensed until it reaches the other end. Even a few intermediate sensing points along the line are usually not considered practical. However, once the pulse does appear at the output of the delay line, it appears on one wire and no further selection is required. To specify the location of a given pulse it is necessary to divide time into cycles which repeat over and over, where the time for one cycle is equal to the time required for a pulse to travel the length of the line. Each cycle is subdivided into individual pulse periods equal in number to the number of binary digits stored in the line. Each subdivision of time may then be assigned one of a series of numbers from zero to the storage capacity of the line. To gain access to any given binary digit the number representing its time of arrival at the output of the delay line (which is also the time of entry) is placed in a counter. At the start of one of the cycles, pulses are supplied to the counter to cause it to count toward zero in synchronism with the individual pulse period of the delay line. When the counter arrives at zero, an "and" gate is opened to allow the pulse, if any, which is emerging from the delay line at this time to pass into other computer circuits. A 1 or a 0 is represented by the presence or absence, respectively, of a pulse at this time. When more than one delay line is used, some of the digits of the number which represent the desired storage location are applied to a matrix to select the appropriate line in the same way that electrostatic tubes or arrays of cores would be selected.

Magnetic Drums. In the case of magnetic drums, the binary digits are stored as small magnetized areas on the surface of a revolving cylinder. Access to a spot on any one "track" is accomplished by substantially the same procedure as is used for acoustic delay lines. The delay in the drum is obtained from the time required physically to transport the spot in its circular path. The drum may be used in two different ways. If separate magnetic heads are used for recording and sensing the binary digits, the digits may be recirculated in the same manner as in the case of delay lines. A track operating in this way is sometimes called a "revolver." The other mode of operation involves the use of the same magnetic head for recording and sensing. With this scheme, the digits are not continually erased and rewritten, but instead they may be left on the drum surface indefinitely. However, it then becomes necessary to synchronize the drum position with the circuits used for access. A "timing track," which consists of a special track with a uniform series of magnetized spots permanently recorded, may be used for this purpose. The pulses obtained from the timing track can be used to control the drum speed, or the drum may be allowed to run at its own speed and the pulses used to control the access circuitry.

Practical pulse repetition rates for drums are in the order of 100 kilocycles, which is less than for acoustic delay lines by a factor of, roughly, 20. Also, the access time for comparable storage capacities is proportionately greater. Both of these properties are strong disadvantages, but magnetic drums have nevertheless found wide application because of their relatively low cost.

Magnetic Tape. The storage principle used for magnetic tape is substantially the same as for magnetic drums, although, because of tape-handling problems, the maximum practical pulse repetition rate is much less. However, the access procedure is radically different. The amount of information that can be stored on tape is almost unlimited, because pieces of tape can be spliced together to form very long lengths. The problem of physically handling the tape becomes acute, of course, when unduly long lengths are used, but even with short lengths of tape the problem of locating a desired spot is of importance. As a general rule, no attempt is made to assign numbers to the storage locations on tape (although it is possible), as is done with all of the other storage devices which have been described. Instead, information is usually recorded along the length of the tape in sequential fashion as it passes under the magnetic head without regard to the exact position of any particular bit of recorded information. When sensing the information, the tape is passed by the magnetic head, and the circuits which respond to the pulses from the head must be prepared to accept pulses at any time because the time of their arrival is not known.

When, as is usually the case, the recording is not being done continuously, the tape-drive mechanism must be stopped when not recording. Otherwise, large sections of unused tape would pass by the heads, and this procedure would not only waste tape but would make the access problem even more severe. Since the tape-drive mechanism cannot stop or start in a time which is short compared with the pulse-repetiton rate of the recorded information, a certain amount of space on the tape must be allowed between each "block" of recorded information. Further, there must be at least some safety factor in the amount of space. Because of the general uncertainty of the location of any information stored on tape, it is usually not practical to alter single bits of information. It is more common to erase an entire block and then record it again in its altered form. Care must be taken that sufficient space for tape starting and stopping is allowed at each end of the block.

Because of these characteristics of tape, computers are usually designed so that access to the desired places on tape is gained by means of programming instead of by built-in equipment. For example, the program may be written so that the blocks of information recorded on the tape can be counted. For another example, if tables of functions are stored on the tape, the arguments and values can be stored in alternate blocks. Then through programming, the computer can examine by a comparison operation all of the arguments until it comes to the right one, at which time it senses the next value of the function.

Consideration of Storage Devices Relative to Stored-program Computers. Of the various storage devices that have been described, magnetic cores and electrostatic storage tubes are the most attractive for stored-program computers in that access to any storage location may be gained with equal ease at any time. The choice between the two in any given application would be based on several engineering and economic considerations, but from the standpoint of computer organization either may be chosen.

Acoustic delay lines and magnetic drums are less desirable because, in the general case, it is necessary to require the computer to wait to place any information in storage or to recall it from storage. Nevertheless, these two forms of storage are used in many machines because they have other properties that are more advantageous. When using acoustic delay lines in a computer employing the serial mode of operation, a reasonably fast and reasonably inexpensive machine can be built because of the very high pulse-repetition rates that are possible. The waiting time can be minimized by writing the program so that at each step the desired storage location is the one approaching the end of the delay line at the time. The outstanding advantage of magnetic drums is the relatively low cost of a given amount of storage, and again, access time can be reduced by writing the program in an appropriate manner. However, the problem of "minimum access programming," as it is usually called, is by no means a simple one. In the case of magnetic tape, the access time is far too great to make tape practical as the principal storage medium in general-purpose electronic computers.

Also, either magnetic drums or tape, or both, are useful storage devices in computers using some other medium for its main, fast-access, storage. Larger storage capacities can be made available at a more attractive cost. The access problem can be side-stepped in large measure by transferring large blocks of information between the fast-access storage and consecutive locations on the tapes or drums rather than by making reference to substantially random locations on them. With this arrangement, all arithmetic operations are performed with the aid of only the main storage. When the capacity of the main storage will be exceeded, a few storage locations are saved for instructions which will record appropriate blocks of intermediate results on the tapes or drums and then call in blocks of more program steps or data, as required.

Tape reels on a computer can be changed readily by an operator. For this reason magnetic tape is frequently viewed as being an input or an output device instead of a storage device. Since the true source of information is seldom, if ever, found on magnetic tape and since invisible spots on a magnetic material are of little value as a final output, the role of magnetic tape as an input-output device could be questioned (compared with meter readings, keyboards, printers, and graph plotters, for example). Regardless of the semantics of the case, magnetic tape is frequently treated as an input and output device from the standpoint of computer organization. Also, magnetic drums are frequently handled organizationally as input-output mechanisms when used in conjunction with magnetic cores or electrostatic storage tubes, even though drums are usually not physically removable from the machine.

Organization of a Stored-program Computer. As with other forms of computers, there are a great many variations in the ways in which a stored-program computer can be organized. The organization which will be described here is patterned after IBM's Type 701 (a parallel, binary machine), although some modifications in details and nomenclature have been made to facilitate explanation of basic principles without confusion from information which is not pertinent. The 701 was chosen because the arrangement of this machine is about as straightforward as any and because all of the fundamental features of stored-program computers are easily illustrated. Other important features found in the 701 and other machines of this category will be described in later sections.

As a general rule, the storage devices which are useful for the main storage in stored program computers are not satisfactory for the temporary storage of numbers during the time that they are undergoing arithmetic operations or controlling the sequence of operations. For this reason, a set of miscellaneous storage registers, each specially adapted to a specific purpose, are employed in addition to the main storage. They may be comprised of any of a variety of storage elements. Conventional bistable flip-flops are frequently used, and for purposes of visualization, the use of flip-flops may be assumed. Three registers are used for storing numbers which enter into the computations. One, known as the "storage register," or S-register (see Fig. 11-3), serves the primary function of storing the multiplicand during multiplication and the divisor during division so that it is not necessary to make repeated references to the main storage during these operations. With the electrostatic storage system, as used in the 701, it is thereby possible in some cases to do nearly all of the regenerating of storage during these two relatively lengthy operations. Numbers are transferred from the main storage to the S-register over a set of parallel wires, one for each binary digit. The accumulator register can be of any one of the forms described in Chapter 4 on binary addition and subtraction, or it can be an adder used in conjunction with a conventional register. The multiplier-quotient, or M-Q register, as the name implies, is for the purpose of storing the multiplier during multiplication and the quotient during division.

For addition and subtraction, numbers are taken from appropriate locations in the main storage and sent to the accumulator. They are sent through the S-register because this path is needed anyway for other purposes. For multiplication, it is necessary as a first step to cause the multiplier to be transmitted from the main storage to the M-Q register. The accumulator and M-Q register are both capable of shifting the numbers in them to right or left. Then, at the start of the actual multiplication process, the multiplicand is obtained from the main storage and placed in the S-register to be added in over-and-over fashion in the accumulator, which shifts to the right one step after each addition. The product as it is built up is shifted into M-Q register as has been described in an earlier chapter. At the conclusion of the multiplication process the double-length product is stored with its high-order digits in the accumulator and its low-order digits in the M-Q register. If it is desired to retain the entire product, two storage locations in the main storage are required and two program steps are used to transfer it from

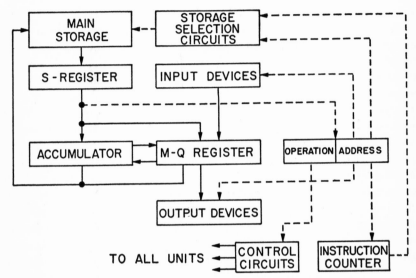

Fɪɢ. 11-3. One arrangement for a stored-program computer.

the two registers. Division is substantially the reverse of multiplication. The dividend is placed in the accumulator (or the accumulator and the M-Q register if a double-length dividend is required) and the divisor is stored in the S-register. As the division process proceeds, the digits in the accumulator are shifted to the left with the result that the final remainder appears in the accumulator and the quotient in the M-Q register. In Fig. 11-3, all paths used for the data and results are indicated by solid lines.

The problem is now to control the transmission of data between the main storage and the three registers in the arithmetic portion of the machine. This function is to be accomplished through the use of numbers representing program steps, and these numbers are to be stored in the main storage along with the numbers representing data. The instruction counter, the operation-address register, and the control circuits are the major units which are used for accomplishing this purpose.

The instruction counter has two functions. First, it keeps track of the program step that the computer is executing at any given time. Normally, a pulse is sent to the instruction counter at the conclusion of each arithmetic operation to step it up by one count; but for altering or repeating a program the contents of the address part of the operation-address register may be transferred to the instruction counter to replace the number there. The second purpose of the instruction counter is to control the storage-selection circuits when a number representing a program step is being sensed in the main storage. The nature of this control would depend upon the choice of storage device used for the main storage, as described in previous sections. The paths to and from the instruction counter are indicated in Fig. 11-3 by dotted lines, as are all of the paths which transmit information pertaining to the control or programming of the computer.

Before describing the function of the operation-address register, the meaning of the term, "address," must be explained. In its narrowest sense, an "address" is a number which represents a storage location in the main storage. Usually, each location is assigned one of a series of consecutive numbers from zero to the storage capacity of machine. Then, when an address is sent to the storage-selection circuits, access is gained to the storage location represented by that address. By this definition the number in the instruction counter is more than an abstract number used for counting program steps; it is an address also, because it prescribes the storage location from which a number representing the program step is to be taken. As will be explained further later, an address can be used to designate other things. For example, it is used to specify the desired input or output mechanism when sending information to or from the computer. Also, the address specifies the number of shifting steps that are to take place in a shift operation.

The operation-address register is used for storing the "instruction," which has been previously referred to as the number which represents the program step. An instruction consists of two parts, known as the operation part and the address part. The operation part specifies the operation to be performed, which may be an arithmetic operation such as add or multiply, or which may be any one of a long list of other operations such as the transfer of a number from one place to another or the causing of a magnetic tape unit to rewind. This part of the instruction causes the computer to perform the indicated operation by means of control circuits, which are described more fully in a later section. As the name implies, the address part of the instruction specifies the addresses of the operands when the main storage is involved or the input-output device, the number of shifts, and so on, as the case may be in other types of operations. In the 701, as well as in several other computers, the address part of the instruction contains only one address, and machines of this type are called "single-address" computers. Some computers contain as many as four addresses per instruction. The nature of the individual operations is somewhat different in multi-address computers from the ones found in single-address computers, but the general organization of the two types of machines can be quite similar. Incidentally, the address part of the register is a counter as well as a register and is used for keeping track of the shifts in a shift instruction or during a multiplication or a division.

During operation, the computer alternately comes under the control of the instruction counter and the operation-address register. To visualize the sequencing of the computer functions, assume that the program is initially stored in the main storage with at least the first few instructions in the lowest numbered addresses. The various items of data may be at any desired addresses. If the instruction counter is initially at zero, the control circuits first cause the instruction at address zero to be taken from the main storage and sent to the operation-address register. (The fact that the path is through the S-register is incidental.) Normally, the instruction is rewritten at address zero so that it may be used again. The computer then performs the operation indicated by the digits in the operation part of the address register. Upon completion of the first operation, control is returned to the instruction counter, which has in the meantime been stepped from zero to one. The instruction at address one is now caused to be sent from the main storage to the operation-address register, after which the second instruction is executed under control of this register, and so on. In other words, each program step consists of two parts, which are (a) the securing of the instruction and (b) the execution of the instruction. Reference to the main storage may be made during each part; in (a) the storage selection circuits are under control of the instruction counter and in (b) they are under control of the address part of the operation-address register.

For a further understanding of a stored-program computer, it becomes necessary to consider the list of instructions which the computer is able to perform. In any practical computer this list would involve a mass of detail, the description of which would be well beyond present purposes. Chapter 12 on programming describes a simplified list of instructions with sample programs illustrating its use. Here, the discussion will be limited to two outstanding features of instructions which can be built into computers of the stored-program variety.

The basic problem of altering a program or repeating portions of it is solved in the stored-program computer by a "jump" (sometimes given other terms such as "branch" or "transfer") instruction. The jump instruction causes the address part of the instruction, which is in the operation-address register, to be sent to the program counter to replace the number there. The result is that the uniform sequence of addresses from which instructions are obtained is terminated, and a jump is made to some other address. Then, because the program counter receives one pulse to be counted for each program step, the selection of instructions from sequentially numbered addresses is resumed at the new address and is continued until another jump instruction is encountered. The great usefulness of jump instructions arises from the possibility of using some criteria in the computer to control whether or not the jump is actually made. It is common practice to include at least two jump instructions, with one causing the jump to be made unconditionally and another causing the jump to be made or not under control of the sign of the number which is in the accumulator at the time. Other jump instructions may be included which are conditional upon different factors. It is not necessary that the factor be within the computer; for example, in some applications the jump might well be made dependent upon the time of day.

A second important feature of the instructions in a stored-program computer is that they are indistinguishable from the data. The programmer must keep track of which is which. Occasionally a certain amount of confusion results, but it is useful to be able to perform arithmetic operations on instructions. The addition or subtraction of a constant from the address part of an instruction is an operation which is performed frequently when using sub-programs. Another example of the usefulness of the feature is in the storage of tables when the arguments form a uniform sequence. To find the address of the value corresponding to any given argument, it is sufficient to perform a simple computation on the argument and then use the result as the address part of an appropriate instruction. A time-consuming searching process is thereby avoided. Arithmetic operations on the operation part of an instruction can be of considerable value too, but they usually fall in the category of tricks, any one of which can be used only on the machine for which it was devised. Also, as a result of the interchangeability of instructions and data, the program can be arranged so that extensions of the program can be entered into the computer through the input devices under control of the program itself in the same manner that new data are entered.

The input and output devices are shown connected through the M-Q register in Fig. 11-3. That the M-Q register is used in this way is incidental; it just happens to be convenient. However, some temporary storage of some sort is usually needed between the input and output devices and the main storage because the various units are not synchronized with one another. When an instruction calls for a number to be sent from main storage to an output device, for example, the output device may not at that particular instant be prepared to accept it. Then when the output device is ready to accept the number, the timing in the arithmetic part of the computer may not be at the right point for transmission. Another factor, which is probably even more compelling, is the fact that the form of the number may be different in the two places. In particular, in the 701 numbers are transmitted 36 bits at a time to and from main storage, but only 6 bits at a time to and from magnetic tape. Both the timing and the change of form problems can be solved through the use of "buffer" storage, as it is sometimes called.

Control Circuits. The objective to be accomplished by the control circuits in a stored-program computer is the causing of all the individual units of the computer to perform in such a manner that the instructions in the main storage are sensed in the proper sequence and executed. In general, the units are controlled by sending pulses to them over a set of wires which may be called "command lines." Each command line is for a specific purpose, such as transferring a number from one register to another, shifting the number in a register, resetting a flip-flop, or any one of a multitude of other functions. Usually it is necessary to send pulses, appropriately sequenced in time, over several different command lines to execute any one instruction. The circuit arrangement to be used in any given case for distributing the control pulses on the command lines depends in large measure on the organization of the computer as a whole, and in existing machines great variations will be found when comparing one computer with the next. Two general methods of assembling control circuits which can be used in a wide range of machine organizations will be outlined.

One possible organization for the block labeled "control circuits" in Fig. 11-3 is given in Fig. 11-4. The basic source of pulses is a continuously running multivibrator (MV) which drives a ring counter indicated in the figure as the "clock ring." Timed pulses are obtained from each stage of the clock ring, and one complete set of timed pulses is called a "cycle." At least two cycles are required to perform any arithmetic or other operation; one cycle, called the "instruction cycle," is used to transfer the instruction from the main storage to the operation-address register, and then at least one "execution cycle" is needed for the actual operation. The timed pulses from the ring are, therefore, sent through a switching network which distributes them to the various command lines as called for by the operation and the status of certain signals applied to the switching network as "miscellaneous inputs."

Among the more important miscellaneous input signals are signals from a flip-flop in the computer which indicates whether an instruction cycle or an execution cycle is being performed at the time. An instruction is obtained from storage during an instruction cycle and executed during an execution cycle. During an instruction cycle the signals from the clock are sent to appropriate units for the transfer of the instruction

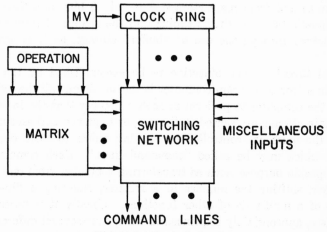

FIG. 11-4. Control circuits.

from the main storage to the operation-address register. Recall that during an instruction cycle the storage-selection circuits are under control of the instruction counter. One of the last pulses in the cycle is used to alter the instruction-execution flip-flop to cause the next cycle to be an execution cycle. In general, all instruction cycles are exactly alike, but there is a different type of execution cycle for each arithmetic or other type of operation that the computer can perform. Further, some operations, notably multiplication and division, require many execution cycles, not all of which are alike. Also, the execution cycles for conditional jump operations depend upon the conditions as supplied to the switching network through some of the miscellaneous input lines.

The major factor controlling the computer during an execution cycle is the number which was placed in the operation part of the operation-address register by the immediately preceding instruction cycle. The digits of this number are applied to a matrix which has one output line for each operation the computer is capable of performing. The output signal from this matrix together with certain signals from miscellaneous inputs then controls the distribution of the clock pulses to the command lines to cause the execution of the indicated operation. For all operations which refer to the main storage, the particular location selected will be the one indicated by the number in the address part of the operation-address register. For operations which require more than one execution cycle, a counter must be provided, and output signals from the counter are among the miscellaneous input signals to the switching network. A command line is used to pulse the counter at the completion of each cycle; when the counter indicates that the required number of cycles have been completed, a pulse on a different command line causes the instruction-execution flip-flop to call for the next instruction cycle. During the execution of the instruction one of the command pulses was used to advance the instruction counter by one step so that the instruction located in the next sequentially numbered address will be sensed unless the operation was a jump, in which case the next address will be the one which was transferred into the instruction counter from the address part of the operation-address register.

Although it is a relatively straightforward matter to assemble control circuits along this pattern which will make a computer capable of performing any list of operations that might be desired, minimizing the number components is usually a complex puzzle. Boolean algebra is a useful tool, but it is not wholly adequate, not only because of the multiplicity of signals involved, but also because the timing of the signals is a parameter which the designer can vary and which falls outside the scope of Boolean notation. Much is left to the ingenuity of the designer.

A second system for assembling control circuits avoids the use of a clock. Instead, a series of delay units is used for generating the timed command pulses needed for transferring the instruction from the main storage to the operation-address register. Also (in its most straightforward form), there is a set of delay devices to correspond to each operation the computer is capable of performing. The basic concepts of this type of control will be explained with reference to Fig. 11-5, which shows an abbreviated set of circuits in block diagram form. Assume that a pulse is applied at the point marked X. This pulse will travel to the right in the figure; and, as it passes through the delay units, appropriately timed pulses may be taken from the junctions. The timed pulses are sent along command lines to the required units in the computer for sensing the instruction in the main storage and transferring it to the operation-address register. This much of the functioning corresponds to an instruction cycle in the previous arrangement. The command lines are indicated in the figure as unmarked arrows pointing downward.

When the pulse emerges from the first set of delay devices it is applied to a set of "and" switches, one of which is opened by a signal from the matrix. The matrix, as before, is under control of the digits in the operation part of the operation-address register. The pulse will now travel along the set of delay devices corresponding to the particular operation

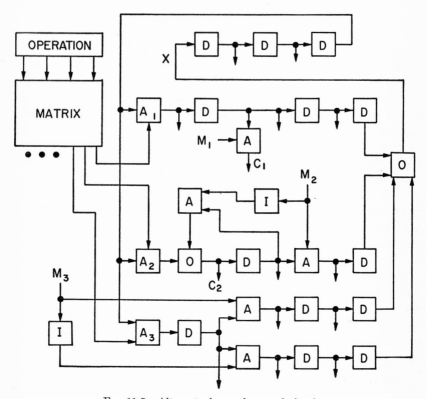

FIG. 11-5. Alternate form of control circuits.

which is to be performed. The path of the pulse from this point may now branch or loop in any of a variety of fashions under control of miscellaneous conditions in the computer. For example, if the A_1 switch is the one which is open, the pulse will appear on command line C_1 or not, according to the status of miscellaneous signal M_1. When the operation corresponding to A_2 is to be performed, the pulse will traverse a closed loop as long as no signal is present on M_2. Presumably one of the command lines, say C_2, leads to a counter which controls M_2, and when the loop has been traversed the desired number of times a signal will be applied to M_2 so that the pulse can leave the loop and continue to the right.

Loops of this type are useful in multiplication, division, and shifting operations. In cases where the pulse passes through A_3, the path branches under control of M_3 so that two quite different sets of command lines can be pulsed with a minimum of switching. Regardless of which operation was executed, the pulse will eventually appear at one of the inputs to an "or" switch to be returned to point X. The next instruction will then be sensed and executed.

As with the other system of control, the problem of minimizing the number of delay devices and other components is a complex puzzle with no straightforward method of solution. It should be noted, however, that it is not necessary to have a different set of delay devices for each operation, because in most computers many of the operations are similar to one another. A single set of delay devices may than be used for all operations in a given category with signals from the matrix being used as miscellaneous inputs to gate the command pulses as required. In some computers it may be necessary to operate the main storage or other units on a fixed-cycle basis. In this case, synchronization problems may be encountered because it will not always be known which part of the computer will finish first when certain operations, such as shift, are being performed. Synchronizing circuits similar to the ones described in Chapter 3 on switching networks may be used to cause the unit finishing first to wait for the other.

Synchronous and Asynchronous Computers. The two methods for designing control circuits which were described in the previous section are representative of two design philosophies, either one of which may be continued much further in the design of a computer. In the first method, the timing of all operations is under control of the "clock," and, therefore, all operations take place in synchronism with the clock. Each operation requires an integral number of complete clock cycles. Because of the definite time relationship between the period of the clock and the execution of the operations, computers functioning in this way are said to be "synchronous" computers.

In an "asynchronous" computer there is no fixed time reference for the execution of the operations. Instead, one operation is commenced as soon as the previous one is completed. To accomplish this purpose, the circuits must be arranged so that, at the completion of each operation, a signal is generated which may be used to initiate the next one. In Fig. 11-5 the delay devices and switching circuits were arranged so that the path of the pulse was continuous; when the pulse arrived at the end of one set of delay devices it was immediately entered into another set. The philosophy of asynchronous operation may be extended to apply to the individual parts of each operation. For example, the time required for handling the carries in an addition operation depends upon the number of carries that happen to occur. Rather than wait an amount of time required for the maximum number of carries, plus a safety factor, the asynchronous adder described in Chapter 4 on binary addition and subtraction may be used. In this case the path of the control pulse would be through the carry circuits of the adder during this portion of the operation. The asynchronous multiplier, which was described in Chapter 4 on binary multiplication and division, could be used in a similar manner. With this type of multiplier the loop for the control pulse would be in the multiplier itself instead of in the control circuits as shown in Fig. 11-5. The pulse would be circulated by passing it along the carry or the shift lines as dictated by the digits of the multiplier until a counter indicated that all multiplier digits had been sensed. Then, through a switch operated by the counter, the pulse would be returned to the control circuits.

It is not clear that either the synchronous or the asynchronous system has any outstanding advantages over the other. It would seem that the organization of a synchronous machine would tend to be more systematic and, therefore, perhaps easier to design, understand, and service. On the other hand, there is the possibility of making an asynchronous machine somewhat faster because it is not necessary to use a complete "cycle" of time for each operation. However, with either type of machine, the limiting factor with regard to speed is usually in the main storage unit because, in most cases, it has been possible to develop practical arithmetic circuits capable of operating on the numbers as fast as they can be taken from and sent to storage. An outstanding exception to the rule is in the operations of multiplication and division. For this reason it is sometimes desirable to execute multiplication and division in asynchronous fashion in a machine which is otherwise synchronous. Many other compromises in the two design philosophies are to be found, particularly in the input and output units, which cannot in a practical sense be synchronized with the very high electronic speeds of the arithmetic unit.

A-C and D-C Systems. Another criterion by which computers may be classified is in the manner by which signals are transmitted through switching networks and from one part of the machine to another. In one type, all of the signals are pulses. Even the storage registers are of the dynamic type, and the output signals from such devices are represented by the presence or absence of pulses. Machines in this category are known as a-c (alternating-current) computers. The SEAC, which was built by the National Bureau of Standards, was the first computer in which the a-c technique was employed extensively.

At the other extreme is found a class of machines known as d-c (direct-current) computers. In a d-c computer each signal is represented by a steady-state voltage, which is maintained at one of two levels according to whether the signal is a 1 or a 0. The voltage level is changed, of course, when the signal is changed, but during the time that the signal is being used it is held constant. All of the storage devices used in the registers are flip-flops or some other type of mechanism that produces steady-state output signals. All flip-flops are caused to transfer back and forth between their two stable states during computations by means of "pull-over" circuits actuated by steady-state signals and not by pulses. An outstanding example of a d-c computer is the ORDVAC, which was built at the University of Illinois.

Not all machines can be classified as definitely one type or the other. For example, IBM's 604, 650, and 701 computers each contain many circuits employing pulses as well as many circuits of the d-c type.

It is not clear that either the a-c or the d-c technique is superior to the other. With the a-c technique a serious design difficulty is encountered from the fact that all pulses applied to an "and" switch must arrive at the same time for an "and" function to exist. Since the passage of a pulse through almost any component introduces a delay, the design of an arrangement which will cause all pulses to arrive at the desired points at the desired times can be a very complex puzzle. Also, when using an inhibiter, it is necessary in practical circuits that the inhibiting pulse be applied slightly before the arrival of the pulse to be inhibited, and it must be maintained until a time which is slightly later than the pulse to be inhibited has disappeared. Further, the requirement of retiming and reshaping of signal pulses by means of clock pulses throughout the computer is certainly an undesirable feature of the a-c technique. On the other hand, the fact that pulses may be passed through condensers and transformers causes certain circuit isolation and voltage level setting problems to be much simpler with the a-c technique than with the d-c technique. Apparently no two machines, one a-c and one d-c, of sufficiently similar capabilities and history have been found for accurate comparison of such factors as cost (of the machine as a whole), reliability, and ease of servicing. These factors in the relative merits of the two design techniques seem to be matters of opinion.

Other Forms of Computer Organization. The arrangements which were described in the sections on externally programmed, plugged-program, and stored-program computers do not exhaust the variations by which a computer may be caused to proceed through the desired sequences of operations. For one thing, any two, or even all three of the sequencing means may be combined. As an example, IBM's Card Programmed

Calculator (CPC) uses punched cards as an external programming means together with a plugboard. Briefly, each card contains an instruction which causes the computer to proceed through a certain set of program steps that are wired on the plugboard. The instructions, as recorded on the cards, are, therefore, highly flexible. Combinations of stored-program techniques and externally programmed techniques may be found in almost any stored-program computer which includes an instruction for sensing an input device. Since new instructions as well as data may be entered through the input device, the program itself may be used to call in instructions from an external source for continuing the sequence. Some interesting possibilities can be visualized through the use of a plugged program together with a stored program, but this combination has not been exploited.

In the organization of a stored-program computer it is not necessary that storage locations be used interchangeably for instructions and data. The Harvard Mark IV computer, for example, is a stored-program machine which has separate storage locations and separate transmission paths for instructions and data. Arithmetic operations cannot be performed on instructions in the same sense that this function is possible in computers with interchangeable instructions and data, but there is provision for altering or repeating sequences of operations under control of the computed results. There are advantages to keeping instructions and data separated, such as the relative simplicity of certain aspects of programming. However, the vast majority of stored-program computers have been designed with interchangeable instructions and data because of the many useful programming procedures which are thereby made possible.

Another form of organization for a stored-program computer can be obtained by using an idea found in the digital differential analyzer, which was explained in the preceding chapter. It might be described as a "no-address" computer, in that each instruction specifies only an operation. The operation and the number or numbers to which it applies must be stored in the same location, that is, at the same address. The addresses are inspected sequentially, and at each address the indicated operation is performed on the data found there. Again, the possibilities are interesting; but, so far as is known, no machine functioning in this way has ever been put to use.

Special-purpose Computers. For the most part, the computer organizations which have been described are for "general-purpose" machines, where a general-purpose machine is one that is capable of solving a wide variety of problems, the nature of which may not be known prior to the design of the machine. When a computer is to be applied to a specific type of mathematical problem, special features may be incorporated to aid in its solution, and it then becomes known as a special-purpose computer. These special features may range all the way from one or two special instructions in an otherwise general-purpose computer to an entirely different organization throughout. An example of a machine with a radically different organization is the digital differential analyzer, which is intended primarily for the solution of differential equations. Another special-purpose computer bearing little resemblance to any general-purpose machine is the USAF—Fairchild Specialized Digital Computer, which was designed specifically for solving simultaneous linear equations.

Word Length. The term, "word," is used to signify any group of digits that is handled as a unit in a computer. Usually a word is one number when referring to data, or it is one instruction, although there are exceptions to this definition. Most computers operate with a fixed number of digits in each word, and in the design of such machines a decision must be made concerning the number of digits in each word, or the word length to be used. If the word length is made large enough to handle the largest numbers expected to be encountered, much storage space and other equipment will be wasted for those problems requiring less accuracy in their solution. If a short word length is chosen, two or more words may be used to store each number when long numbers are necessary, and arithmetic operations may be performed in parts by following a so-called "multiple-precision" technique. However, many extra program steps are required to execute multiple-precision operations with a resultant waste in storage space and also with a waste in time. Word lengths which have been used vary from 15 binary digits including sign (equivalent to about $4\frac{1}{2}$ decimal digits) in MIT's Whirlwind I to 23 decimal digits in the Harvard Mark I.

The choice of word length is most difficult for general-purpose computers when it is not known what mathematical problems the machine is to solve. Some studies have indicated that the choice is not critical, but that there is an optimum word length for the "average" problem somewhere in the range of 10 to 12 decimal digits (or the binary equivalent).

The number of digits in an instruction, as well as the accuracy of computations, enters into the choice of word length. The number of digits in an instruction depends upon the number of different operations the computer is capable of performing, the number of addresses in each instruction, and the size of the addresses. In the interests of conserving storage space it is desirable to adjust the number of digits in an instruction or the number of digits in the word so that one is an integral multiple (usually one or two) of the other.

There is no inherent reason why the words have to be of fixed length. A computer can, by means of appropriate instructions together with an appropriate organization, be caused to perform arithmetic and other operations on numbers of varying length. The increments in size may be as small or as large as desired. In a decimal machine, increments as small as one decimal digit are advantageous, in which case each individual digit location in the main storage is addressable. An address in an instruction then refers to the first digit in a word, and the remaining digits are stored in successively higher-number address positions. The number of digits to be used at any given time may be indicated by a special counter, by a special character in the accumulator, or by other means. Appropriate instructions must be included for altering the word length. Another scheme is to include the word length as a part of each instruction. Machines in this category are known as "variable word length" or "variable field length" computers in contrast to "fixed word length" computers.

Storage Capacity. Another important decision which must be made during the design of any computer has to do with capacity of the storage medium. In order to solve very complex problems at high speed it is desirable to have a large storage capacity; yet, in the interests of high reliability and low cost, the storage capacity should be made as small as possible. Clearly, a compromise is required. However, in some cases other considerations arise that help in the determination of the proper storage capacity. For example, in a plugged-program computer, a rough upper limit to the number of storage locations that can be used profitably is set by the number of program steps available on the plugboard.

In a stored-program computer the upper limit to the number of storage locations in the main storage unit that can be used is set only by the problem to be solved. Nevertheless, beyond a certain point, a "law of diminishing returns" becomes apparent because of the possibility of introducing blocks of new data or instructions into storage at reasonably high speed. It should be noted that most computations applied to sequenced computers are highly repetitive in nature (otherwise, it would be as easy to solve them on a desk machine as to prepare the program). Because of this fact, the time required to complete the operations specified by one filling of the storage unit of a given size may be comparable with the time required for refilling the storage unit. When this condition exists, a larger sized storage unit would increase the over-all speed of the computer by only a small factor. This line of reasoning applies best to computers which use a random-access, high-speed, storage medium such as electrostatic tubes or magnetic cores for the main storage and which use magnetic tape or drums for auxiliary storage. For machines of this nature, the optimum main storage capacity appears to be in the range of 1000 to 4000 words.

Single-address and Multiple-address Computers. As has been mentioned, a computer may be organized with each instruction containing one, two, three, or four addresses. More than four would be possible, but the incremental advantages of each address beyond four diminishes rapidly.

For single-address computers it is customary to execute the instructions as they are found in sequentially numbered addresses (except for jumps) under the control of an instruction counter in the manner described in the section on stored-program computers. The address in the instruction may refer to the location of one of the operands entering into the computations in the case of an arithmetic operation, or it may refer to the number of shifts, the identity of an input or output device, or something else in the case of a different kind of operation. With this arrangement a simple addition operation usually requires three instructions. The first instruction is used to cause one operand to be transferred from the specified address to the accumulator. The second instruction causes the other operand to be transferred from its specified address to the accumulator to be added to the first operand. Then the third instruction is used to transfer the sum from the accumulator to the desired address in storage.

The two addresses in a two-address computer could be used to specify the locations of two operands, or a shift and the location of one operand, or any of a variety of other combinations. However, the second address is probably most commonly used to specify the location of the next instruction. With this arrangement, the instruction counter is not a counter; instead, it is only a storage register. A counting action is not needed because instructions are not necessarily taken from sequentially numbered storage locations; each instruction is essentially a jump instruction. For conditional jump operations, one address may be used to specify the location of the next instruction when the condition is satisfied (such as positive sign for the number in the accumulator at the time), and the other address may be used for the location of the next instruction when the condition is not satisfied. A two-address system with one address specifying the location of the next instruction is particularly useful in computers employing magnetic drums (or some other storage medium which is not of a random-access type) for main storage. By judicious positioning of the instructions on the drum, the computer can be caused to waste much less time waiting for the next instruction to appear at the sensing heads than when the instructions are positioned randomly. The finding of the proper addresses for the instructions is part of the procedure known as "minimum-access programming."

An example of the use of an instruction in a three-address computer would be an arithmetic operation where the addresses of the two operands are specified as well as the address of the location where the result is to be stored. With this arrangement only one instruction would be required to perform the addition operation that required three instructions in the single-address machine. Several different variations are possible when one or more of the addresses are used to specify locations of subsequent instructions.

In a four-address computer, at least one of the addresses is almost always used for the location of the next instruction because there is little, if any, use for more than three addresses for other purposes.

As a general rule, as the number of addresses in each instruction is increased, the number of instructions required and the time required to solve any given problem are decreased because each instruction is able to accomplish more. On the other hand, a multiple-address computer is usually somewhat more complex than a corresponding single-address machine. Also, more storage space is required for a multiple-address instruction than for a single-address instruction, and in many cases the extra space is largely wasted because the extra addresses are not always needed. There is some reason to believe that the preparation of a program can be made a simpler and more straightforward process for single-address machines than for multiple-address machines, but this point is subject to question. Successful machines of each type have been built.

Floating-point Computers. The floating-point feature can be installed in any of the computer organizations which have been described. In most cases it will probably be found desirable to use special counters for storing the exponent parts of the numbers entering into the computations. For each arithmetic operation, the required shifts are made under control of the counters and under control of circuits for sensing nonzero digits in the shifting register. A pulse is sent to the exponent counter each time a shift is made. While a great many details in many parts of a computer are affected by adoption of the floating-point system, no new principles are involved, and appropriate extensions of the control systems used for fixed-point computers can be used.

Index Registers. Innumerable special features can be found in the various computers which have been built. Among the more important features in some machines is a set of registers, called "index registers." In these machines, which are usually of the single-address type, each instruction specifies an index register as well as an operation and an address. For each operation, the number stored in the indicated index register is automatically added to the address, and the sum is then the actual address which is used. A "load index register" instruction is needed for transferring a number from storage into the indicated index register so that the numbers stored in the index registers may be changed during computations. Index registers facilitate the use of sub-programs as will be described in the next chapter. A computer built at the University of Manchester in England was the first to employ index registers, although with this machine the term used to designate them (collectively) was "B tube."

Repeat Counter. Another useful feature is a "repeat counter" which can control the number of times an instruction is repeated. A "load repeat counter" instruction is used to transfer the desired number from storage to the repeat counter. Then, each time the instruction to be repeated is executed, a pulse is sent to the counter to count it down toward zero, and the repeating is continued until the counter reaches zero. Usually it is desirable to alter the address part of the instruction each time it is repeated. For this purpose, the register storing the address part of the instruction may be made capable of counting, and the pulses which are sent to the repeat counter may be sent to this counter also. Functions such as adding a long list of numbers stored at sequentially numbered addresses are very easily and rapidly accomplished with a repeat counter, where an iterative loop of some sort would be required otherwise. Also, the repeat counter is useful in transferring large blocks of information between the main storage and an input or output mechanism. In this case, the number of words to be transferred is placed in the repeat counter.

Input-output. In some respects the subject of input and output mechanisms for a computer can be as extensive as the subject of the arithmetic operations themselves. In particular, for computers intended for accounting applications, the preparation of voluminous information for machine consumption and the subsequent preparation of records, reports, bills, checks, and other documents are problems that can easily overshadow the arithmetic problems. In many cases even the machine work is largely sorting, collating, and other nonmathematical operations that can be accomplished to some extent through appropriate control of multiple input and output mechanisms.

Relative to the arithmetic operations, the outstanding characteristic of practically all input and output devices is that they are slow in comparison with the speeds attainable with electronic components which may be used in the arithmetic and control portions of a computer. There are some problems, particularly in the scientific field, that involve long sequences or operations on relatively small amounts of input and output data; and, for these problems, input and output speeds are not important. However, in a surprisingly large number of cases even in the scientific field, it is found that time required for input-output functions is an appreciable fraction of the time required for the computations. For this reason, it is desirable that the computer be organized in such a way that the computations can proceed simultaneously with the input-output functions. One way of accomplishing this purpose is through the use of buffer storage. For example, if punched cards are the input medium, a card full of data may be transferred to buffer storage during the time that the computer is processing the data corresponding to the previous card. At the completion of the operations, the data are transferred at high speed from the buffer storage to the main storage in the computer. An alternate method is to arrange the functioning of the system so that arithmetic operations can be performed between individual operations of the input-output mechanism. In the card-input example, the few milliseconds of time between the sensing of individual holes may be sufficient to allow the computer to execute a reasonably long sequence of arithmetic operations. Both of these schemes have been used successfully.

Error Detection and Correction. Because of the multiplicity of components in a large computer, the detection and correction of errors is a constant battle. It would, of course, be desirable to develop components to a state of reliability such that a computer would function for years without error. However, it is not essential that this objective be obtained; in fact, the success of computing machinery is due in large measure to the fact that procedures have been worked out for making effective use of a computer even when components are randomly and frequently deteriorating beyond the point of usefulness.

An error may be placed in one of the three categories according to whether it was caused by a complete failure of a component, the marginal operation of a component, or a random malfunctioning of a component. Actually, an engineer attempting to repair a defective computer must consider other sources of errors. For example, the internal wiring may include some incorrect connections, particularly if the computer is new or if modifications have been made recently. Also, in the course of searching for a defect it can happen that wires will be disconnected and then reconnected improperly. Further, the computer may be in perfect condition with the defect occurring in the program. Even "tested" programs can fail when unforeseen and previously unencountered parameters are used. Here, it will be assumed that the computer is designed properly and that the program is correct. For the most part, all errors regardless of source are detected by the same methods, but important differences arise in the means used for locating defective components.

One method of sensing errors is through the use of error-detection circuits, some of which have been discussed in previous chapters. The storage and transmission of information within a computer is easily checked through the use of redundancy bits. Also, it is not difficult to incorporate checking circuits for adders and other arithmetic devices if appropriate codes are chosen. However, with many computers it has not been found possible to devise practical checking facilities for the entire machine; the control circuits, in particular, can be very difficult to check completely. The other means of detecting the presence of errors is through programming. The nature of program checks depends upon the problem. For example, the solution to an algebraic equation may be checked by observing (through programming) whether or not the result fits the equation. For other types of problems it may be necessary to solve the problem by a second method, which is as different as possible from the first method, and compare the results.

After an error is detected, either by the error-detection circuits or by programming, the computer may be automatically stopped for repairs. The source of an error is usually relatively easy to find when the error is caused by the complete failure of a component, for example, a filament burn-out in a tube. Test programs that require the functioning of all components in the machine or the suspected region of it are useful aids in locating components which have failed completely.

Probably a more common type of component failure is a gradual deterioration until a point is reached where the component causes intermittent failures. The operation of the component is then said to be "marginal." Test programs are helpful in locating marginal components, although they are not when the marginal component creates errors only rarely. It is usually desirable to increase the frequency of the failure of the component by varying some parameter in the machine. For example, if the cathode emission of a tube in a flip-flop circuit is low, the operation of the circuit may be critically dependent upon the grid bias voltage. Therefore, by altering the grid bias the circuit may be caused to fail consistently so that it can be located easily. Since this method is useful for locating components about to fail as well as components which have already caused errors, the best way to treat errors caused by marginal components is to prevent them as much as possible by periodic machine inspection.

Sources of errors are most difficult to find when they are of a random nature. An example of a random error would be found in the case where a few loose flakes of cathode coating material in a tube were dropping off and causing temporary grid-to-cathode short circuits. Another example might be a condenser with a dielectric which occasionally breaks down with a very small arc and then heals. The search for sources of random errors is a puzzle with no fixed pattern for solution. Almost every computer engineer seems to have had the experience of searching for many days or weeks for an elusive defect. Sometimes the frequency of the error can be increased somewhat, in which case the error would probably belong in the marginal category. In the example of the loose flakes of cathode material, a light tapping of the tube might cause the flakes to fall more frequently. On the other hand, after a few flakes have fallen the tube might, for a time, be better than before. In the case of the condenser the frequency of the arcing could probably be increased by increasing the voltage across it, but this step might be impractical because of the location of the condenser in the circuit. Defective connections in the wiring are another source of substantially random errors that are difficult to locate.

In general, error-detection methods do not indicate the nature of the source of an error. Since an error may not be caused by the complete failure of a component, it may not recur for a long period of time. Therefore, it may be preferable to repeat the portion of the problem where the error occurred and then continue instead of stopping the machine. The repeating may be accomplished through the program, and the attention of an operator is not necessarily required. In some applications it is desirable to continue the computations for other reasons. For example, if an error occurs in a computer which is computing the direction of fire for an antiaircraft gun, there is no point in correcting the mistake because the target will have moved. Yet, the next shot might be successful. In contrast to these examples, when searching for the source of an intermittent error, it is desirable to be able to stop the computer on the very step where the error occurs. Then, by studying the status of information in the various registers it is sometimes possible to deduce the location of the defective component. For this purpose, error-detection circuits are necessary; program checks seldom detect an error until one or more steps later.

For very long programs, catastrophic failures such as loss of power are worrisome. To avoid having to restart a problem at the beginning when failure of this type occurs, all intermediate results may be recorded at periodic intervals on punched cards, magnetic tape, or some other medium whereby they can be re-entered into the computer. When this precaution is taken, computations may be resumed at the point where intermediate results were last recorded. In this connection, storage devices are often classified as "volatile" or "nonvolatile" according to whether they lose or retain, respectively, information when power is removed. Electrostatic storage, for example, is volatile, and most magnetic storage devices are nonvolatile. To make use of nonvolatile storage in minimizing the effects of power failures, it would be necessary not only to "stop" the computer before the voltages had collapsed an appreciable amount, but also it would be necessary to stop the computer at a point where computations could be resumed. The latter requirement might be difficult if a relatively slow-speed input-output device were in operation at the time.

Chapter 12

PROGRAMMING

The methods used for programming a computer so that it will proceed through the desired sequences of operations depend greatly on the way in which the computer has been organized. In particular, programming methods are quite different for externally programmed, plugged-program, and stored-program machines. Although interesting and important techniques have been worked out for certain externally programmed and plugged-program machines, the outstanding advances in programming methods have been made in connection with computers of the stored-program variety. For this reason, the term, "programming," frequently implies that the program is stored. Further, it is generally assumed that with a stored program the computer will be able to perform arithmetic and other operations on instructions in the program as well as on items of data, although a few stored-program machines have been built where the program and data have been kept separate. In this chapter, the subject will be confined to stored-program machines that store instructions and data interchangeably.

For each stored-program computer there is a list of instructions that the computer is capable of executing. When preparing a program to solve any given problem, the programmer must be familiar in some detail with the steps the computer will take when following each instruction in the list. Although the instruction lists of most computers contain certain basic instructions, such as add, multiply, shift, and others, the details in the steps taken to execute the instructions can vary considerably from one machine to the next. Also, there are many miscellaneous instructions which may or may not be incorporated into any given machine. Because of the extensive variations which may be found in the instruction lists, the program used to solve a given problem on one machine may seem to bear little resemblance to the program used to solve the same problem on another machine. However, the same principles of programming can be applied to practically all computer organizations where the instructions are stored interchangeably with the data. These principles will be explained and illustrated through the use of a "specimen" machine. The instructions in the instruction list for the specimen machine have been chosen mainly for their usefulness in illustrative programs, but at the same time there has been an attempt to make the list realistic.

Instruction List for the "Specimen" Machine. A 5-digit, single-address, decimal organization has been chosen for the "specimen" machine. Each word will consist of five decimal digits with sign, and any word may represent either an item of data or an instruction. When a word is used to represent an instruction, the first two digits will serve as a code to indicate the operation to be performed, and the last three digits will represent the address; the sign will not be used in the case of an instruction. Normally, the computer will start by executing the instruction found at address 000 and will continue by executing instructions found at sequentially numbered addresses except when a jump type of instruction is encountered. Besides the one thousand storage locations (designated by addresses 000 through 999) in the main storage unit, there will be one other storage register, called the accumulator, which will enter into the various operations as described in the instruction list. A knowledge of the material in the previous chapter, which explains how a computer can be made to proceed through a sequence of instructions, should be helpful but not necessary.

Instruction	*Code*	*Description*
STOP	00	The computer stops regardless of the digits in the address part of the instruction.
RESET AND ADD	01	The accumulator is reset to zero, and the number at the indicated address is then placed in the accumulator.
ADD	02	The number at the indicated address is added to the number in the accumulator, and the sum is left in the accumulator.
SUBTRACT	03	The number at the indicated address is subtracted from the number in the accumulator, and the difference is left in the accumulator.
MULTIPLY	04	The number at the indicated address is multiplied by the number in the accumulator, and the product is left in the accumulator. (This instruction is somewhat irregular in that products of more than five digits will not be possible.)

Instruction	Code	Description
DIVIDE	05	The number in the accumulator is divided by the number at the indicated address. The quotient is left in the accumulator, and the remainder is lost.
SHIFT RIGHT	06	The number in the accumulator is shifted to the right a number of places indicated by the number in the address part of the instruction. Digits shifted to the right from the units position are lost.
SHIFT LEFT	07	The number in the accumulator is shifted to the left a number of places indicated by the number in the address part of the instruction. Digits shifted to the left from the tens thousands position are lost.
STORE	08	The number in the accumulator is placed in the storage location indicated by the address part of the instruction. The previous contents of this storage location are lost; the number in the accumulator is unchanged.
STORE ADDRESS	09	Same as STORE except that the number in the accumulator is assumed to be an instruction, and only the three digits corresponding to the address part of the word are sent to storage. The digits corresponding to the code in both the accumulator and address location are unaffected.
JUMP	10	The next instruction is taken from the address indicated by the address part of this instruction instead of the next sequentially numbered address position.
JUMP IF MINUS	11	Same as JUMP if the number in the accumulator at the time is negative (zero is assumed to be positive); otherwise, the next instruction is taken from the next sequentially numbered address position.
READ	12	One word from the input mechanism is placed in storage at the indicated address. The previous number at this address is lost.
PRINT	13	The word at the storage location indicated by the address is recorded by the output mechanism. The number in storage remains unchanged.

Basic Programming Technique.   To illustrate the basic procedure which is used to cause a computer to proceed through a sequence of operations, the instructions required for the "specimen" computer to compute $xy + z^2$ and print the result will be shown.   Assume that means have been provided for placing the program and the data in the main storage unit of the computer. The first instruction will appear at the storage location designated by address 000, and the other instructions are placed in the storage locations designated by successively higher numbered addresses. The data, x, y, and z, may be stored at any convenient addresses not needed for instructions; in this example, locations 009, 010, and 011 will be used. Recall that when a storage location is used for storing an instruction, the sign is not used, the first two digits represent the operation in coded form, and the last three digits indicate the address part of the instruction. All five digits with sign are used as one number when storing an item of data.

Address	Contents of Address		Remarks
000	RESET AND ADD	009	Places x in the accumulator.
001	MULTIPLY	010	Forms xy in the accumulator.
002	STORE	012	Places xy at address (location) 012 for temporary storage.
003	RESET AND ADD	011	Places z in the accumulator.
004	MULTIPLY	011	Forms z^2 in the accumulator.
005	ADD	012	Forms $xy + z^2$ in the accumulator.
006	STORE	012	Places $xy + z^2$ at address 012 for temporary storage. (The previous contents of 012 are lost.)
007	PRINT	012	The number representing $xy + z^2$ is printed.
008	STOP	---	Computer stops. The address part of this instruction is of no consequence.
009	x		
010	y		
011	z		
012	[ ]		Reserved for temporary storage.

In the above program the purpose and function of each instruction is explained through the comments in the "remarks" column. Several different variations in the program may be worked out. One minor variation is that location 012 need not be reserved as a place for the temporary storage of intermediate results. Location 009, for example, would serve this purpose just as well, because after the first instruction x does not enter into the problem again so that location 009 is no longer needed for its storage.

Note the desirability of stopping the computer on step 008. If the computer is not stopped, it will automatically proceed to interpret the items of data as instructions. Since the digits of x, y, and z could represent any of the instructions, all manner of unpredictable and unwanted operations might result.

Elementary Logical Program. In the example of the previous section, the computer proceeds uniformly through sequentially numbered address locations to obtain its instructions. In many problems it is necessary or desirable to alter the sequence of operations in accordance with the data. A simple illustration of a problem of this type is the finding of the largest of the three numbers, x, y, and z, and printing the result. Such a problem is more a problem of logic than a problem of arithmetic, although certain arithmetic operations are employed in its solution. When the computer compares two numbers (by subtracting one from the other) JUMP instructions are used to cause one sequence of instructions or another to be followed in accordance with which of the two numbers was the larger. The finding of a program which employs as few instructions as possible is an intriguing puzzle; a program using one or two less instructions than certain "obvious" programs will be explained. As before, the instructions will be found in consecutive address locations, but in this case the computer will not necessarily follow them in sequence because of the JUMP instructions. The locations, 013, 014, and 015, will be used for storing x, y, and z, respectively, and location 016 will be used for temporary storage.

Address	Contents of Address		Remarks
000	RESET AND ADD	013	Places x in the accumulator.
001	SUBTRACT	014	Subtracts y from x.
002	JUMP IF MINUS	005	Computer takes next instruction from address (location) 005 if $y > x$; otherwise, it proceeds to 003.
003	RESET AND ADD	013	Places x in the accumulator again.
004	JUMP	006	Causes computer to take next instruction from 006.
005	RESET AND ADD	014	Places y in the accumulator.
006	STORE	016	Note that the computer will arrive at this step from 005 when $y > x$, but from step 004 when $y < x$ with the result that the accumulator contains the larger of x and y. This number is stored in 016.
007	SUBTRACT	015	Subtracts z from the larger of x and y.

Address	Contents of Address		Remarks
008	JUMP IF MINUS	011	If z is largest, next step is taken from 011; otherwise, from 009.
009	PRINT	016	The larger of x and y (which is now known to be the largest of the three) is printed.
010	JUMP	012	Causes computer to take next instruction from 012.
011	PRINT	015	Causes z to be printed. The computer arrives at this step only when z is largest.
012	STOP	---	Computer stops.
013	x		
014	y		
015	z		
016	[ ]		Reserved for temporary storage.

Again, several variations in the program are possible. For example, a STOP instruction instead of a JUMP instruction could have been placed in location 010. With this change, the computer would stop on step 010 or 012, depending on the relative sizes of x, y, and z. In this elementary example, the change would be trivial; but in cases where a program of this type is a part of a larger program, the termination of the part is more likely to be of consequence.

Program Loops. In many problems of a highly repetitive nature, a program prepared in a "straightforward" manner would consume an unduly large number of instructions. Through the use of JUMP instructions it is possible to prepare a relatively short program (program "loop") through which the computer will proceed over and over again the desired number of times. The loop may comprise substantially the entire program, but in most practical examples a loop would pertain to only a small portion of it. Any one program may contain many loops which may interlock one another in a complex manner. As a simple example of a loop, a program for preparing a list of the squares of the integers from 1 through 125 will be presented.

Address	Contents of Address		Remarks
000	RESET AND ADD	010	The number at address (location) 010 is increased by 1 (from $+00000$ to $+00001$ the first time through the loop).
001	ADD	011	
002	STORE	010	

Address	Contents of Address		Remarks
003	MULTIPLY	010	The number (+00001 the first time)
004	STORE	013	is squared and printed.
005	PRINT	013	
006	RESET AND ADD	010	The quantity, +00125, is subtracted
007	SUBTRACT	012	from the number with the result that
008	JUMP IF MINUS	000	the program will be repeated until the
009	STOP	---	number is increased to +00125.
010	[+00000]		
011	+00001		
012	+00125		
013	[ ]		

In this program, storage locations 010, 011, and 012 were used for the storage of constants which were not data in the usual sense of the word. The brackets around the number in 010 signify that this particular quantity is changed during the course of the computations. Note that in this example it was not necessary to store all of the numbers from 1 through 125 as data; instead, it was possible to generate them by means of the program.

Modification of Instructions. As has been mentioned, one of the outstanding features of most stored-program computers is their ability to modify an instruction (particularly the address part of an instruction) by means of the same arithmetic circuits that are used for performing computations on the data. A frequently encountered application of this facility is the performing of the same operation on a series of numbers which are located in sequentially numbered addresses. For example, assume that it is desired to accumulate and print the sum of the squares of a series of numbers, x_i, where i varies from 1 to 100. Assume, also, that these numbers are stored in addresses, 300 through 399, inclusive. One program which may be used for this purpose is shown below. Again, brackets are used to signify quantities that will be changed during the course of the program.

Address	Contents of Address		Remarks
000	RESET AND ADD	[300]	These two program steps cause the
001	MULTIPLY	[300]	square of the specified number to be placed in the accumulator. The first time through the loop the specified number is the one found at address 300.
002	ADD	016	Location 016 is used to store the ac-
003	STORE	016	cumulated sum of the squares.

Address	Contents of Address		Remarks
004	RESET AND ADD	018	In 018, a number representing the instruction RESET AND ADD 398 is stored, and this number is placed in the accumulator. Recall that the code for RESET AND ADD is 01.
005	SUBTRACT	000	The number in 000 (which is an instruction) is subtracted. The difference will not be minus unless the address part of the number in 000 has been increased to 399.
006	JUMP IF MINUS	014	
007	RESET AND ADD	000	The address part of the number (instruction) in 000 is increased by 1.
008	ADD	017	
009	STORE	000	
010	RESET AND ADD	001	The address part of the number (instruction) in 001 is increased by 1.
011	ADD	017	
012	STORE	001	
013	JUMP	000	The process will be repeated. Each time through the loop the next successive number in the series will be squared and accumulated because of the altered addresses of the instructions in 000 and 001.
014	PRINT	016	The computer will arrive at step 014 (from 006) only after all squares have been formed and accumulated.
015	STOP	---	
016	[+00000]		
017	+00001		
018	+01398		

An important extension of programs of this type is in generalizing them so that they will function properly by merely inserting one number representing the length of the series. One variation in the ways by which the preceding program can be generalized will be presented. The number representing the first address of the series (300 in this example) is placed in address 023, and the number representing the length of the series (100 in this example) is placed in address 024. Address 024 is used as a counter; the number stored there is reduced by 1 each time the program loop is traversed, and when the count becomes negative, the process is terminated.

Address	Contents of Address		Remarks
000	RESET AND ADD	023	The address parts of the instructions
001	ADD	010	in 010 and 011 are set equal to the
002	STORE	010	number in 023.
003	RESET AND ADD	023	
004	ADD	011	
005	STORE	011	
006	RESET AND ADD	024	The number in the counter is reduced
007	SUBTRACT	026	by 1.
008	STORE	024	
009	JUMP IF MINUS	021	
010	RESET AND ADD	[000]	The square of the appropriate number
011	MULTIPLY	[000]	is formed and accumulated with the
012	ADD	025	sum being placed in 025.
013	STORE	025	
014	RESET AND ADD	010	The address parts of the instructions
015	ADD	026	in 010 and 011 are increased by 1.
016	STORE	010	
017	RESET AND ADD	011	
018	ADD	026	
019	STORE	011	
020	JUMP	006	The program is repeated, except for the first group of instructions, which are needed only once.
021	PRINT	025	The computer will arrive at 021 (from
022	STOP	---	009) only after all 100 squares have been formed and accumulated.
023	+00300		
024	[+00100]		
025	[+00000]		
026	+00001		

With this particular arrangement one detail that should not be overlooked when the program is used a second time is that the address parts of the instructions in 010 and 011 and the number in 025 should be reset to zero. In this "specimen" machine the number in 025 would be reset to zero if the following three instructions were inserted at the beginning of the program.

RESET AND ADD   025
SUBTRACT   025
STORE   025

The address part of 010, for example, could be reset to zero by using the SHIFT instructions as follows.

RESET AND ADD	010
SHIFT RIGHT	003
SHIFT LEFT	003
STORE	010

The STORE ADDRESS instruction is of considerable value in programs of the above type. A substantial reduction in the number of program steps can be achieved, and the need for resetting to zero the address parts of the instructions in 010 and 011 in the illustration is eliminated. The required alterations in these addresses can be achieved by substituting the following five instructions in place of the first six instructions in the illustration and by eliminating instructions 014 through 019.

000	RESET AND ADD	023	The address parts of the instructions
001	STORE ADDRESS	010	in 010 and 011 are replaced by the
002	STORE ADDRESS	011	number in 023, and that number is
003	ADD	026	increased by 1.
004	STORE	023	
023	--300		The first two digits are of no consequence.

The JUMP instruction would be altered to include this group of instructions in the loop, and, of course, a renumbering of all instructions would be necessary.

Sub-programs. When a sequence of instructions is to be used frequently, but not in the uniformly recurring manner of the previous examples, a technique known as "sub-programming" is advantageous. By preparing the sequence of instructions as a sub-program, it is possible to arrange the "main" program so that the computer will jump to the sub-program, perform the desired standard sequence of operations, and then return to the main program. Actually, the summing of the squares of a series of numbers when considered as an integrated operation might be a good example of a program to be made into a sub-program if this operation is required frequently. However, another example has been chosen to illustrate sub-programming because it is somewhat less complex, and also because some other interesting points of programming are introduced incidentally. The sub-program to be explained is one for computing the square root of a number. The computation of the square root is required frequently in many problems. If the sequence of instructions for extracting the square root were inserted in the main program each time it was needed, an unduly large number of storage locations in the computer would be consumed. From the standpoint of storage space it is preferable to write the square-root program once as a sub-program, and use the relatively few instructions which are required to refer to it each time a square root is needed.

Before proceeding to the example itself, a useful notation relating to addresses will be explained. Often when preparing programs it is inconvenient to specify the exact address to be used in each and every instruction. Instead, the notation, $L(x)$, which signifies the address (location) where x is stored whatever that address might be, may be used. With this definition, an instruction such as ADD $L(+00003)$ means that 3 should be added to the number in the accumulator. Of course, before the program is executed by the computer, the actual number representing the address, $a = L(x)$, must be inserted in the address part of the instruction by the programmer either directly or by means of other instructions in the program. Also, it is frequently convenient to refer to the number stored at a given address by the notation, $C(a)$, which means the "contents" of the address (location). If x is stored in a, $C(a) = x$. To appreciate more fully the meaning of the notation, observe that the equations,

$$L[C(a)] = a$$

$$C[L(x)] = x$$

follow directly from the definitions.

For computing the square root, the iterative formula,

$$b_{k+1} = \frac{1}{2}\left(b_k + \frac{x}{b_k}\right)$$

will be used with $+00317$ (the largest possible square root in a five-digit machine) as the first approximation, b_0. Successive approximations will decrease monotonically toward the desired value. The constants, $+00317$ and $+00005$, may be stored as appendages to the sub-program, or they may be at some other known storage locations. Since the square root is to be computed by an iterative process, the sub-routine will contain a loop, and this loop will be traversed repeatedly until $b_{k+1} = b_k$. Assume for purposes of illustration that the first instruction of the sub-program is at address 350. The number, x, for which the square root is desired, is at address 363 and the b_k are stored at 364.

Address	Contents of Address		Remarks
350	RESET AND ADD	$L(+00317)$	The number for b_0 is placed in the accumulator.
351	STORE	364	The approximation, b_k (b_0 the first time through the loop), is placed in 364.

Address	Contents of Address		Remarks
352	RESET AND ADD	363	The quantity, $b_k + x/b_k$, is formed
353	DIVIDE	364	in the accumulator.
354	ADD	364	
355	MULTIPLY	$L(+00005)$	A division by 2 with a rounded
356	ADD	$L(+00005)$	quotient is effected by multiplying
357	SHIFT RIGHT	001	by 5, adding 5 in the units position, and dividing by 10 (shifting right). The accumulator now contains b_{k+1}.
358	SUBTRACT	364	If $b_{k+1} < b_k$, the loop, starting with
359	JUMP IF MINUS	361	instruction at 351, is to be repeated. Instruction at 361 is needed to restore the contents of the accumulator to b_{k+1}.
360	JUMP	[ ]	Sub-program returns to main program.
361	ADD	364	See remarks above.
362	JUMP	351	
363	x		
364	b_k		

In order for the main program to be able to use a sub-program, two important conditions must be satisfied. Any parameters of the sub-program, such as x in this example, must be placed where the sub-program can find them, and the proper address must be placed in the JUMP instruction which causes the return to the main program. The instructions which provide for the entry into a sub-program and the return from it are commonly referred to as the "linkage." In particular, the JUMP instruction which causes the return from the sub-program to the main program (the one at address 360 in this example) is called the "link" instruction. As an example of the use of the sub-program, assume that the main program has arrived at a step where the next instruction is to be taken from address 100, and it is desired to compute the square root of the number in address 750. The square-root sub-program may be utilized by the following instructions in the main program.

Address	Contents of Address		Remarks
100	RESET AND ADD	750	$C(750)$ is placed at 363, where the sub-
101	STORE	363	program can find it.
102	RESET AND ADD	105	The number representing the link in-
103	STORE	360	struction is obtained from 105 and is placed at the appropriate address in the sub-program.

Address	Contents of Address		Remarks
104	JUMP	350	Computer jumps to the sub-program.
105	JUMP	106	See above remarks.
106	Continuation of main program		The sub-program returns the computer to this step. The square root of $C(750)$ is now at 364.

With above method of linkage, all steps in the placing of the link are accomplished by the main program, and new instructions for this purpose are required each time the sub-program is used. By making use of the facility that the operation part as well as the address part of an instruction can be modified by the program, it is possible to employ two less instructions in the main program for each entry into the sub-program at the expense of two instructions at the beginning of the sub-program and one special constant. When a sub-program is used many times in one program, a considerable saving in storage space can be achieved in this way.

Address	Contents of Address		Remarks
100	RESET AND ADD	750	These two instructions are the
101	STORE	363	same as before.
102	RESET AND ADD	102	The number, 01102, is placed in
103	JUMP	348	the accumulator. The next instruction is taken from 348, which is the new beginning of the sub-program.
104	Continuation of main program		The sub-program returns the computer to this step.

348	ADD	$L(09002)$	The sum, $01102 + 09002 = 10104$,
349	STORE	360	which is equivalent to JUMP 104, is formed in the accumulator and then placed in 360 as the link instruction.

350		
.	The main body of the square	
.	root sub-program is the same	
.	as before.	
364		

By using the STORE ADDRESS instruction, the linkage can be made equally conservative of storage space and possibly somewhat more straightforward. In this example, different addresses will be used for the linkage instructions in the main program to emphasize that the link instruction in a sub-program must provide for return to the "next consecutive" step in the main program regardless of the location of the instruction that caused the jump to the sub-program. Assume that the computer has arrived at step 620 and that the square root of the number at address 506 is desired.

Address	Contents of Address		Remarks
620	RESET AND ADD	506	These two instructions are the
621	STORE	363	same in principle as before.
622	RESET AND ADD	622	The number, xx622 (the first two
623	JUMP	348	digits are irrelevant in this case), is placed in the accumulator, and the next instruction is taken from 348.
624	Continuation of main program.		The sub-program returns the computer to this step.

348	ADD	$L(00002)$	The sum, xx622 + 00002 = xx624,
349	STORE ADDRESS	360	is formed in the accumulator. The address part of this number is placed in 360, which already contains the code for JUMP in the operation part.
350 · · · 364	The main body of the square root sub-program is the same as before.		

In all of the linkage examples which have been cited, the same method was used for placing the parameter where the sub-program could find it. Another frequently used method for locating the sub-program parameters is to place them immediately after the instructions that cause the jump to the sub-program. Then, if x is the number for which the square root is desired, a linkage arrangement employing the STORE ADDRESS instruction as illustrated in the next example could be used. Prior to the arrival of the computer at step 622, x must be placed at 624 by instructions not shown. Note that in this case, the link must provide for a return to the main program at a step that is 2, instead of just 1, steps beyond the JUMP instruction which caused entry into the sub-program.

Address	Contents of Address		Remarks
622	RESET AND ADD	622	Same as corresponding instructions
623	JUMP	346	in previous examples except that the first instruction of the sub-program is now at 346.

Address	Contents of Address		Remarks
624	x		
625	Continuation of main program.		

346	ADD	L(00002)	The sum, xx622 + 00002 = xx624,
347	STORE ADDRESS	352	is formed in the accumulator. The address part is placed in 352, which contains the instruction involving the location of x.
348	ADD	L(00001)	The sum, xx624 + 00001 = xx625,
349	STORE ADDRESS	360	is formed, and the address part is placed in the link instruction.

350⎤
   ⎜ The sub-program is the same in principle as before. Changes in details
   ⎜ will result from the fact that the address part of the instruction in 352 will
   ⎜ be altered by the program and from the fact that storage location 363 will
364⎦ no longer be needed for the storage of x.

In some of the above examples, the signs of certain numbers which relate to instructions have been disregarded in cases where only the magnitudes were of primary consequence. Actually, for the program to function properly, the signs of these numbers must be chosen correctly. A more detailed discussion of signs will be omitted because it would most likely add confusion without aiding in the explanation of programming principles. In many computers, special "magnitude" instructions are provided which facilitate arithmetic operations involving only magnitudes and not signs.

Library of Sub-programs. Many sub-programs are likely to be useful in more than one problem. The need for extracting the square root, for example, is encountered in a wide variety of problems. Much programming effort can be saved if sub-programs can be retained in a "library" of some sort from which they can be "withdrawn" and inserted in other programs as needed. The outstanding factor to be considered in the formation of a library arises from the need for being able to place a sub-program at any set of consecutive addresses in computer storage instead of one fixed set such as 348 to 364.

Assume, for example, that in the preparation of the program for the solution of some problem the square root is needed, and addresses 348 to 364 happen to have been employed for the storage of other instructions or data. The square-root sub-program can be moved to some other part of the storage, say addresses 448 to 464, by adding 100 to the address where each instruction of the sub-program is stored and by adding 100 to the address part of each sub-program instruction which refers to another part of the sub-program. Note that in the square-root sub-program the address parts of some instructions, particularly the SHIFT instruction, should be the same regardless of where the sub-program is stored. The address parts of the instructions involving constants should also remain unchanged if special addresses are assigned for the storage of constants. On the other hand, if the constants are stored as part of the sub-program, the instructions which refer to the constants must be altered by adding 100 to the address parts.

Since the altering of a sub-program to fit it into any set of consecutive addresses in storage is a routine job, it is possible to prepare a "positioning sub-program" which will make it possible for the computer to relieve the programmer of this work. However, one difficulty of consequence is encountered. The positioning sub-program must, by some means or other, be able to distinguish which of the instructions are to have their address parts modified and which are not. One reasonably simple means of identification which can be used in some computers (including the "specimen" computer) is to employ the sign of the number which represents an instruction. Previously, the signs of these numbers have been ignored because they were not used for anything. The convention might be used that all instructions represented by a positive number should not be altered, but all instructions represented by a negative number should have the appropriate constant added to their address parts. Of course, any constants in the sub-program must then be stored as positive numbers; otherwise, the positioning sub-program will incorrectly interpret them as instructions to be modified. Signs used in this manner are sometimes called "tags." Other means for making it possible for the positioning sub-program to identify the instructions to be modified would be to use extra storage locations to list the addresses of the instructions to be modified. After the sub-program to be positioned has been properly modified, the extra storage locations are no longer needed and may be employed for other purposes. Since the details of positioning sub-programs vary tremendously from computer to computer and since no new programming principles are introduced (once the possibility of a positioning program is recognized), the subject will not be discussed further here.

When assembling a library of sub-programs it is important to record not only the sub-programs themselves but also as much pertinent data as are available about each. In the example of the square root sub-program, a graph of the required time as a function of the parameter, x, would be useful. In other cases where approximations or cumulative round-off errors are involved, the accuracy of the result as a function of the various parameters would be important. Also, sub-programs are likely to respond in peculiar and unexpected ways when certain combinations of parameters are used or when certain errors are made. The person preparing the sub-program might be well aware of its limitations, but unless these limitations are recorded, the full value of the sub-program as a library item will not be realized.

Interpretive Programs, First Type. An important extension of the sub-program concept is the "interpretive" program. When an interpretive program is used, each step in the main program is "interpreted" and executed in a manner specified by one of a set of sub-programs. Interpretive programs of many different forms and variations have been developed; two have been selected for presentation here and, for lack of a better designation, they are referred to as first and second types, respectively.

Consider the situation where all items of data are represented by complex numbers of the form, $x + jy$, where j is the square root of minus one. With complex numbers, the arithmetic operations are not as simple as with real numbers. For examples, addition and multiplication in the complex number system are represented by the following equations.

$$(x_1 + jy_1) + (x_2 + jy_2) = (x_1 + x_2) + j(y_1 + y_2)$$

$$(x_1 + jy_1)(x_2 + jy_2) = (x_1x_2 - y_1y_2) + j(x_1y_2 + x_2y_1)$$

While it is possible to program the computer so that it will perform all the necessary steps for each operation in the complex system, it would be desirable to relieve the programmer of this burden. The sub-programming procedure, as described previously, allows some reduction in programming effort, but it is possible to simplify program preparation much further. Through the use of the interpretive program, each instruction, such as ADD, can be interpreted to mean the addition of two complex numbers, and the jump to the appropriate sub-program is made automatically and without any special link or other instructions being provided by the programmer (once the interpretive program has been prepared).

For some purposes, particularly in forming loops and sub-programs which are not related to the fact that the data are in complex number form, it will be necessary for the ADD and other instructions to be interpreted in their normal way. To distinguish which instructions pertain to complex numbers, the signs of the numbers representing instructions may be used as tags. In the example to be presented, a minus sign will be used to signify that a complex-number operation is to be performed, and a plus sign will indicate that the instruction is to be interpreted in the usual way. Note that the programmer must be careful if the signs are used as tags for some other purpose such as in the positioning subprogram described in an earlier section.

The convention will be used that the two parts x and y, of a complex number will be stored in two consecutive address positions. To specify the location of a number it is sufficient to give the address of the real part, and it is understood that the imaginary part is located at the next higher numbered address. Then, to illustrate by a simple example, all the programmer needs to prepare to add two complex numbers and print the sum are these instructions.

075	(−) RESET AND ADD	124
076	(−) ADD	151
077	(−) STORE	120
078	(−) PRINT	120
079	(+) STOP	---

The real parts of the two numbers are taken from addresses 124 and 151, and 120 is used for temporary storage of the real part of the sum. Addresses 125, 152, and 121 play analogous roles for the corresponding imaginary parts. The main program does not start at address 000; instead, in this example, the first instruction of the main program is found at address 075. The computer follows the interpretive program and not the main program for its detailed instructions. Therefore, it is the interpretive program which should start at address 000.

Before describing the interpretive program itself, one of the sub-programs will be explained. Assume that the sub-program for adding two complex numbers is stored with its first instruction at address 500. In principle, this sub-program does the same thing as the ADD instruction for ordinary numbers; that is, the number at the specified storage location is added to the number already in the accumulator, and the sum is left in the accumulator. However, the accumulator built into the computer is not capable of holding both the real and imaginary parts of a complex number at the same time. For this reason, two addresses, numbers 998 and 999, in the main storage are reserved for use as a sort of "acting" accumulator. The effect of the complex ADD sub-program, then, is to cause the addition of the complex number at the specified location to the complex number in 998 (and 999).

Address	Contents of Address		Remarks
500	RESET AND ADD	004	The address of complex number to
501	STORE ADDRESS	503	be added is placed in 503. (The interpretive program will have placed this address in 004.)
502	RESET AND ADD	998	The real parts are added, and the
503	ADD	[ ]	sum is placed in 998.
504	STORE	998	
505	RESET AND ADD	503	The address of the imaginary part
506	ADD	L(+00001)	of the complex number to be added
507	STORE ADDRESS	509	is formed by adding 1 to the address of the real part. The result is stored in 509.
508	RESET AND ADD	999	The sum of the imaginary parts is
509	ADD	[ ]	formed and placed in 999.
510	STORE	999	
511	JUMP	009	The computer takes its next instruction from 009, which is in the interpretive program.

An analogous sub-program will be needed for each type of instruction which can pertain to complex numbers. Besides the arithmetic operations, it is desirable to be able to interpret instructions such as STORE, PRINT, and SHIFT, as operations to be performed on complex numbers. The instruction, STOP, presumably has the same effect regardless of the type of number under consideration and may therefore be treated as an ordinary instruction always.

The interpretive program serves the function of examining each instruction in the main program and causing a jump to the proper sub-program for actual execution. Note that even though an instruction in the main program may be accompanied by a plus sign, which indicates that only ordinary numbers and not complex numbers are involved, a separate sub-program is needed for each type of instruction. The program could be arranged so that the computer would execute the instruction directly, but this procedure would be of no use because the interpretive program makes use of the accumulator for its functioning, and the results of execution would therefore be ruined in most cases. When the interpretive program finds an instruction accompanied by a plus sign, a jump to address 040 (arbitrarily chosen) is made where an analogous interpretation for real numbers is made. Another "acting" accumulator, say storage location 997, is used for real numbers.

For the interpretive program to start properly, the address of the first instuction in the main program is placed as the address part of the instruction at 000. The interpretive program is as follows.

Address	Contents of Address		Remarks
000	RESET AND ADD	[075]	The number representing the instruction to be interpreted (the first one of which is at 075 in this example) is placed in 003.
001	STORE	003	
002	JUMP IF MINUS	005	If the instruction is accompanied by a minus sign, the computer jumps to 005. Otherwise, it jumps to 040 where a program for interpreting the instruction in ordinary fashion is stored.
003	JUMP	040	
004	[	]	
005	SHIFT RIGHT	003	The two digits representing the operation code are shifted to the right-hand end of the accumulator, and 12 is added to the result.
006	ADD	$L(+00012)$	
007	STORE ADDRESS	008	The number representing the operation code, increased by 12, is used as the address to which the computer jumps from step 008.
008	JUMP	[ ]	
009	RESET AND ADD	000	These four instructions have the effect of increasing the address part of the instruction at 000 by 1 and then causing a jump to 000 for the interpretation of the next instruction in the main program. The sub-programs provide for a return to 009.
010	ADD	$L(+00001)$	
011	STORE	000	
012	JUMP	000	
013	JUMP	L (r and a)	The computer arrives at one of these JUMP instructions from 008, and from here goes to the appropriate sub-program. (Recall that the code for ADD is 02; the jump to 500 is made from 014 since $02 + 12 = 14$.)
014	JUMP	500	
015	JUMP	L (sub.)	
016	JUMP	L (mult.)	

The part of the interpretive program which starts at 040 and which is for interpreting the instructions in an ordinary way is not shown. However, its function is substantially the same as the instruction found at addresses 005 through 008 except that jumps are made to sub-programs which are intended for real numbers instead of complex numbers.

Observe that when the desired sequence of operations is accomplished through the medium of an interpretive program, the computer never does arrive at step 075 or any other step in the main program. Instead, the instructions of the main program are executed by transferring them to the accumulator and address 004 for interpretation. As a result of this situation, instructions of the JUMP type in the main program require further explanation. If a JUMP instruction in the main program is interpreted in the ordinary way (that is, if it is accompanied by a plus sign), the computer will jump to the specified address, which could be at any point in storage. In particular, it could be at a location such that the computer would leave the interpretive program altogether. For some applications this effect would be highly useful. However, if it is desired that the JUMP instruction cause a jump to some other step in the main program while keeping the interpretive program in effect, the JUMP must be accompanied by a minus sign. A sub-program for JUMP is needed to make the required alterations in the interpretive sub-program. It is necessary that the address part of the instruction stored at 000 be changed to the address of the instruction which is to be interpreted after the jump; this alteration takes the place of increasing by 1 the address part of the instruction at 000. The following three instructions, arbitrarily stored at 580 to 582, may be used for a sub-program for JUMP.

Address	Contents of Address		Remarks
580	RESET AND ADD	003	The address part of the JUMP instruc-
581	STORE ADDRESS	000	tion from the main program (which
582	JUMP	000	was placed in 003 by the interpretive
			program) is placed in 000. Return is
			made to 000 in this case, instead of 009,
			because it is not necessary to increase
			the address by 1.

The sub-program for JUMP IF MINUS is slightly more involved, but it follows the same principles. Here, the "IF MINUS" applies to the complex number stored in the "acting" accumulator. The "sign" of the complex number may be taken from either the real or the imaginary part by using the sign of the number stored in 998 or 999, respectively.

The same interpretive program may be used for all problems where the data are represented by complex numbers. After it has been prepared for one problem, the detailed procedure by which it functions need no longer be of concern to the programmer. However, the programmer must keep in mind the addresses in storage which are consumed by the interpretive program and all of its sub-programs, because these addresses will not be available for use in the main program.

Other categories of problems to which interpretive programs of this type can be applied are multiple-accuracy computations (that is, where each number is so long that two or more locations are required for its storage), floating-point computations, matrices, and multi-dimensional vectors.

Interpretive Program, Second Type. The second type of interpretive program which will be described is similar in basic principles to the first, but it is much more general in its applications. Instead of merely interpreting each existing kind of operation or instruction in some special way, it becomes possible to create (in effect) any number of new operations which are not built into the machine.

To illustrate how new operations can be created by means of an interpretive program, a simplified example has been worked out for the "specimen" machine. It should be understood that almost any practical interpretive sub-program for any real machine would probably differ vastly from the example, but the important concepts can be found in this simplified version. In the organization of the "specimen" machine, the first two digits of each word were used as a code to indicate the various instructions the machine is capable of executing. With two digits, one hundred different instructions can be represented, but only the codes from 00 to 13 were actually used. By using interpretive programming techniques, these same two code digits can be made to represent any one hundred instructions the programmer desires, except that the required auxiliary sub-programs must not be so elaborate that the storage capacity of the machine is exceeded. Some of the selected instructions may be substantially the same as the "built-in" instructions, but in the general case there is no relationship between the list of instructions which are formed by programming and the list of "built-in" instructions which was given at the beginning of this chapter.

Suppose, for example, that the extraction of the square root is a frequently encountered operation and that it is desired to form a special instruction for it. The code, 30, might be selected for the square root instruction so that the number, 30721, will have the meaning: "extract the square root of the number found in address position 721 and leave the result in the accumulator." As in the original examples, the sign of a number has no significance when the number is used to represent an instruction. Also, it will be assumed that ordinary numbers (not complex) are involved, although complex numbers or other special situations can be handled easily with appropriate sub-programs and minor modifications in the interpretive program. As in the interpretive programs of the first type, the computer never arrives at a program step which contains an instruction of the main program. Instead, each instruction in the main program is "interpreted" in accordance with the details of the interpretive program together with all of its sub-programs. Since the instruction counter which is built into the computer is needed to control the progress of the machine through the interpretive program and the sub-programs, an extra storage location (009 in the example below) is used as an "acting" instruction counter to cause the interpretive program to interpret the main program instructions in the proper sequence. Further, the "accumulator" referred to in the square root instruction or in other programmed instructions is not the accumulator built into the computer, but is a particular storage location (say 999) which is reserved for the purpose. In other words, an interpretive program executes an instruction of the main program in a manner roughly analogous to the way the computer itself executes an instruction of the interpretive program. The procedure by which an interpretive program functions is explained in the "remarks" column of the following example.

Address	Contents of Address		Remarks
000	RESET AND ADD	009	The contents of the instruction
001	STORE ADDRESS	004	counter (the address part of 009) is
002	ADD	$L(+00001)$	placed in 004 and then increased
003	STORE	009	by 1.
004	RESET AND ADD	[ ]	The instruction to be interpreted is placed in the accumulator.
005	SHIFT RIGHT	003	The operation part of the instruction is caused to appear as the two lowest-order digits.
006	ADD	$L(+00009)$	The code representing the operation or instruction to be performed
007	STORE ADDRESS	008	is modified by the addition of 9,
008	JUMP	[ ]	and the resulting number is used as an address to which a jump is made.
009	—	[ ]	Instruction counter. Initially, the address of the first instruction to be interpreted is placed here.
010	JUMP	xxx	
011	JUMP	xxx	Jump table. The jump to the appropriate sub-program is made from here. The square-root sub-program is assumed to start at 600.
⋮			
039	JUMP	600	

The sub-programs can be substantially the same as described in earlier sections. However, certain alterations in the linkage are required. In the case of the square-root sub-program, for example, note that address

Programming

004 will contain the address of the instruction being interpreted, and the instruction being interpreted in turn contains the address of the number for which the square root is desired. Therefore, the following sequence of instructions can be placed at the beginning of the square-root sub-program for the purpose of placing the number where the sub-program can find it.

Address	Contents of Address		Remarks
600	RESET AND ADD	004	Places the address of the instruction
601	STORE ADDRESS	602	in 602.
602	RESET AND ADD	[ ]	Places the address of the number for
603	STORE ADDRESS	604	which the square root is desired in 604.
604	RESET AND ADD	[ ]	Places the number where the sub-pro-
605	STORE	xxx	gram can find it.

With the system as described, the square-root sub-program must also contain an instruction which will cause the result to be placed in the "acting" accumulator. The return link is simply a JUMP 000 instruction in this case.

An outstanding extension of the interpretive program principle arises from the fact that the instructions formed by the sub-programs need not be limited to the single-address variety. A convention may be adopted whereby a group of two or more address positions may be used for each instruction, and an interpretive program can be prepared which will interpret the instructions in any multi-address fashion. By this means a single-address computer can be made to appear to a programmer as a multi-address computer of any desired form (after the interpretive program has been worked out). Conversely, a multi-address machine can be made to function in single-address fashion from a programmer's viewpoint. The ability to make one machine appear like another one has proved to be of great value in computer design. Before a new machine is actually built, programs for it can be tested and corrected on some existing machine. By this means, the need for certain improvements in the organization of the new machine can frequently be discovered at an early stage of design when it is not difficult to make changes.

Although it is probably obvious to most readers, it should be noted that the time required to execute a given number of steps in the main program is increased by a large factor in most cases where an interpretive program is used.

Programming when Index Registers Are Available. As was explained in the previous chapter, a computer may be equipped with one or more

index registers. When index registers are available, the computer is usually so organized that certain digits in each instruction are reserved for
specifying which index register is to be used and, in some machines, for
specifying the amount (usually 1) by which the contents of the index
register should be altered. In the examples which have been presented
to illustrate various programming techniques, it may have been observed
that the addition of 1 to the address part of an instruction was a frequently encountered requirement when a program loop of any sort was
involved. In most cases the traversing of the loop was terminated when
the address reached some predetermined number. The number of instructions involved was dependent upon the detailed requirements of the
situation, but it was always at least three. With index registers, the
number of instructions required for this function can be reduced to one
because built-in circuits cause the number in the specified index register
to be added to the address before execution of the instruction, and at the
same time the number is increased by 1 (or some other specified amount)
in an automatic fashion. Further, succeeding jumps in the program can
be made automatically in accordance with whether or not the number
in the index register has reached some preset value.

Besides facilitating the preparation of program loops, index registers
are found useful in numerous miscellaneous ways. No examples will be
given because, although index registers have been incorporated in many
computer designs, the details and elaborations vary so greatly from machine to machine that the value of an example worked out for a "specimen" machine would be severely limited.

Assembly Programs. When a single program contains hundreds or
thousands of instructions, its preparation contains problems which are
not encountered to any extent in short programs where the programmer
can remember the purpose and effect of each instruction. If, during the
preparation or correction of a long program, it is necessary to alter the
program by as little as inserting one instruction, it frequently happens
that numerous changes throughout the program must be made. Not only
are the storage locations of the instructions modified, but also certain
constants and the address parts of many instructions are usually affected.
For this reason it is extremely difficult to prepare a long program without
errors even after the logic of the program has been worked out perfectly.
For the purposes of reducing the labor and chances for error involved
in program preparation, techniques have been worked out whereby the
computer itself is given the job of assigning storage locations to the instructions and data and of determining the address parts of all instructions which refer to storage locations. With these techniques the programmer writes the program in sections with some sort of symbolic

notation to describe the storage locations and addresses. An "assembly program" is then used to assemble the sections and compute the actual storage locations and addresses from the symbolic notation.

The basic idea behind at least one form of assembly program is to use a symbolism whereby one series of numbers designates the major sections of the program; a second series, separated from the first by a dash or some other mark, designates the instructions within the section; and a third series designates instructions inserted after the initial writing of the program. A portion of the eighth section of a program might then appear as follows.

Address	Contents of Address	
8–12	JUMP	8–15
8–13	RESET AND ADD	10–2
8–14	SHIFT RIGHT	002
8–15	STORE ADDRESS	8–17
8–16	ADD	2–1
8–17	JUMP	15–3

The meaning of the instruction at 8–13, for example, is that the number representing the second instruction in the tenth section of the program is to be placed in the accumulator. The assembly program will assign an actual address in storage for the symbol 8–13; also, it will assign an address for 10–2 and place it in the address part of the instruction. The assembly program will not affect the address part of the shift instruction because no storage locations are involved and no alterations are to be made.

Suppose that through an oversight or for some other reason it is desired to insert a new instruction, say ADD 5–2, between instructions 8–13 and 8–14. A study of the example will reveal that it will be necessary to alter the storage assignments of all instructions after 8–13. Also, the address parts of some, but not all, of the instructions must be changed. However, if a symbol such as 8–13–1 is assigned as the address (location) of the inserted instruction, there will be no need for any reshuffling of symbols by the programmer. Since with this system of notation each address will be represented by different symbols and no two symbols will represent the same address, it is possible to make all changes in address assignments by means of the assembly program.

Numerous complexities in assembly programs are encountered in certain cases. One important case is in the assembling of a program with help of a library of sub-programs. Some means must be provided for distinguishing one sub-program from another; otherwise address 1–1 would mean one thing in one sub-program and something else in another (it is assumed that the same symbolic system is used for the sub-programs). Also, situations arise where it is desirable to cause particular instructions in two different sub-programs to refer to the same address where the symbolic addresses as stored in the library are not the same.

Another complexity arises when the assembly program and the program being assembled are too extensive to fit into the storage unit of the computer. The procedure in this case is to divide the program into parts and assemble one part at a time. Since the instructions in one part may refer to the addresses in another part, it is not always possible to convert the address part of each instruction from symbolic form to an actual address on the first pass through the machine. By using a part of the storage unit for maintaining a file of unassigned addresses, the assembly of the program can be completed the second time it is entered into the computer. A further requirement of the assembly program is that it record the assembled program in forms suitable for subsequent use by the computer and suitable for visual reference by the programmer.

Most practical assembly programs for real machines are themselves long and complicated and may require literally months to prepare. The usefulness of an assembly program comes, of course, from the fact that, once prepared, it can be used without alteration for the assembly of innumerable other programs.

The "Speed-coding" System. A different approach to the problem of simplifying the preparation of long programs is to provide, by interpretive sub-program techniques, a set of instructions which are much more comprehensive than those built into the machine. By this means it is possible in many cases to eliminate all sub-programs and certain other complicating factors in the program as prepared by the programmer; in fact, it is not even necessary that the programmer understand sub-programming techniques at all. Another advantage of the system is that the number of instructions which must be written to solve a given problem can be reduced by a large factor. The name, "speed-coding," was first applied to a system of this type which was prepared at IBM for the 701 computer. Other groups have worked out analogous systems for different computers; the systems have been given other names in some cases.

As in the case of an assembly program, the speed-coding interpretive program is long and involved and requires a matter of thousands of instructions with its usefulness being derived from the fact that, once prepared, it may be used by programmers who have no knowledge of how it works. The programmer need be familiar only with the list of "programmed instructions" which the speed-coding system provides. Included in the list are instructions for square root, sine, arc tangent, exponentials, and logarithms, all of which would normally require sub-programs when using the "built-in" instructions of the computer. Also, several input and output instructions are included which allow the programmer to move an entire block of information from one place to another with only one instruction. To handle situations where it is desirable to modify an instruction, a set of index registers (referred to as R-quantities in this case) and an address counter are provided by the speed-coding system. The index registers function in principle by the procedure described previously, and by means of the address counter it is possible to replace selected addresses with new ones or to add address increments in a variety of manners.

A further convenience included in the speed-coding system are special instructions for the automatic checking of computations. By placing a START CHECK instruction at the beginning and an END CHECK instruction at the end of the series of instructions to be checked, the computer will be caused to proceed through the sequence twice and to generate a check sum each time. The computer will then compare the two check sums and, if they are equal, it will skip the instruction immediately following the END CHECK; but, if there is a discrepancy, that instruction will be executed. In the event an error is detected, the programmer may control the course of action the computer is to follow by having placed an appropriate instruction in the position immediately following the END CHECK instruction.

The basic ideas employed in writing a program in the speed-coding system are substantially the same as when writing a program using "built-in" instructions. There are a great many differences in detail, however, because of the considerable differences in the nature and quantity of the individual instructions. An instruction in the speed-coding system consists of two operations, four addresses, and a digit relating to the index registers. One operation and three of the addresses are used for arithmetic and input-output functions in a manner similar to that of a three-address computer. The other operation together with the fourth address are used for jump, address modification, and error-checking functions, although there are many interrelationships between the two operations. All items of data are handled through the speed-coding system as floating-point numbers even though the computer is a fixed-point machine.

In spite of the relative complexity of the individual instructions in the speed-coding system, the over-all task of preparing a program for a given mathematical problem is made easier because many of the confusing factors arising from sub-programming are avoided through the interpretive process and because many less instructions in the "main" program are required. An outstanding disadvantage of the speed-coding system is that the great number of instructions consumed in the interpretive process cause more time to be required for calculations in the speed-coding system than when the program is prepared entirely in terms of "built-in" instructions.

An interesting combination of assembly program and speed-coding concepts is the use of an assembly program to prepare address assignments for a program written in terms of speed-coding instructions.

Tracing Programs. It seems to be almost axiomatic that a program when first prepared will not work. Occasionally programmers are able to write short programs that are totally free from errors, but for a long program the places where typographical errors, unforeseen circumstances, and mistakes in logic can arise are so numerous that the chances of getting it right the first time are extremely small. In spite of the difficulty a human being has in discovering errors by a mental checking process, the computer usually will show up errors in programming very quickly by a failure to arrive at the right answer. The computer, then, is the best tool the programmer has for perfecting his programs. However, the computer will show only the existence of an error; it will not indicate precisely what or where the error is. The programmer still has the job of deducing the source of the error from the behavior of the computer, which may be peculiar to say the least.

To assist the programmer in locating errors in a program, "tracing programs" may be used. A tracing program is basically an interpretive program which functions in the same general manner as other interpretive programs which were described by means of examples in earlier sections. When a tracing program is used, the computer does not execute the instructions of the main program directly; instead, each instruction is "interpreted." The interpreting in this case accomplishes the same end result as direct execution, except that certain additional features are added. For example, each instruction may be caused to be printed as it is executed so that the programmer can have a record of what the computer actually does. By studying this record, the path of the computer through the main program can be determined to see whether or not it was following the various jump instructions as expected. The address parts of the instructions can be observed to indicate whether or not the desired items of data entered into the computations at each point. Tracing programs can also be used to obtain a printed record of the contents of the accumulator or of other registers at the end of each program step. With this information the progress of the computations for a sample set of parameters can be compared with the results obtained from a desk machine in an effort to locate the mistake.

Innumerable variations can be worked out for special cases. For example, if the programmer is interested only in knowing the sequence of program steps that the computer followed, the tracing program can be altered so that it will be limited to printing information relative to jump instructions. In other applications, computed values will be needed only at certain intermediate points in the program instead of at each program step. Since the progress of the computer through the main program is much slower when a tracing program is used, it may be important from a purely time consideration to limit the scope of the tracing functions.

Diagnostic Programs. If errors are being encountered which place the computer and not the program under suspicion, special programs known as "diagnostic" programs can frequently be used to locate the source of the errors. A diagnostic program is to be distinguished from a test program, although the dividing line between the two is not at all well defined. A test program is generally employed to determine whether or not the computer, or some particular portion of it, is working properly. This purpose is accomplished by exercising each element in the computer as thoroughly as practical by means of appropriate instructions in the program and then observing to see that the proper response is obtained. Since the proper response may consist of a check sum or some other number obtained after a long sequence of operations, there may be no indication of the source of an error in the event that the existence of an error is sensed. On the other hand, diagnostic programs are generally employed after a defect is known to exist, and the purpose is to find the defect.

The details of any specific diagnostic program would be dependent upon the engineering details of the computer under consideration. However, there are a few considerations which appear to apply to nearly all computers. For one thing, for a diagnostic program to work, the computer must be functioning well enough "to get a program off the ground"; that is, the instructions of the program must be executed properly, and therefore certain portions of the computer must be in good condition. For this reason it is difficult to prepare a program that will properly diagnose an error in some of the important control circuits of the machine. Errors originating in the power supply are also difficult to locate by means of diagnostic programs. It is usually necessary to check these parts of the computer through the use of oscilloscopes, voltmeters, and other test instruments.

Although it would be desirable to have one all-inclusive diagnostic program that would indicate the cause of an error regardless of its source, it is generally more feasible to employ a set of specialized programs, each of which pertains to a relatively small portion of the machine. Frequently when errors are encountered, the approximate location of the source is known, and in this case the appropriate diagnostic programs may be selected to aid in finding the trouble quickly. In instances where incorrect results are being obtained with no indication whatsoever of the cause, the specialized diagnostic programs are still of great value, although it is then necessary to examine the entire computer in some systematic manner such as would be used when testing a new machine.

For IBM's 701, for example, a library of at least seventy different diagnostic programs has been assembled. One of the simplest (and surprisingly useful) programs is merely a blank card to be fed through the card reader; many clues to error causes can be obtained if the card fails to feed properly or if extraneous digits are entered into the machine. Most of the diagnostic programs are highly specialized and pertain to such things as controls for a particular instruction, the instruction counter, a specific property of the electrostatic storage unit, drum addressing circuits, or the printer circuits. The medium through which the programs present the results of their diagnosis to the operator is usually a stopping of the computer at a point where the pertinent data are readily observable in the various registers. Instructions for interpreting the data are recorded in the library along with the programs. Some of the diagnostic programs are capable of generating relatively elaborate reports on the output printer.

BIBLIOGRAPHY

Books

Calculating Instruments and Machines, D. R. Hartree, University of Illinois Press (1949).

Giant Brains, E. C. Berkeley, John Wiley and Sons, Inc. (1949).

High-Speed Computing Devices, Staff of Engineering Research Associates, Inc., McGraw-Hill Book Co., Inc. (1950).

Synthesis of Electronic Computing and Control Circuits, Staff of Harvard Computation Laboratory, Harvard University Press (1951).

Programs for an Electronic Digital Computer, M. V. Wilkes, D. J. Wheeler, and S. Gill, Addison Wesley Press, Inc. (1951).

The Design of Switching Circuits, W. Keister, A. E. Ritchie, and S. H. Washburn, D. Van Nostrand Company, Inc. (1951).

Faster Than Thought, B. V. Bowden, Sir Isaac Pitman and Sons, Ltd. (1953).

Automatic Digital Calculators, A. D. Booth and K. H. V. Booth, Butterworth Scientific Publications (1953).

Periodicals

"Transactions of the IRE, Professional Group on Electronic Computers," Institute of Radio Engineers.

"Digital Computer Newsletter," Office of Naval Research, Mathematical Sciences Division.

"Computers and Automation," Edmund C. Berkeley and Associates, New York.

"The Journal of Computing Systems," The Institute of Applied Logic, St. Paul, Minn.

"Journal of the Association for Computing Machinery," Association for Computing Machinery, New York, N. Y.

Other Publications

"Proceedings of a Symposium on Large-Scale Digital Calculating Machinery," *Annals of Harvard Computation Laboratory,* Vol. 16 (1948).

"Proceedings of a Second Symposium on Large-Scale Digital Calculating Machinery," *Annals of Harvard Computation Laboratory,* Vol. 26 (1951).

"Review of Electronic Digital Computers," Joint AIEE-IRE Computer Conference, 114 pages, Dec. 10–12, 1951 (Published February, 1952).

"Proceedings of the Electronic Computer Symposium," University of California, Sponsored by Los Angeles IRE Professional Group on Electronic Computers in cooperation with Department of Engineering, University of California, 220 pages, April 30, May 1–2, 1952.

"Proceedings of the Association for Computing Machinery," Meeting at Mellon Institute, Pittsburgh, Pa., 305 pages, May 2–3, 1952 (Published by Richard Rimbach Associates, Pittsburgh, 1952).

"Proceedings of the Association for Computing Machinery," Meeting at University of Toronto, Toronto, Ontario, 160 pages, Sept. 8–10, 1952 (Published by Sauls Lithograph Co., Washington, D. C.).

"Review of Input and Output Equipment Used in Computing Systems," Joint AIEE-IRE-ACM Computer Conference, 142 pages, Dec. 10–12, 1952 (Published March, 1953).

"Convention Record of the IRE 1953 National Convention; Part 7, Electronic Computers," 71 pages, IRE, 1953.

Proceedings of the IRE, Computer Issue, October, 1953.

"Commercially Available General-Purpose Electronic Digital Computers of Moderate Price," *Publication No. 111043*. Available from U. S. Dept. of Commerce, Office of Technical Services, Washington 25, D. C. ($1.25), 41 pages (May, 1952).

"Convention Record of the IRE 1954 National Convention; Part 4, Electronic Computers and Information Theory," 144 pages, IRE (1954).

"A Survey of Automatic Digital Computers," Report 111293, U. S. Department of Commerce, Office of Technical Services, Washington 25, D. C. ($2.00) 109 pages (1953).

Papers Devoted to Specific Machines

Automatic Sequence Controlled Computer:

"The Automatic Sequence Controlled Calculator," H. H. Aiken and G. M. Hopper, *Electrical Engineering*, Vol. 65, pp. 384–391 (Aug.–Sept., 1946); pp. 449–454 (Oct., 1946); pp. 522–528 (Nov., 1946).

IBM Pluggable Sequence Relay Computer:

"The IBM Pluggable Sequence Relay Calculator," W. J. Eckert, *Mathematical Tables and Other Aids to Computation*, Vol. III, pp. 149–161 (July, 1948).

ACE:

"Automatic Computing Engine of the National Physical Laboratory," M. Woodger, *Nature* (London), Vol. 167, pp. 270–271 (Feb. 17, 1951).

NAREC:

"Design of the Naval Research Laboratory Computer," D. H. Gridley and B. L. Sarahan, *Electrical Engineering*, Vol. 70, p. 111 (Feb., 1951).

Bibliography

"Electronic Circuits of the NAREC Computer," P. C. Sherertz, *Proc. IRE*, pp. 1313–1320 (Oct., 1953).

CSIRO Mark I:

"An Automatic Computer in Australia," T. Pearcey, *Mathematical Tables and Other Aids to Computation*, Vol. VI, pp. 167–172 (July, 1952).

"An Electronic Computer," M. Beard and T. Pearcey, *Journal of Scientific Instruments*, Vol. 29, pp. 305–311 (Oct., 1952).

BARK:

"The BARK, A Swedish General Purpose Relay Computer," G. Kjellberg and G. Neovius, *Mathematical Tables and Other Aids to Computation*, Vol. V, pp. 29–34 (Jan., 1951).

ENIAC:

"The Electronic Numerical Integrator (ENIAC)," A. Goldstine and H. H. Goldstine, *Mathematical Tables and Other Aids to Computation*, Vol. I, pp. 97–110 (July, 1946).

"The ENIAC," D. R. Hartree, *Nature* (London), Vol. 158, pp. 500–506 (Oct. 12, 1946).

"Electronic Computing Circuits of the ENIAC," A. W. Burks, *Proc. IRE*, Vol. 35, pp. 756–767 (Aug., 1947).

"The ENIAC," J. G. Brainerd and T. K. Sharpless, *Electrical Engineering*, Vol. 67, pp. 163–172 (Feb., 1948).

CALDIC:

"The California Digital Computer," P. L. Morton, *Mathematical Tables and Other Aids to Computation*, Vol. V, pp. 57–61 (April, 1951).

SWAC:

"Characteristics of the Institute for Numerical Analysis Computer," H. D. Huskey, *Mathematical Tables and Other Aids to Computation*, Vol. IV, pp. 103–108 (April, 1950).

"The SWAC—Design Features and Operating Experience," H. D. Huskey, R. Thorensen, B. F. Ambrosio, and E. C. Yowell, *Proc. IRE*, Vol. 41, pp. 1294–1299 (Oct., 1953).

Burroughs Computer:

"The Burroughs Laboratory Computer," G. G. Hoberg, *Report on AIEE-IRE Computer Conference*, pp. 22–29 (Feb., 1952).

University of Manchester (and Ferranti) Computer:

"The University of Manchester Universal High-Speed Digital Computing Machine," T. Kilburn, *Nature* (London), Vol. 164, pp. 684–687 (Oct. 22, 1949).

"The University of Manchester Computing Machine," F. C. Williams and T. Kilburn, *Report on AIEE-IRE Computer Conference*, pp. 57–61 (Feb., 1952).

"The Design, Construction, and Performance of a Large-Scale General-Purpose

Digital Computer," B. W. Pollard, *Report on AIEE-IRE Computer Conference,* pp. 62–70 (Feb., 1952).

"Multiplication in the Manchester University High-Speed Digital Computer," A. A. Robinson, *Electronic Engineering,* Vol. XXV, pp. 6–10 (Jan., 1953).

"Digital Computers at Manchester University," T. Kilburn, G. C. Tootill, D. B. G. Edwards, and B. W. Pollard, *The Proceedings of the Institution of Electrical Engineers,* Part II, Vol. 100, pp. 487–500 (Oct., 1953).

"The Construction and Operation of the Manchester University Computer," B. W. Pollard and K. Lonsdale, *The Proceedings of the Institution of Electrical Engineers,* Vol. 100, pp. 501–512 (Oct., 1953).

IBM CPC:

"The IBM Card-Programmed Electronic Calculator," J. W. Sheldon, and L. Tatum, *Report on AIEE-IRE Computer Conference,* pp. 30–36 (Feb., 1952).

General Electric Computer:

"A General Electric Digital Computer," B. R. Lester, *Annals of the Harvard Computation Laboratory,* Vol. 26, pp. 65–70 (1951).

UNIVAC:

"The UNIVAC System," J. P. Eckert, J. R. Weiner, H. F. Welsh, and H. F. Mitchell, *Report on AIEE-IRE Computer Conference,* pp. 6–16 (Feb., 1952).

"Punched Card to Magnetic Tape Converter for UNIVAC," E. Blumenthal and F. Lopez, *Report on AIEE-IRE-ACM Computer Conference,* pp. 8–11 (March, 1953).

"The Uniservo—Tape Reader and Recorder," H. F. Welsh and H. Lukoff, *Report on AIEE-IRE-ACM Computer Conference,* pp. 47–53 (March, 1953).

"Input Devices," L. D. Wilson and E. Roggenstein, *Report on AIEE-IRE-ACM Computer Conference,* pp. 53–58 (March, 1953).

"Output Devices," E. Masterson and L. D. Wilson, *Report on AIEE-IRE-ACM Computer Conference,* pp. 58–62 (March, 1953).

Elecon 100:

"The Elecon 100 General Purpose Computer," A. Auerbach, *Report on ACM Meeting,* pp. 47–51 (May, 1952). Also in *U. S. Dept. of Commerce Publication No. 111043,* pp. 24–30 (May, 1952).

EDVAC:

"The Electronic Discrete Variable Computer," S. E. Gluck, *Electrical Engineering,* Vol. 72, pp. 159–162 (Feb., 1953).

"A Digital Computer Timing Unit," R. M. Goodman, *Proc. IRE,* Vol. 39, pp. 1051–1054 (Sept., 1951).

University of Toronto Computer:

"The University of Toronto Model Electronic Computer," R. F. Johnston, *Proceedings of ACM Meeting at University of Toronto,* pp. 154–160 (Sept., 1952).

IBM 701:

"The Logical Organization of the New IBM Scientific Calculator," M. M. Astrahan and N. Rochester, *Report on ACM Meeting*, pp. 79–83 (May, 1952). Also in *Proceedings of Electronic Computer Symposium*, University of California, pp. XIX 1–7 (April–May, 1952).

"Engineering Experience in the Design and Operation of a Large Scale Electrostatic Memory," J. C. Logue, A. E. Brennemann, and A. C. Koelsch, *Convention Record of the IRE*, Part 7, Electronic Computers, pp. 21–29 (March, 1953).

"Diagnostic Programming Techniques for the IBM Type 701," L. R. Walters, *Convention Record of the IRE*, Part 7, Electronic Computers, pp. 55–58 (March, 1953).

"Engineering Organization of Input and Output for the IBM 701 Electronic Data Processing Machine," L. D. Stevens, *Report on AIEE-IRE-ACM Computer Conference*, pp. 81–85 (March, 1953).

"IBM Magnetic Tape Reader and Recorder," W. S. Buslik, *Report on AIEE-IRE-ACM Computer Conference*, pp. 86–90 (March, 1953).

"Magnetic Tape Techniques and Performance," H. W. Nordyke, *Report on AIEE-IRE-ACM Computer Conference*, pp. 90–95 (March, 1953).

"The System Design of the IBM 701 Computer," W. Buchholz, *Proc. IRE*, Vol. 41, pp. 1262–1275 (Oct., 1953).

"Engineering Description of the IBM Type 701 Computer," C. E. Frizzell, *Proc. IRE*, Vol. 41, pp. 1275–1287 (Oct., 1953).

"The Arithmetic Element of the IBM Type 701 Computer," H. D. Ross, *Proc. IRE*, Vol. 41, pp. 1287–1294 (Oct., 1953).

"The IBM 701 Speedcoding System," J. W. Backus, *Journal of the Association for Computing Machinery*, Vol. 1, pp. 4–6 (Jan., 1954).

"The IBM Magnetic Drum Calculator Type 650," F. E. Hamilton and E. C. Kubie, *Journal of the Association for Computing Machinery*, Vol. 1, pp. 13–20 (Jan., 1954).

"LEO," J. M. M. Pinkerton and E. J. Kaye, *Electronic Engineering*, Vol. XXVI, pp. 284–291 (July, 1954); Part 2: "Operation and Maintenance," E. H. Lenaerts, pp. 335–341 (Aug., 1954); Part 3: "A Checking Device for Punched Data Tapes," E. J. Kaye and G. R. Gibbs, pp. 386–392 (Sept., 1954).

ORACLE:

"The Logical Design of the Oak Ridge Digital Computer," C. L. Perry, *Proceedings of ACM Meeting at University of Toronto*, pp. 23–27 (Sept., 1952).

"The Oak Ridge Automatic Computer," J. C. Chu, *Proceedings of ACM Meeting at University of Toronto*, pp. 13–17 (Sept., 1952).

SEAC:

"The Incorporation of Subroutines into a Complete Problem on the NBS Eastern Automatic Computer," NBSMDL Staff, *Mathematical Tables and Other Aides to Computation*, Vol. IV, pp. 164–168 (July, 1950).

"The Operating Characteristics of the SEAC," Electronic Laboratory Staff of NBS, *Mathematical Tables and Other Aids to Computation,* Vol. IV, pp. 229–230 (Oct., 1950).

"Provision for Expansion in the SEAC," A. L. Leiner, *Mathematical Tables and Other Aids to Computation,* Vol. V, pp. 232–237 (Oct., 1951).

"The National Bureau of Standards Eastern Automatic Computer," S. N. Alexander, *Report on AIEE-IRE Computer Conference,* pp. 84–89 (Feb., 1952).

"Engineering Experience with the SEAC," R. J. Slutz, *Report on AIEE-IRE Computer Conference,* pp. 90–94 (Feb., 1952).

"SEAC Input-Output System," S. Greenwald, *Report on AIEE-IRE-ACM Computer Conference,* 31–36 (March, 1953).

"Input-Output Devices Used with SEAC," J. L. Pike, *Report on AIEE-IRE-ACM Computer Conference,* pp. 36–38 (March, 1953).

"Auxiliary Equipment to SEAC Input-Output," R. C. Haueter, *Report on AIEE-IRE-ACM Computer Conference,* pp. 39–44 (March, 1953).

"Operational Experience with SEAC," E. F. Ainsworth, *Report on AIEE-IRE-ACM Computer Conference,* pp. 44–47 (March, 1953).

"SEAC," S. Greenwald, R. C. Haueter, and S. N. Alexander, *Proc. IRE,* Vol. 41, pp. 1300–1313 (Oct., 1953).

"Dynamic Circuit Techniques Used in SEAC and DYSEAC," R. D. Elbourn and R. P. Witt, *Proc. IRE,* Vol. 41, pp. 1380–1387 (Oct., 1953).

RAYDAC:

"The Raytheon Electronic Digital Computer," R. M. Bloch, R. V. D. Campbell, and M. Ellis, *Mathematical Tables and Other Aids to Computation,* Vol. III, pp. 286–295, 317–323 (Oct., 1948).

"A Digital Computer for Scientific Applications," C. F. West and J. E. DeTurk, *Proc. IRE,* Vol. 36, pp. 1452–1460 (Dec., 1948).

"The Raytheon Electronic Digital Computer," R. M. Bloch, Vol. 26, *Annals of Harvard Computation Laboratory,* pp. 50–64 (1951).

"The RAYDAC System and Its External Memory," K. M. Rehler, *Report on AIEE-IRE-ACM Computer Conference,* pp. 63–70 (March, 1953).

"RAYDAC Input-Output System," W. H. Gray, *Report on AIEE-IRE-ACM Computer Conference,* pp. 70–76 (March, 1953).

"Operating Experience with RAYDAC," F. R. Dean, *Report on AIEE-IRE-ACM Computer Conference,* pp. 77–80 (March, 1953).

MANIAC:

"MANIAC" (Los Alamos Scientific Laboratories), H. B. Demuth, J. B. Jackson, E. Klein, N. Metropolis, W. Orvedahl, and J. H. Richardson, *Proceedings of ACM Meeting at University of Toronto,* pp. 13–17 (Sept., 1952).

ONR Relay Computer:

"The Office of Naval Research Relay Computer," J. J. Wolf, *Mathematical Tables and Other Aids to Computation,* Vol. VI, pp. 207–212 (Oct., 1952).

Institute Blaise Pascal Computer:

"Report on the Machine of the Institute Blaise Pascal," L. Couffignal, *Mathematical Tables and Other Aids to Computation*, Vol. IV, pp. 225–229 (Oct., 1950).

Whirlwind I:

"The Whirlwind I Computer," R. R. Everett, *Electrical Engineering*, Vol. 71, pp. 681–686 (Aug., 1952). Same title and author: *Report on AIEE-IRE Computer Conference*, pp. 70–74 (Feb., 1952).

"Evaluation of the Engineering Aspects of Whirlwind I," N. H. Taylor, *Report on AIEE-IRE Computer Conference*, pp. 75–78 (Feb., 1952).

"Diagnostic Programs and Marginal Checking in the Whirlwind I Computer," N. L. Daggett and E. S. Rich, *Convention Record of the IRE*, Part 7, Electronic Computers, pp. 48–54 (March, 1953).

IAS Computer:

"A Description of the Electronic Computer at the Institute for Advanced Studies," G. Estrin, *Proceedings of ACM Meeting at University of Toronto*, pp. 95–109 (Sept., 1952).

"Diagnosis and Prediction of Malfunctions in the Computing Machine at the Institute for Advanced Study," G. Estrin, *Convention Record of the IRE*, Part 7, Electronic Computers, pp. 59–61 (March, 1953).

"The Electronic Computer at the Institute for Advanced Study," G. Estrin, *Mathematical Tables and Other Aids to Computation*, Vol. VII, pp. 108–114 (April, 1953).

MONROBOT:

"The MONROBOT Electronic Calculators," E. J. Quinby, *U. S. Dept. of Commerce Publication No. 111043*, pp. 7–12 (May, 1952).

CADAC:

"The CADAC," R. E. Sprague, *U. S. Dept. of Commerce Publication No. 111043*, pp. 13–17 (May, 1952).

Bell Laboratories Computers:

"A Bell Laboratories Computing Machine," F. L. Alt, *Mathematical Tables and Other Aids to Computation*, Vol. III, pp. 1–13 (Jan., 1948), pp. 69–84 (April, 1948).

"The Bell Computer, Model VI," E. G. Andrews, *Electrical Engineering*, Vol. 68, pp. 751–756 (Sept., 1949). Same title and author: *Annals of Harvard Computation Laboratory*, Vol. 26, pp. 20–31 (1951).

"Use of a Relay Digital Computer" (Model V), E. G. Andrews and H. W. Bode, *Electrical Engineering*, Vol. 69, pp. 158–163 (Feb., 1950).

"Biquinary System Calculator," G. R. Stibitz, U. S. Patent 2,486,809 (Nov. 1, 1949).

"Digital Computer" (Floating decimal point system), S. B. Williams, U. S. Patent 2,538,636 (Jan. 16, 1951).

"A Review of the Bell Laboratories' Digital Computer Developments," E. G. Andrews, *Report on AIEE-IRE Computer Conference*, pp. 101–105 (Feb., 1952).

Binac:

"The Binac," A. A. Auerbach, J. P. Eckert, R. F. Shaw, J. R. Weiner, and L. D. Wilson, *Proc. IRE*, Vol. 40, pp. 12–29 (Jan., 1952).

Harvard Mark III:

"The Mark III Calculator," B. L. Moore, *Annals of Harvard Computation Laboratory*, Vol. 26, pp. 11–19 (1951).

ORDVAC:

"The ORDVAC," R. E. Meagher, and J. P. Nash, *Report on AIEE-IRE Computer Conference*, pp. 37–43 (Feb., 1952).

EDSAC:

"The Design of a Practical High Speed Computing Machine. The EDSAC," *Proc. Roy. Soc. London* 195A, pp. 274–279 (1948).

"An Ultrasonic Memory Unit for the EDSAC," M. V. Wilkes and W. Renwick, *Electronic Engineering*, Vol. XX, pp. 208–213 (1948).

"The EDSAC—An Electronic Calculating Machine," M. V. Wilkes and W. Renwick, *Journal of Scientific Instruments and of Physics in Industry*, Vol. 26, pp. 385–391 (Dec., 1949).

"The EDSAC," M. V. Wilkes and W. Renwick, *Mathematical Tables and Other Aids to Computation*, Vol. IV, pp. 61–65 (April, 1950).

"Programme Organization and Initial Orders for the EDSCA," D. J. Wheeler, *Proc. Roy. Soc. London*, A, 202, pp. 573–589 (Aug. 22, 1950).

"The EDSAC Computer," M. V. Wilkes, *Report on AIEE-IRE Computer Conference*, pp. 79–83 (Feb., 1952).

"Experience with Marginal Checking and Automatic Routining of the EDSAC," M. V. Wilkes, M. Phister, and S. A. Barton, *Convention Record of IRE*, Part 7, Electronic Computers, pp. 66–71 (March, 1953).

ERA 1101:

"Minimum Access Programming," D. P. Perry, *Mathematical Tables and Other Aids to Computation*, Vol. VI, pp. 172–182 (July, 1952).

"Design Features of the ERA 1101 Computer," F. C. Mullaney, *Report on AIEE-IRE Computer Conference*, pp. 43–49 (Feb., 1952). Same title and author: *Electrical Engineering*, Vol. 71, pp. 1015–1018 (Nov., 1952).

JAINCOMP-B1:

"The JAINCOMP-B1 Computer," D. H. Jacobs, *U. S. Dept. of Commerce Publication No. 111043*, pp. 1–6 (May, 1952).

Circle Computer:

"The Circle Computer," J. Greig, *U. S. Dept. of Commerce Publication No. 111043*, pp. 18–24 (May, 1952). Same title and author: *Mathematical Tables and Other Aids to Computation*, Vol. VII, pp. 249–255 (Oct., 1953).

CEC Model 30–201:

"Model 30–201 Electronic Digital Computer," L. P. Robinson, *U. S. Dept. of Commerce Publication No. 111043*, pp. 31–36 (May, 1952).

Logistics Computer:

"The Logistics Computer," R. S. Erickson, *Proc. IRE*, Vol. 41, pp. 1325–1332 (Oct., 1953).

Remington Rand Type 409-2:

"The Remington Rand Type 409-2 Electronic Computer," L. P. Crossman, *Proc. IRE*, Vol. 41, pp. 1332–1340 (Oct., 1953).

Illiac:

"Diagnostic Programs for the Illiac," D. J. Wheeler and J. E. Robertson, *Proc. IRE*, Vol. 41, pp. 1320–1325 (Oct., 1953).

Digital Differential Analyzers:

"Fundamental Concepts of the Digital Differential Analyzer Method of Computation" (MADDIDA), R. E. Sprague, *Mathematical Tables and Other Aids to Computation*, Vol. VI, pp. 41–49 (Jan., 1952).
"The Serial-Memory Digital Differential Analyzer" (MADDIDA), J. F. Donan, *Mathematical Tables and Other Aids to Computation*, Vol. VI, pp. 102–112 (April, 1952).
"Applications of the CRC105 Decimal Digital Differential Analyzer," E. Weiss, *Trans. IRE*, PGEC-1, pp. 19–24 (Dec., 1952).
"The Design of the Bendix Digital Differential Analyzer," M. Palevsky, *Proc. IRE*, Vol. 41, pp. 1352–1356 (Oct., 1953).

Special Purpose Computers:

"The USAF-Fairchild Specialized Digital Computer" (for simultaneous linear equations), J. J. Stone, *Mathematical Tables and Other Aids to Computation*, Vol. VII, pp. 35–37 (Jan., 1953).
"A Special Purpose Digital Computer" (Haller, Raymond and Brown, Inc.; for simultaneous linear equations), J. P. Walker, *Mathematical Tables and Other Aids to Computation*, Vol. VII, pp. 190–195 (July, 1953).

INDEX